THE 20th CENTURY
AND THEN WHAT?

AUDREY KERRY-WARD

THE 20th CENTURY AND THEN WHAT?

A PHILOSOPHICAL VIEW OF LIFE

Matador
5 Weir Road
Kibworth Beauchamp
Leicester LE8 0LQ, UK
Tel: (+44) 116 279 2299
Email: books@troubador.co.uk
Web: www.troubador.co.uk/matador

ISBN 978 1848761 179

British Library Cataloguing in Publication Data.
A catalogue record for this book is available from the British Library.

Typeset in 11pt Bembo by Troubador Publishing Ltd, Leicester, UK
Printed in the UK by TJ International, Padstow, Cornwall

Matador is an imprint of Troubador Publishing Ltd

Dedicated to the Children of the future

ACKNOWLEDGMENTS

I would like to thank my daughter Kerry Sneddon, son in law Alistair Sneddon, and friends Brian Barnard, Alice Webb, John Collinson, Jane Ingham, Lorraine Wren, for patiently listening to my droning about 'my book' and returning only love and support. Jane Lindo for committing my words to type over and over again and correcting my grammar whenever necessary. And Dennis Lindo for putting up with it all. Mr Brian Pateman and Victoria McCann for lending their expertise to my medical questioning. Sue Littleford whose constructive editing enhanced the clarity of the text. My friend the late Barbara Wilks whose ultimate faith in my work lived on in my heart to inspire and encourage me to complete the task I had undertaken. Last but not least a very special thank you to Nina Clifton, who, after kindly offering to review this book, concluded that it is a well written, constructed and researched work that provokes thought and inspires hope.

Contents

PROLOGUE

1996

Adam gazed at the skies to see the dawn breaking on the day that would bring his plans to fruition. As he had slept in a bed for the night, and not in a shop doorway, he had gained the bodily strength he needed to fulfil his purpose. The stale smell of sweat hung around his body, but today he had the luxury of a sink and water. He made his way to the washroom of the hostel carrying the last of the clean clothes that he had. How wonderful it would be to feel clean and alive again.

At the street door he stretched away the sleep of the night and took a deep breath. The ubiquitous stench of exhaust fumes was so intense that Adam had to step back into the building to let a little unpolluted air into his lungs. As he sat on a chair in the corridor his thoughts were filled with visions of good health. Having to cope with asthma was very hard and proved a hindrance to living a full life sometimes. However, he had had the condition since his early teens and had learned to live with the situation. His thoughts carried him deeper, to think of the number of babies who were born with it nowadays, and those who soon contracted asthma if they evaded it at birth.

Thoughts of his own ill health nudged memories of his life. He began to remember Jane and their life together. It seemed a lifetime, and not a mere six months ago, that they had separated. They had been reasonably happy for the four years they had been together. They had had a lovely home in a suburban area and all the trimmings of a successful couple were theirs – two large cars, huge television, video recorder, a large collection of video tapes, CD player, automatic washer, dishwasher, three telephones, two mobile phones, a boat, holidays abroad and a very large mortgage. By means of Jane's high salary as a computer advisor, and Adam's mediocre one as a laboratory technician at a drug company, they managed their financial commitments adequately. However when he lost his job a year ago funds became inadequate and everything went wrong. He tried desperately to find another job but with over three million people unemployed, most job applications went unacknowledged.

Jane remained in her job but she was not prepared to tolerate his unemployment. She was not going to support him and continue to pay the mortgage, even though her salary was much higher than his had been. This was the age of the woman; she could manage quite well on her own without having an unemployed man in tow to drag her down. Separation came quickly and he was left with the responsibility of selling the house and finalising the finances. However houses were not selling – the market was at rock bottom, with properties remaining unsold after periods of years. No one had the money or security to contemplate house moves these days. The mortgage was already in arrears, as they had not paid it for six months because of other financial commitments. When he went to the building society to explain his joblessness, they swiftly repossessed the house. It was sold at auction at a greatly reduced price so that the building society could recover the monies outstanding to them. To his dismay he learned that there was no exoneration as to the interest incurred on the loan. Thousands of pounds were still due to be paid so this would render him a debtor for the rest of his life, even in the event of his acquiring a well-paid job. Everything else that he and Jane had owned was also repossessed when creditors learned of their plight. Homeless and in debt, he began his new life on the streets: sleeping wherever he could and begging the food he ate. He was not alone: there were thousands like him who shared the same fate.

It was a matter of principle that had lost him his job. Although the animals used for experimentation at the laboratories where he worked were fed and housed very well, their purpose was to endure suffering. He was reaching a point where inflicting this on them was making him unwell. He couldn't sleep, he couldn't eat, he couldn't think rationally. Jane, however, stepped in to do the last by impressing on him that people would die and suffer if experiments on animals were not carried out. He battled daily with his conscience, trying to persuade himself that she was right. However, one day at work he heard a horrific scream that made him shiver. "That sounded as if someone was having the skin ripped from their body," he said to a colleague, who smiled in reply – "Probably was just that, who knows what the big boys along the corridor are up to." Without hesitation, Adam left the room and began to run along the passageways. Reaching an area marked 'No Unauthorised Admittance', he waited. As he did so he recalled rumours saying that experiments on sheep, pigs, chimps, etc. were being executed within the building for the purpose of cloning them to produce organs for human transplantation. There seemed to be jubilation amongst the workforce about the prospect as it would create great wealth for the company and the country's economy, when people around the world started to buy the hearts, kidneys, etc. that were to be produced. The scientist who arrived to tap in the entrance code to the high security unit was unaware of Adam's presence. As the door began to open he pushed the man away from it violently and took his place. The sight that greeted him beyond the doorway took his breath away as no more did he wonder about the horrific screams. The creatures that had been given life in there consisted of legless torsos showing malfunctioning organs attached to them. They were suffering an agony that only sudden death could end. Within minutes he was being held by security guards and was escorted out of the building. His job was over.

That night Jane arrived home to find him curled upon the floor crying unstoppable tears, but regarded his plight as that of a loser. Like most other ladies of the age she preferred to disregard sentiment in the belief that life was to be played to be won.

Rising from the chair Adam sighed and headed for the street door again. It was five in the morning and time to move on to the long journey ahead. As usual the streets were blocked with motor vehicles. They were parked at all angles – on pavements, street corners and alleyways as though they had been dumped there, never to be retrieved. This, together with the shrieking rats that were tearing frantically into the piles of refuge in the streets and alleyways, portrayed a vision of devastation and decay. The early morning skies received no respite from attack as aeroplanes thundered across the skies, one after the other, to leave their foul-smelling fumes to pollute the atmosphere.

Adam's pace was slow going as he had to rest from time to time. He heard the bells of a distant church and realised that it was already 8am.

"Watch where you're going, mate." He had reached a main road where the vision before him had rendered him sightless for a moment. "I am sorry," he offered the man whom he had accidentally bumped into. It was crazy. The road was filled with vehicles, their horns hooting, their brakes screaming. Two cars had actually come to a standstill whilst their owners stood in the road shouting at each other – then they began to fight. Other vehicles were swerving around the situation, blaring their horns as they went. Adam absorbed this familiar sight with the increasing belief that the average motorist depicted the failure of the human race.

Another half an hour on and he had reached the High Street of the city where throngs of people marched to and fro. Some were there just for sake of shopping, whilst others were 'pre-work' shoppers. The only venues left for this pursuit were the large superstores, where everything from a pin to a penguin could be bought.

The small shops had each in their time been forced to close with the coming of a competition they couldn't match. Shopping for most had developed into a kind of religion – no longer was it just a case of necessity.

Adam stopped and looked through the large window of the superstore. Inside people were being shackled to wheeled trolleys and then, quickly and unsmilingly, joined to lines of others. They were all shoving each other; frantically reaching out at the items piled high on the shelves. Soon their trolleys were laden to the top. Piped music percolated through ceiling-high speakers. At three-minute intervals the music was stopped whilst promotions were announced. Rote-trained voices told that fish was selling at well below market prices today, whilst dustbins were being offered with £2 off. Feet immediately clambered to the left and to the right, ambitious to secure the items before stocks ran out and depression set in. At the checkout tills, queues of people were stamping their feet, waving their hands, and shaking their heads. Anguished words were being exchanged between customers as to their rights of service priority. The sense of urgency hung savagely in the atmosphere; there was no time for delay. The clock was ticking away these people's lives – they had so much to do with little time left to do it.

Walking on, Adam had to pass the back of the store where cars were parked. There he saw a hotchpotch of squashed and dented shopping trolleys. The speeding motorists, who were so intent on reaching the exit points, did not seem to notice the innocent, abandoned vehicles, even as they drove into them.

Moving on, he pondered the movement of time where the week had become a day and a day an hour. As for the minute itself, well this had become extinct when everybody realised that they had none to spare to give to anyone else.

Back on the main road his thoughts were shattered by the sudden sound of gunfire assaulting his ears. Further ahead was a young man running along the pavement. In his hand was a revolver smoking with the shots it had fired. The pavement was strewn with bodies – some still, some moving. People were diving into doorways or passageways trying to escape the bullets. No one was saved; the young man's aim was accurate. People dropped to the ground one by one. Whilst Adam had seen newspaper headlines reporting these sorts of horrific happenings, he never thought that he would witness such a scene himself. There was a telephone booth on the other side of the road but he could not reach it because of the dense march of traffic. Despite the gunfire, and the horror accompanying it, no vehicles had come to a halt. The speeding, weaving and hooting continued on both sides of the road. He would have to go in search of another booth on his side so that he could call the police. Doubling back on himself he ran as fast as his breathing would permit. He could see another booth in the distance. Reaching it, he gasped for breath before stepping inside. The telephone dangled before him – the coin box was missing. A robotic voice gurgled from the mouthpiece, "Out of order – out of order – out of order". He remembered the superstore – there would be a telephone there that had not been vandalised.

On his way back to the store he found a little smirk lurking in his mind. He was thinking of the telecommunication system, recalling how difficult it was to speak to a human being by telephone. Phones these days were answered by technological robots that requested that one tap a series of numbers into the telephone, to give, or access, information required. He recalled the occasions when this time-consuming procedure had left him so frustrated that he had slammed down the phone, particularly so if his call had been answered with a recorded message saying – "there is a queuing system, please hold the line," followed by recorded music and advertising slogans. On top of this, frustration had increased knowing it was he who was paying for this wasted call. His thoughts made him stop in his tracks and turn back. He never wanted to make any more telephone calls, and what was the use of contacting the police anyway – by the time they had weaved their way through the congested traffic, the gunman would have shot everyone in sight and escaped the scene of the crime. He shrugged his shoulders and realised that he was succumbing to the attitude of society in general – 'what's the use of bothering, nothing I can do'.

Continuing his journey, he listened to the message in his footsteps. Perhaps his mind would clear once he had rid himself of the portrait of selfishness. If he could reach the countryside the touch of nature might renew his energy, and let him forget the people who were long lost in a fever of consumership and greed.

Though many vehicles had left the sanctuary of parking spaces, the back roads were still cluttered with immobile cars. The only sounds were from moving traffic in the middle of the roads – aeroplanes in the sky – car alarms – and blue-flashing, screaming burglar alarms on houses. There were no sounds of people. All the roads that Adam had walked along had been empty of human life. There were rows and rows of houses, but all gave the appearance of vacancy behind the closed silent doors. It was like walking through a ghost town. His loneliness would have cherished communication with another person. Just a 'hello' or 'nice day' would have spurred him on, whereas a smile from someone could have inspired him to think that life was worth living after all. But then another sound filled his ears. It was the grouped voices of children – a noise seldom heard these days. Because of reports of children being murdered, raped or abducted, parents were afraid to allow their kids to play out on the streets anymore. Instead, fun-seeking was now a solitary activity for children, with television and the computer their only companions. As he walked on he remembered the time of his own childhood and that of children throughout history. Times when groups of children played happily together in the roads, repeating games that their own parents and grandparents had played. Hopscotch, marbles, rounders, cricket, cowboys and indians, tick, top and whip, doctors and nurses, mummies and daddies, skipping, football and a never-ending list. Most of these historic games were being lost to time.

He reached the source of the voices – a school playground. He dared not stand and watch the children in case an adult attendant saw him as a potential child offender. His thoughts sank to the pit of despair. How very sad that the trust we should learn to have for each other had been reduced to the total mistrust of everyone. No longer did the measure of good outweigh the measure of bad. Walking slowly he allowed himself to observe the children in the playground.They looked so pale and lethargic. Many of them were gasping for breath – some were pulling inhalers out of their pockets and applying them to their mouths. The government, and health authorities, repeatedly insisted to the public that asthma was caused mainly by cigarette smoke.Adam reflected his own asthmatic condition and its exacerbation when he was subjected to the horrors of vehicle exhaust fumes. Smiling, he pondered the number of people who chose to disregard the real problem of the nation's failing health, for surely air pollution could not be masked indefinitely. He heard one child shout to another, "I am not allowed to run about – it might damage my heart, I could have a heart attack". Adam could not believe his ears. Six, seven and eight year olds showing the stress and neurosis of their elders. Why should this be when all a child should know is fun and laughter? Could it be because of the pressure of the classroom where a child is made to learn those things beyond the comprehension of its own mind? Where it is made to conform to the rules of government and powers beyond, stating that all children must be at a certain level of learning at specific ages? That all children should be the same? Having succeeded in taking away the individuality of the public in general, was it now the beginning of cloning the next generation? He pitied the kids' lot in life. Already their freedom of living was controlled, with restrictions never before imposed on children throughout the history of the human race. The whistle blew and the children began their miserable march back to the classroom where they would stay until home time, when waiting parents would bundle them into cars for the journey home.

It felt as if the sun was becoming hotter and Adam's feet were beginning to burn. He sat on a nearby wall, a handkerchief protecting his head. Everyone was being urged to stay out of the sun.The reduction of the ozone layer meant that now there was little protection from the sun's rays. There was much warning that they could rapidly cause skin cancer.This was just one of the many health risk warnings that came daily from the media.The government and health authorities were so intent on implementing preventative healthcare schemes that the country was in a permanent state of neurosis. When he stood to walk on, he could hear the radios of passing cars. Warnings were being issued about the weather. The announcements stated that with the heat of the day, and the lack of wind, carbon dioxide levels were dangerously high and could cause death. People were being urged not to use their cars unless it was really necessary. But then, how else could they get from A to B? The public transport systems were only readily available on main routes, and fares were unaffordable anyway.

"Do you want a nice time love?" The voice behind him brought Adam quickly back to reality. He looked round and saw a girl at his heel. She was small and pretty, and looked to be about twelve or thirteen years old. She smiled sweetly at him.

"Do you not want a nice time then?" she said. He innocently smiled back at her.

"I am sorry, what do you mean?"

Between the moment of his asking and her answering, he knew exactly what she meant. He could not believe that a little girl was asking him if he wanted sex with her. "I am sorry," he said, "I don't want a nice time."

She turned away from him and walked away raising two fingers in the air as she went. He looked about him and realised that he was walking through an estate of houses. His questioner was not the only girl he saw. There were several young ladies standing at different points along the road. He watched them approach slowing cars, and climb into the passenger seats as vehicles stopped.

Through the open doors of houses he passed, he observed groups of young people lying about on furniture or floors. Their faces looked blank as he walked by unobserved. Further along the road, young men sat on pavement edges. Some of them were talking in blurred speech whilst others leaned one against the other saying nothing. They looked at him without expression as he approached – a syringe lay on the floor beside them. The drugs they had used had not yet taken over their whole being. It would be later when their nightmares would begin to render their minds out of control. This would be the time when crimes of theft, murder or rape might occur.

"What are you staring at?" a voice came behind him. He turned to see a tall well-built man standing there. He felt apprehensive but ventured to speak.

"I suppose I'm wondering just what makes people sink to this level".

"Are you now," the man gruffed, "I suppose you're round here looking for a bit of pleasure. Don't suppose you know what it is like never to have had a job or had anyone to care for you. Don't suppose you've ever been in a no-hope situation."

Adam smiled at the man and asked him to have a good look at him. Then he told him his own story. The man's attitude quickly changed and he slapped Adam on the back.

"I'm sorry mate, but all the same you have at least tasted the good life."

A large car drew up at the kerbside and the man glanced over his shoulder.

"Don't look up," he warned.

Four men got out of the car and looked about them. Two of them made their way up the front path of one of the houses whilst the other two scurried around to the back. When they had gone the man tugged at Adam's sleeve.

"Don't look back. Just keep walking."

The sound of gunfire echoed behind them and shouting was heard. Without conversation, the two of them walked the length of two roads. At the third, the man tugged at Adam's sleeve again.

"Not safe for you to walk on your own - better come home with me for a while."

The man opened the gate of a property numbered 17 and ushered Adam along the path. Inside the house, he made a pot of tea for them both and explained the happenings they had just witnessed. The men who had alighted from the car were some of the big boys in the drug world. The house they visited would have been that of a drug dealer who owed them money. Without preamble they would have gained access to the house and killed the offending debtor.

"It's not usually guns they use," he told Adam, "they're too noisy. "Knives are their favourite weapons, quieter you see?"

"It happens a lot then?" Adam asked.

The man nodded "Oh yes, all the time, it's a drug empire around here. Nearly all the kids are on them and there's a dealer on every corner making a fortune out of them."

"But how do they pay for them if they haven't got jobs?"

"Honestly mate, were you born yesterday? By selling their bodies and thieving, what else? Girls round here are prostitutes from the age of eight upwards. Mothers too; they are all on the game. And the lads? Well thieving is all they know, same as their dads, uncles and friends."

"What about the police, don't they do anything?"

The man shook his head. "What can they do mate? The only way the police are going to catch anyone at it is to have a tip-off, and no one's going to risk getting shot or knifed are they? Anyway they're just after the big boys aren't they? The drug kings so to speak. Mind you, if they succeed in catching any of them what happens? They get them into a courtroom and some clever-speaking lawyer gets them off the hook. It's a charade right enough."

It was Adam's turn to shake his head.

"Yes, you're right there".

The man continued, "The drug problem is so widespread that it would take an army of police to curb it. It's completely out of hand. Even little kids in primary schools are into it now".

Adam sighed, "It's frightening to realise that children are committing horrible crimes as it is. What will happen if they become drug addicts as well?"

"I know – children used to be taught the difference between right and wrong and knew they had to suffer a punishment if they broke the rules. Now there's no punishment for them. If they break the law the police can do nothing about it. All they can do is take them into custody for a few hours then they have to release them, because the law states that juvenile offenders can't be punished. If they break the law at their school there's nothing the teachers can do either, because they're not allowed to enforce punishment. At the end of the day children have been given a licence to do anything they want to do. I never thought I would see the day when a whole society could be terrorised by kids. It doesn't bear thinking about but that's the way it is."

Adam nodded his head in agreement and then stood to leave. The man stood too.

"I'll walk with you until you're off the estate, too dangerous for you to walk on your own," he said.

Adam was glad to be on the open road again, and turned to wave to his protector as he walked back in the direction of the main road. The cup of tea and the rest had given him a little more strength to continue his journey. It might be nightfall before he reached the countryside but it did not matter. He could not stand another night in a makeshift bed in the centre of a smelly city – tonight he would feel the softness of the grass beneath his body as he slept.

Another hour of walking left him breathless and tired again. The heat of the sun bore down even though it was nearing the end of September. He remembered not too many years ago when the beginning of October announced the start of winter, when snow was likely to fall. Now the few flurries of snow that came soon filtered into the air without leaving a store of water to fill the reservoirs. Water was becoming scarcer and scarcer. The government had already made an official proclamation that the climate had changed. 'Weather conditions are becoming warmer and warmer and water supplies are dangerously low', the announcement stated. Everyone was being urged to use less water and rationing was becoming commonplace. Many trees were dying in the extreme heat, but giving them water to survive was not allowed. Despite the shortage of water, however, commercial ventures were privileged in their use of it. Car washes for instance, for whilst trees were dying, cars were being kept clean. Then there were the football and cricket grounds – they must be ready for man's sport at all cost, so the sprinkler systems could offer days of rain for them if needs be. Adam's thwarted vision of man's insanity added to the sudden fatigue that had overcome him. He could see a church on the next block. If he could find the strength to get there, he would be able to sit out of the sun for a while until he recovered.

With relief he opened the gate to the churchyard and stumbled his way over the old gravestones. He reached the door of the church only to find it locked. Crying quietly to himself he mumbled into his hands, "If this is the House of God, why does He keep His door locked?" Walking slowly backwards he looked up first to the sky and then to the church. All the windows were covered with meshed wire. On one wall there was a burglar alarm, and on the other, a security light. His tears increased to a sob as he recognised the total abandonment of love. Even the church was preaching mistrust – was there no sanctity anywhere? And why should God have treasures to protect anyway? He sat cross-legged on a gravestone; his fatigue turning to the illness he had felt for a week or so.

His aim that day was to get to the countryside and reach it he would. He sat for as long at it took to gain the strength needed, then continued with his steps slow and lumbering. He was passing a health centre now and wondered if he should go in – perhaps if the staff there saw how ill he was a doctor might give him medication. He pushed open the door to see a room full of desolate people with staring eyes. With the total absence of conversation, laughter or smiles, the whole area represented an abyss of depression. But then, wasn't it recognised that this was the major illness of the day, and was one which would increase in the twenty-first century, so why was Adam so overcome by the vision? Making his way over to the fortressed reception area, he stood to be noticed. A windowed panel was opened and a lady's face appeared.

"Yes?" she asked.

He suggested that he might see a doctor. The rapid reply was that there were no appointments left for that day nor the day after or the day after that.

"But please, I am ill, I *must* see a doctor".

The lady asked for his name, address and postcode. Deliriously, he gave the first and pondered the next, deciding that he could only quote his last address. Upon receiving the information she tapped it into the computer in front of her then turned to him.

"You don't appear to be registered with us, Mr Seymour," she said, then turned back to the computer and tapped again at the keys. "You are not listed at the address you gave, either".

Adam coughed on his words – "Er, well – no, I used to live there but I don't live anywhere at present".

"Well, I'm sorry Mr Seymour, but people of no fixed abode are not entitled to be registered with a GP. Of course a doctor would see you if there were time for him to do so, but we don't have any free appointments for the next two weeks. The only thing I can suggest is that you take yourself off to the Accident and Emergency Department at the hospital and they will attend to you."

With this the lady closed the window panel tightly and walked away from it. Adam could not move, and felt that his feet were anchored to the floor. His vacant eyes stared into a vacuum of nothingness, whilst he pondered the human race. How had it fallen to such depths of uncaringness that people were able to turn their backs on others in need of help? How had it succumbed to the pressure that advocated that individual privacy was not a right any more, and that personal information about oneself be revealed on demand so that it might be stored in computer databases for all to access at will. He turned around slowly to see each person in the waiting room staring in his direction. However, he could see in their eyes that they were oblivious to his plight anyway. But then, a man stood and began to walk towards him.

"You all right, mate?" he asked.

Adam shook his head but tried to smile a grateful acknowledgement.

"Perhaps if I could have a drink of water!" The man took his arm and led him out of the room into the corridor.

"Wait here a minute, mate, I'll get the key."

Adam looked up to see a surveillance camera pointing at him and thought back to the waiting room where he had seen himself on a television screen. There were cameras spying on people everywhere – superstores, football grounds, shopping arcades, seaside promenades, airports, office blocks, blocks of flats – and now, even here in a health centre. Was there no privacy – was respect for people and life gone forever? He shrugged as he recalled a novel, called *1984*, which told of people being watched for twenty-four hours a day by cameras which operated through TV screens within their homes. Not only did the screens watch, they talked too and constantly bellowed out the instructions that the ruler of the land (Big Brother) insisted people follow to the letter. Whilst the event of such a ruler had not materialised in 1984, he reflected present times and wondered if 1996 could be the year of Big Brother's conception.

"All right, mate?" the man returned, key in hand, and unlocked the toilet door.

Inside Adam felt relieved to detect the absence of a camera. He slouched over the sink and thrust his hands under the cold water tap. First he drank, and then he splashed his burning face with water.

"Listen, you go and sit down on the loo seat for a bit, you look as if you can't stand much longer," the man said.

Adam thankfully obeyed and shut the cubicle door.

"Who'd have thought that it would come to this?" the man called from beyond the door. "I mean, that a sick person can't get treatment when it's needed. Mind you, these days GP's have got to devote most of their time to preventative medicine, so they don't have much to spare to treat people with a current problem. All to do with money isn't it? Governments want NHS spending cut and think that by doling out preventative drugs to one and all, no one will ever get sick. It's like me; I came to see the doctor once because I was having trouble hearing. It took him fifteen seconds to discover I had wax in my ears, and for the rest of my ten minute slot, he lectured me on the perils of smoking, drinking, being overweight, not exercising and not taking preventative drugs. And do you know, he was so intent on persuading me to reform my health-destroying habits that he forgot the reason for my visit and didn't prescribe a cure for my blocked ears." He started to laugh uproariously.

Inside the cubicle Adam could not fail to smile at the man's contagious laughter. Nor could he disagree with the words spoken, or wonder what the man would think of the medical future. For example, with DNA testing now established, it would be possible to predict what diseases people were likely to develop in coming years. With this system in place doctors would have the option to refuse acceptance to their list of people regarded as potentially high maintenance patients. In the past it was pot luck whether a GP's practice had a majority of generally healthy patients on its list to constitute a lucrative business, or whether it had a majority of chronically sick people needing regular expensive medication to render the practice financially unviable. DNA testing would mean that GP practices would never again have to take this gamble.

There came a hammering on the door with a voice booming out "What's going on in there?" The man called back harshly.

"A sick man is having a drink of water and a sit down, there's no law against that yet is there?"

Adam unlocked the cubicle door and leaned against the frame. The man looked at him with concern.

"You all right, mate?" he said. "Take no notice of them, if you're not ready to move yet just stay where you are. They can't throw you in jail for it you know."

Adam smiled and the man continued to talk.

"Mind you, that might be a good idea, at least you'd have a bed and three meals a day. Not to mention a television, sports facilities and a chance to get a degree whilst you're in there."

He linked his arm through Adam's to lead him along the corridor. "I've heard it said that drug companies give doctors prizes for promoting their wares", the man said as they walked. "Not just any old prize, but holidays and the like! Wonder if that's true?"

Instead of offering the confirmation that pharmaceutical knowledge had given him, Adam merely replied, "I wonder?"

At the street door the man again viewed Adam with concern. "Are you sure you're going to be all right?" he asked. "I'd feel happier if I thought you'd be admitted to hospital if you weren't." He sighed and shook his head. "But with the way things are there's no guarantee of that".

Adam understood what the man was thinking because of his awareness that hospitals had to 'close their doors' when there was a shortage of beds. In these situations, when ambulance crews attended those who had been taken ill, or involved in an accident, they might have to journey many miles before finding an alternative hospital that could receive their patient. He turned to the man to shake him by the hand.

"I'll be fine" he assured. "Thanks for all you have done for me. Just got to get on with life eh? Like the unfortunate hospital doctors who have the dilemma of deciding which of two patients is to be admitted to hospital to occupy one available bed".

"True enough my friend, take care of yourself and good luck," said the man as he waved Adam a cheery farewell.

It was nearing 5.30pm now as Adam plodded his way towards the hills. Another couple of hours and he should be there. He took a bite of the chocolate bar the man at the health centre had given him, and felt overcome at remembering his kindness. How refreshing it was to know that there was still some measure of kindness left in the uncaring world of today. He popped the bitten bar back into his pocket thinking that he would save the rest for his moments of victory.

Walking over a motorway bridge he began to cough and gasp for breath again. He leaned on the barrier hoping to breathe air. But there was no air; there was just a stale taste of pollution with the atmosphere choking with fumes. Below, eight lanes of roadway were filled with vehicles travelling at a speed no more than a standstill. Engines roared whilst exhaust pipes puffed out vapour. Long, heavy lorries formed parades of tail-holding elephants, whilst cars resembled contrasting lines of wriggling caterpillars eager to develop wings. As the heat spiralled into the sky the blasting horns heralded a road to hell. Adam escaped the bridge as quickly as his ill health would permit. The hills were there, beckoning him in the distance; he must go on.

Passing two large buildings now, he recognised them to be the baby centres. The first was the one where women came daily to acquire the abortion of unborn babies that had been conceived inconveniently. Here 75,000 tiny bodies a year, after being stripped of their stem cells, were consigned to the belly of the incinerators for consumption. The second was the place where women came daily to conceive a child by means of artificial insemination. As long as she had the money to pay for treatment, a woman could decide how many children she would like to bear and also when she would like to do so. Furthermore, when the technology of genetic engineering became more advanced, there would be the opportunity for parents to select some of the features they would like their child to have. Then, if their babies carried genes which would render them fat, thin, small, big, homosexual, criminal, slow learning etc. these could be replaced with more suitable ones. Genes that might cause illnesses or deformities would be treated the same way, if the parents wanted the guarantee of a healthy child. For those prepared to pay the fee, the centre could also provide genetic therapy for naturally conceived babies, as well as those artificially conceived. All potential parents would be at liberty to choose the child of their needs. Adam shivered at the thought of man-made babies and wondered how these supercilious efforts to deny nature would affect the human race.

Through his gasps for breath, Adam murmured to himself, "nearly there now." Another half an hour and he would be sitting under a tree looking down on the city. He took another bite of his chocolate bar to give him strength to climb the hill. Exhausted, he reached the top and slumped down on the grass. He smiled to himself, feeling a wave of happiness surge over him. How glad he was to have completed his pilgrimage; tonight he would be sleeping nearer the stars. He leaned his back against an old birch tree and unwrapped the remaining chocolate bar. How far away the city seemed now. In a distant field he could see the large farm buildings that were used to house animals. He remembered his childhood days, when cows and horses, chickens and goats, pigs and geese, were familiar farmyard sights and wandered freely in open spaces. Now all animals, apart from some sheep and a few dairy herds, were locked away in pens inside buildings for twenty-four hours a day. They never saw the light of day from birth till death. All they represented were eating machines, forced to consume any concoction that man chose to feed them. Hormone injections, antibiotics, genetically engineered fodder and the brains and flesh of other animals, all administered to these vegetarians in order to swell their flesh with profit.

He reflected on his thoughts of two years ago. It was then that he began to believe that it was time to re-evaluate his life. Now, here on this lonely hill, life was evaluating him. He wondered if it were not time for society itself to take a good look at its structure to ponder the future of twenty-first century people, for they faced the social and moral dilemmas that signalled that life's purpose had been lost.

Where could the many, many people who regularly asked of life 'what's it all about?' look for answers? He lay down, his eyes flickering on a sky unnaturally ablaze with fire. Circling his mind were the words, 'the more man learns, the less he knows,' and before his eyelids closed he said out loud, "The twentieth century – and then what?"

PART 1

What *Is It* All About?

CHAPTER ONE

The Reason

Although scientists have estimated that the 'Big Bang' which created the Earth occurred between ten and thirteen billion years ago, there is obviously no way that any mere mortal will ever be able to prove the age of our home. However, there is one fact that has been proven, and this is that our planet is one of the smaller ones in the solar system, and measures only 25,000 miles around the equator. Hence, it has been suggested that Earth is just an inconceivably insignificant mote in the universe. Because astronomical and planetary exploration has not discovered any other suitable habitat for *Homo sapiens* to occupy, it has also been said that for the foreseeable future human beings will be confined to living on the only planet in the universe that can support human life.

Some people assume that the Earth came about through a freak of nature, and that the existence of the human species is down to evolution. Whilst the first conjecture will remain eternally unprovable, scientific research offers what is thought to be the truth of the second. This tells that after the Earth's matter had been knocked into shape for billions of years, both by the meteors and violent weather conditions that bombarded it, that four plus billion years ago minerals and gases began to form that produced ingredients adequate to sustain life. The consequence of these occurrences was that cells were born to the oceans that had formed during the evolutionary process. From here other sea life forms evolved, by way of genetic reproduction, and this development affected the production of oxygen. When the build up of oxygen in the oceans reached superfluous proportion, it began to escape into Earth's atmosphere where it headed towards the skies. Here it eventually formed a layer of ozone that would protect the Earth from ultraviolet radiation, which is damaging to nearly all organisms. With this in place, organisms left the sea and headed to the Earth's surface to prepare the path for ongoing developments. Then, millions of years on, there was an explosion of life, with plants and wildlife ready to lay the foundations of a perfect planet. Whilst the plants and trees provided food, drink and shelter for wildlife, and contributed greatly to the development of the Earth, they also continued the production of essential oxygen. The animals' donation to the scheme was in accordance with Mother Nature's ingenious powers of creation. For to each and every species she had given a skill that they would integrate to create, and maintain, the delicate system. When the complex biological network of the planet reached the state of perfection, human life evolved by way of animal reproduction.

Legend has it that 'God' created the world, and that it took him only six days to do it at that. Only a fool would want to believe this. Should this person ever seek to prove his belief, he would need to plant a seed in his garden and note how long it would take for a flower to grow. Then he should observe if blooms appeared without many months of the combination of rain and sunshine. If the same observation were to be made to note how long it takes a tree to reach maturity, then one would have to hope for a lifespan of hundreds of years to complete the survey.

The conception of the Earth is a miracle beyond man's reason and intellect. Whose miracle – whose creation? We will never know the answer to this because no-one will ever be qualified to give it. What we need to acknowledge is that there is a superior power in existence. Then, go on to wonder if this power is nature itself? Why was the planet Earth given to man? Why was a lush green earth cultivated for so long to provide the human race with a home? My mind tells me that if it took billions of years to perfect the planet so that I could live on it, then I must be here on a very important mission.

When I was growing up I was given to believe that life is a test, and that the Earth is a testing ground. I am grateful to my elders for planting this wise thought in my mind, and creating a reason for my life on Earth. Without reason there can be no aim for living and, without aim, there can be no reason for living.

So what is this special mission we are on? Is it to be born, to live, and then to die, as many people believe? My own common sense and logic tell me that this is not the answer. If our lives meant nothing more than this, then why did we not evolve in any old corner of the universe? Say a black hole for instance, for this would be appropriate for this function. Why were we given a highly developed and perfect planet on which to live? When we take into account the vastness of time required to cultivate the Earth before it was ready for human habitation, plus the expanse of the universe itself, we have to ask some questions: is not man's lifespan on Earth so insignificant in comparison? Is it not anything more than a blink of the eye? If this is so, then why is he propelled to Earth for such a short time? Unlike every living animal, insect, plant and micro-organism which is vital to the cultivation and maintenance of the Earth, man has nothing to offer the planet. He does not even contribute to the food chain. In fact, man lives off the Earth, not for the Earth, and absorbs the benefits that others have toiled to give him. Whilst every other living species is vital to the planet's survival, man is not – he is more of a burden. So why is he here?

To me the suggestion of the Earth being 'a testing ground' makes good sense. Like other people who have found inner happiness I believe that the reason for our lives on Earth is to learn important lessons. My theory is that our souls incarnate on Earth, for as many times as it takes, to reach human perfection. Although the concept of it makes me shiver, I have come to a personal decision that our souls are eternal. I cannot for one moment begin to imagine what happens to them once they do become perfect. I would drive myself insane pursuing an answer to this question, as would anyone else. Many, many answers will always be beyond the realms of human cogitation. All that is certain for me is that there is no such creature as a perfect human being living on the Earth's surface. The souls who have reached this stage in their evolution have moved to a destination beyond our contemplation. When it is time for our souls to be born to the Earth, either for the first time, or one of numerous times, we inherit a human body and the characteristics of the species. Human beings have very many faults to overcome, the most debilitating one being selfishness. A baby's first instincts are towards itself when it looks for food and warmth and, to get what it wants it will cry until its needs are met. This innate instinct, which drives us towards self-survival, *is* selfishness. The instinct is a self-destructive one which has been given to us so that we can overcome it. However, one lifetime would not be long enough for a soul to fulfil the task. If someone were to begin to write a book entitled *How to Overcome Selfishness*, they would have to live unlimited lifetimes before they could bring it to a final conclusion.

In each life we are given our souls have certain grades to reach. If they are earthbound for the first time they will have no knowledge of any of life's lessons. There will be so much for them to learn that they will stumble and fall over life's hurdles, without even noticing the one labelled 'selfishness'. Then, second-time comers, third, fourth, fifth and so on might have been so busy trying to achieve the easier of their tasks last time round, that they run out of time before attempting 'the big one'. Even those who have lived enough lifetimes, and learned enough, to qualify them to set forth on their quest to become perfected souls, may not yet have conquered their own selfishness. The theory is that our souls return to the Earth for as many times as it takes to learn the lessons that will lead us to human perfection. So, because the human race will always consist of imperfect souls, the world will never be a perfect one.

The ultimate aim of an advanced spirit is to find perfection in itself despite having to live in an imperfect world. But there are no set rules for achieving this. All that a mere human being can do in life is his or her best, according to personal feelings. As we grow older our beliefs and standards change and transform us. Our views about life when we are twenty will certainly change by the time we reach sixty. It is the same with our soul's lives on Earth. Each time it returns it will develop in different ways. One lifetime might teach one thing and the next, another. This pattern will continue until it is ready to receive the final lesson, the one which highlights the road to perfection. However it will only learn lessons when it is ready to do so – when it has had enough experience. Therefore, as mere human beings we must be gentle with ourselves and realize that we are at the beck and call of our soul, and that in any one lifetime we can only achieve (or not achieve) the tasks set for us for that particular span.

My conception of our lives is that they are journeys to the discovery of our own souls. And they are hard journeys because there are no little arrows saying – 'this way to your soul' or 'three paces forward, ten paces back and then dig for your soul'. The ones who have succeeded in making these discoveries have gone forever and taken their blueprints with them. Finding one's soul is a personal task – and the greatest asset you have to help in your search is *you*. In a world intended to be imperfect the only perfection that can be developed is your own.

How can I prove my assumption that our souls live multiple lives as human beings – I can't! My attitude towards life is that, if you believe, there are no questions, if you don't believe, there are no answers (this is as far as unprovable matters are concerned). Whilst I do not presume to offer any answers, perhaps my thoughts about multiple lives are worth a listen.

The first element to spring to my mind is déjà vu. How many of us have experienced the feeling of having lived an experience before? How many times have you heard it said, 'I have done this before', 'I have seen this place before,' 'I feel as if I've known you for a lifetime' or 'I feel that we have met before'? Could it be that we have known that person for a lifetime – a previous lifetime? And do we *imagine* that we have seen a place before, or *have* we seen it before? Then parents and grandparents are often amazed by the knowledgeable antics of the babies of the family. "This one has been on the Earth before" is a sentence used so often in the history of mankind. Do we use it because we are trained to do so, or might we believe that there is an atom of truth in it? Can we not wonder why little children sometimes know so much of what they have not yet experienced, or learned of life? The saying 'we can learn a lot from children' is often well founded when a child gives us the answer to a problem that we can't sort out ourselves. How could a child do this when its wisdom belongs to mere infancy? What of child prodigies? Why, when there is no family history to indicate similar talents, are some children able to play musical instruments instinctively without having had any lessons? How are small children able to compose music, when the art of composition could take a lifetime to acquire? Brilliance in children comes out in other activities too – perhaps football, mathematics, acting, painting, writing, dancing etc. Skills which should take many years to learn and perfect. Could it be that they have done these things before?

If we are destined to live one life on Earth, and one life only, can we also not ask why are we not all born equal? Why are some of us born to riches and others to poverty, some to health yet others to ill health? Why is it that many people have a lifetime of strife, whilst others escape it and find themselves living quite an easy life? Surely a once-given life of living and dying would put us all on an even keel, wouldn't it? Why should millions be born to a no-hope environment of a famine-bound country, whilst millions more are born to a country of plenty. Not a fair equilibrium for a once-off lifetime!

Then what of our phobias, our fears? Why are some of us terrified of fire, spiders, water, heights, enclosed spaces and so on and so forth? Why should we have these fears when nothing at all has happened in our lifetime to cause them? Could it be that they developed in previous lifetimes?

If my thoughts have inspired you into thinking that yes, there is something in it and we might live more than one life, then you may assume that, consequently, we die more than one death. And of course we do, and this occurs when our souls have completed the tasks undertaken for a particular lifetime and are ready to leave the Earth. However, the way in which our souls choose to release their earthly bodies can often leave living human beings perplexed. For example, if death comes suddenly to human beings at an early age, without there being any physical illness to cause it, the question asked will be, 'Why has this death occurred?' Then, medical experts will certainly be baffled if a perfectly healthy patient dies whilst undergoing a simple routine operation which they perform on a daily basis. If it is an accident that causes a death then people will wonder why just one person died when many others were subjected to the same impact of the incident. And, what of wartime deaths? Who of us does not wonder why some soldiers die whilst others, grouped in the same place at the time of a bomb explosion, live? Not only can the death of a human being signify that a soul has completed the tasks it has set for itself, for another implication is that it has reached perfection and is ready to leave the Earth forever to move onto a higher plane. Furthermore, it might well be that it had chosen death itself to be the task it had to conquer to qualify to go on to advanced learning, or to reach human perfection. This might apply particularly to babies who die in the womb, or shortly after birth, for no apparent reason. Perhaps in these cases it might well have been that just the effort of being conceived, or the trauma of being born, was enough to qualify these souls for advancement, or perfection.

I am indicating here that in order for a soul to advance it must undergo varying degrees of suffering. Perhaps each of us is aware that we cannot feel the pain of others, unless we have experienced that same pain ourselves. How many times have we heard it said, 'you won't know what it feels like unless it happens to you?' We will never appreciate true happiness until we have known unhappiness. We will not respect good health until we have experienced poor health. We won't be happy with our wealth unless we have suffered poverty. We will not be grateful for the food on our plates until we have endured hunger. We will not be aware of true friendship until we have tolerated loneliness. Each time we suffer, our souls grow a little more.

What is a soul? Even those who do not believe in multiple lives must sometimes wonder it's function. From the mouth of a very dear friend of mine (who happens to be an all-out disbeliever) came his definition of the word. He said, "The soul is the part of you that goes onto other things". If we were to think of our soul as being 'the part of us that goes on to other things', where could this be? Perhaps they might hop onto a star and gallop off into eternity; or burrow underground and vegetate into oblivion; or journey to other planets to occupy the bodies of indigenous beings there. Then possibly they could return to planet Earth to continue their education. In the Hindu and Buddhist religions there is a word which describes the function of the soul. This word is karma – a dictionary definition follows: -

> *Sum of person's actions in one of his successive states of existence, viewed as deciding his fate in the next.*[i]

To put it in simpler terms: whatever we put into life we will get out.

When a soul incarnates on Earth it has a tough task to face, for the human species has many construction faults. These are those of selfishness, greed, hate, jealousy and evil. The good news is that the species is blessed with many positive attributes – like love, thoughtfulness, kindness and compassion. The mixture of these ingredients means that life on Earth is like a battlefield for humans where war rages between the strong forces of the 'faults', and the gentle ones of the 'positive attributes'. These go on and on until the day arrives when victory is won to leave faults defeated. All we will know then is the peace that those positive attributes bring. Let's look further at ourselves as human beings and examine our make-up. We like to win over others. Constantly we choose to portray that we are better than the next man. It is important to us that we are able to show that we have more strength, possessions and brains than him. Life to us is about scoring points and vying to be top of the list. It is like a giant competition where nobody knows what the prize for winning will be, but wants it anyway. As human beings we act this way because we have not yet discovered ourselves. We are unsure of who we are, and why we are here and search desperately for the answer. We will do almost anything to prove ourselves to the next man because we believe this could be it.

There is no panacea to cure the frailties of man. Inner happiness is a self-acquired commodity. Being alive means striving to become ourselves; striving to be who we are and recognising what makes us happy. We have been given the gift of life for a very special purpose, and with this gift we have been blessed with an individual personality which belongs to our own soul. Each of us has a special quality that is ours. Our duty should be to develop our gifts and not destroy them. By doing this we destroy ourselves.

Whilst the fundamental basis of our lives is to learn how to be happy and to believe in ourselves, we cannot achieve this without the help of other people. They will set the test papers for our exams from which we will learn how to develop the better qualities of ourselves. During the life we are living now we have to have a 'feel good' spirit in our hearts. This is the only way to find happiness. Often we act in ways we feel will portray messages about ourselves to those around us. Seldom are these actions the ones we need to fulfil personal happiness. Let's ask ourselves, how good do we feel if we have had a big argument with someone whilst attempting to prove our superiority. Are we able to sit back in contentment to believe that the world is a lovely place? Do we feel physically well, or does the matter keep going round in our heads, leading to our developing a headache or a tummy ache? When we have been out with friends and have spent time laughing and joking, do we come home feeling depressed and unwell? On the other hand if our actions have meant hurting someone, do we come home feeling on top of the world? In all honesty I think we all know the answers to these questions. It's all a matter of reaping what we sow isn't it? As the saying of the day goes – 'what goes around comes around'. During our lives we are all responsible for our own actions and must be prepared to accept whatever results they create. If we are happy doing what we do, fine. If we are not, then we have to attempt to change and find a way that will make us happy. Trouble is, it might take a whole lifetime to learn that it's *us* who manufacture the consequences of our lives. Trouble is, it might take a whole lifetime to learn that we should be proving ourselves to ourselves and not the next man.

Planet Earth is dominated by the presence of souls on a mission; some have been here many times; some few times; some not at all. Some will be on their way to perfection; some half way there; some far from it. The consequence of this is that the world will be both wicked and beautiful all at the same time; violence will walk hand-in-hand with peace; cruelty with kindness; sickness with health; bitterness with forgiveness; hate with love. Because the Earth houses souls who are on different levels of learning, this means that happiness will always exist in the world, as will suffering.

Four plus billion years to create a planet of perfection where the human race could live and breathe! For what? So that man could be born to become extinct – or that man could be born to reach the perfection of the planet itself? Nothing on Earth or the universe happens for nothing. Be gentle with yourself and try to believe that there is a reason for your life. You are here to learn how to believe in yourself. This is the way to inner happiness and to the perfection of your soul.

---

i The Concise Oxford Dictionary, 5th Edition (1964) Oxford University Press p661

CHAPTER TWO

The Hope

A master plan – God – what are these things? Who knows, who of us can say, "I know, I am an expert". No one. There is no evidence, no proof. There is no written examination that can be taken to pronounce a hundred per cent pass rate for this one. In spite of tests, studies, archaeological digs, out-of-body experiences, interviews with the spirits, illusions, research, surveys and so on, no one will ever find the answer. Probably because there *is* no answer or perhaps mankind should not have invented something called God in the first place! What we can say, and be sure of, is that there is a superior power out there which is much bigger than we will ever be. What it is is an unknown quantity.

What is the God we think we know of? Our conception might be that we have decided that whoever he is, a lot of wars are being fought in his name. We are indoctrinated from an early age into believing that God is some sort of man who sits on a big throne in the sky. We are told that God is love but when we do wrong he waves his arms about and punishes us by inflicting some terrible suffering on us. Is this cruel unrelenting God the one that asks mankind to love each other? What kind of hypocritical being have we created here to worship? Is this interpretation of God meant to inspire us?

The Church's version of God derives from the Old Testament of the Bible which consists traditionally of three parts. These are: THE LAW – which is the name given to the first five books written by the prophet who laid down the Ten Commandments. THE PROPHETS – which includes the prophetic histories. THE WRITINGS – which are all the books not covered by the previous two (e.g. Psalms). I think that very few of us, regardless of our various religions, would question the truth of the Ten Commandments of which we know, nor the basic principles and morals which the wise philosophers of the day recommended that people strive to achieve. However, the Old Testament advocates the fear of God and his wrath, and tells of evil events which He is supposed to have instigated. Regrettably the Church continues to support the God of the Old Testament without adding to, or deviating from, the conception. Alas, this leaves students of religion confined to an imprisoning inheritance.

A twentieth century comedian[i] always ended his show by saying – "Goodnight and may your God go with you". What a privilege it would be for us to believe in a God of our choice. A faith established by listening to various aspects of religious beliefs with an open mind, and hopefully recognising that there are many interpretations of the elusive God. Following the doctrines of any one cult denies us the freedom to reach out to our thoughts. Throughout history many atrocities have been committed, man against man, in the name of religion. Beliefs have created Gods of evil, ones who propel civilisations towards destruction. Religion inspires notions of a God who tells his followers they must go out and exterminate anyone who does not believe in his cause. With the interpretation of God varying from race to race, group to group, is it any wonder that so much blood is shed, so many tears wept? Is religion not a fight – God against God?

Do I believe in God? My faith is one which leads me to believe that if there were a God my interpretation of this entity would be that it is love – the love that exists in and around all of us. I believe too that the other fellow – old Satan himself – also exists in the same capacity. (Do I believe in Heaven and Hell? I do, but that these places are again within ourselves.) As opposed to the many legends, where God's voice has been heard emanating from a bush, the sky, or anywhere else – I believe that the voices of God, and Satan, come to us as the echo of our own thoughts. My beliefs about God, ourselves, our lives, our hopes have been inspired by the observation of life itself, my father (who taught me how to think), and by the teachings of a chap named Jesus. Jesus, the Jew, born in Bethlehem two thousand years ago. There is cause for controversy here as I pose a contradiction. I state that the Old Testament of the Bible is based on the beliefs of a God-fearing nation, whereas I am now offering testimony to the words of the New Testament. This portion of the book is based on the scribblings thought to be those of four of Jesus' disciples and friends. It seems feasible to think that these men would have remembered as many of his words as they could. However, for me it wouldn't matter if the authors of the New Testament fabricated the plot, and invented the dialogue. If the writings of the book were the fictitious work of a cartoon character, a tramp, an educated dog or a king, my awe would still continue. Why? Because I believe that these wise and well-founded words are ones which could lead us to happiness.

Taking into account that our calendar is derived from the event of Jesus' existence, and our holidays celebrate his birth, life and death – there are still many sceptics who doubt, rightly so, that Jesus ever did exist. This disbelief in Jesus is understandable as the story, as told, amounts to nothing more than a fairy tale. I believe that the simple truth of the matter is that two thousand years ago a baby was born and was named Jesus. As he grew into manhood it was observed that this man was a leader. He had great wisdom and forethought and was a terrific orator. His words conveyed a definite confidence that offered hope to a people struggling for survival, and a place in the world. He seemed to know what he was talking about and very soon people were hanging onto his every word. His followers grew in astounding numbers, and he was dubbed the Christ – which means the Saviour or the Messiah. He was someone who could sort out all their problems for them – he would know the answers. They had been waiting a long time for this prophet to come along and make everything right for them. They never pondered why a god could walk the earth in human form when his place was in the sky. When Jesus told them – *"what I can do, you can do also"*[ii] they didn't ask why. No one questioned him as to how a mere mortal could follow the example of a god.

The New Testament – the story of Jesus' life – was written supposedly sixty years after his death. I believe that before he showed himself as a leader of men – at a thirty-ish age – he was unknown. Accounts of his birth and childhood were no doubt asked of his mother at the time of his notoriety, and embroidered into the storyline which constitutes the New Testament. In the story Jesus was the Christ at birth, and the Christ at death, but no mention was made of this title in the intervening years. Why has the Church never questioned the missing years? Why is it automatically assumed that there was a twenty year hibernation period in Jesus' life? Some have sought an answer as to where Jesus, the child, grew into Jesus the man. It is a theory that can never be proven to the satisfaction of truth, but I for one find it feasible. It is said that Jesus travelled to India in his developing years to study with the yogis and gurus. If this is so then, having sought out the wisest teachers he could find to put him on the right path to understanding life, he would also have been indoctrinated with Hindu beliefs. When he graduated from his learnings he was ready to return to his homeland to pass on his knowledge.

Throughout the centuries the teachings of Jesus have been deciphered in many ways. But as he spoke in parables this is not surprising as the stories he told, which were of moral and spiritual connection, were not meant to convey literal significance. Instead they were an invitation for those who would listen to go away with their own thoughts, from which would come their own conclusions.

Setting aside the myth of the Jesus story I would suggest that some of the words of the New Testament are worth a listen (no matter who wrote them).

Hence, throughout the next paragraphs some of the well known phrases that Jesus supposedly spoke will be introduced. However, I will be taking two liberties here – the first, to convert the words to modern day language, the second, to give my own interpretation of them. Some of the statements written are so blatantly obvious to understand that it is difficult to imagine that anyone could interpret them wrongly. For example, throughout the New Testament the writings indicate that when Jesus spoke he referred to himself as 'the Son of Man', and never as 'the Son of God'. Another easy one is – *'do to other people what you would like them to do to you'.*[iii] The words that Jesus spoke tell me that he was a very positive person. I see no negative glimmers whatsoever. One of his most staggering statements was:
'If you have faith as big as a grain of mustard seed, nothing will be impossible to you. You could say to a mountain "move to another place" and it would.'[iv]

WOW! What an achievement that would be, but surely an impossible one! Was Jesus a comedian as well as everything else? Or can we not see that he was illustrating that we are capable of doing anything we choose to do, once we have achieved confidence and faith in ourselves. 'Faith' was a word used frequently by Jesus. As the people became familiar with his apparent healing powers, they followed him beseeching that he cured them of their illnesses. More times than not, when his 'patients' experienced relief from their sufferings, he would tell them that it was their own faith that had enabled the healing. In one particular incident a sick woman believed that if she could just touch the hem of Jesus' robe, she would be cured. Having felt the presence of her hand on his garment he turned to her and said, *"Take heart daughter; your faith has made you well."*[v]

Before I continue I would like to throw in a little anecdote here which illustrates the attributes of faith and confidence. My dad had suffered ill health for most of his life. He had only one lung and fluid collected frequently around the area. Many visits to the hospital were required so that the liquid could be drained away. At a time in his early thirties my dad became so dangerously ill that doctors pronounced that he would die. As he lay in the hospital bed, in agony because of the long needle inserted into his back, he heard two doctors talking. One said, 'What else can we do for him?' 'Nothing at all,' answered the other. 'He'll be dead before the morning comes'. Dad lay there thinking aloud, 'I am not going to die, I am not, I am not, and I'll show them'. How surprised the doctors were when they walked into the ward the next morning to see dad sitting up in bed. But how surprised he was too. Never did he envisage that the words he had spoken could have saved his life. But they had. He was so overwhelmed by the incident that he pledged to devote all his spare time to the study of the mind. Because of the knowledge he acquired not only did his ailing body survive for another thirty-six years, he developed a positivity which brought peace to his whole being. Having discovered the path which led him to his achievements his desire was to share his knowledge with others – and this he did.

But then, throughout man's evolution it has naturally followed that all positive learning be passed on; be it how to light a fire, to how to be contented. From his words it would seem that Jesus had learned what one had to do to gain inner happiness, and was eager to pass the instructions on to others. I believe that his teachings were not fired at the masses, but at the few who were ready to listen. The man was not an idiot: he knew what life was about. He was aware that the earth is a testing ground for the soul of man. He was in tune with the fact that the perfection of the human race, as a whole, was not the intention of life itself. At one point he said:

The gate to destruction is easy to get through because it is wide as lots of people use it. Few use the gate to life because it is narrow and hard to get through.[vi]

To me this statement means that it's much easier to follow the crowds regardless of their aims or intentions, whereas it is very hard to maintain the principles and beliefs that might lead to personal happiness.

However, given the fact that we all live many lives before we start to get it right, can we ask – how many lives had Jesus lived before the purification of his own soul was effected? It might be that only in his last lifetime, of thirty-odd years, did he finally make it. Up to then he was still struggling with himself. He was a human being and experienced the same turmoils and temptations as any other human being. For example, it is quoted in the New Testament that Jesus was heard to have said *'Get behind me Satan'*[vii] as he heard the voice of Satan asking him to perform magic tricks to prove that he was God. My own explanation as to why he said these words is that he was probably trying to dispel one of his own bad thoughts. As happens to every human being at some point in life, he might have being saying to himself, 'What the hell, everyone else is getting what they want, why shouldn't I? I will do as everyone else does'. Another story is that he went into the mountains to pray to God, and stayed there for forty days and forty nights. My explanation for these field trips is that he just had to get away sometimes to have some time to himself. Every day he had masses of people following him around, asking him questions, asking that he cure them, and imploring him to make everything right for them. The poor guy never had a moment to himself; everyone was taking from him and no one was giving. He must have been drained by people's constant demands on his resources. He had to get away from time to time to recharge his batteries – just the same as every other human being needs to do.

It is reported that he once went into a synagogue and found people selling wares there. He was so furious to see trading being carried out and money changing hands, that he overturned all the stalls and sent the wares flying. His action was as violent as any other normal human being's could have been. He had always preached that you must *'turn the other cheek to the people who would hurt you.*[viii] But Jesus himself was beyond practising his own preaching that day in the synagogue as he lost his self-control to become the victim of his offended feelings.

By the time of his death he had a highly sophisticated spirit, which merited his soul's perfection. As the nails were savagely hammered into his feet, and his hands; as the blood eked from his human flesh; as he was suffering the pain of this agonising death, he uttered two statements. The first one echoed the thoughts of any other man in this situation:

My god, my god why have you forsaken me.[ix]

He was questioning was there really a God in heaven, he was wondering what his life had been about and why his efforts had been in vain. He had done nothing to deserve the punishment he was receiving. His thoughts lulled him into silence for a while. Then, before slipping into the unconsciousness of death he said of his executioners:

Forgive them, they don't know what they are doing.[x]

In making this statement he was saying to his friends and followers 'I have forgiven them, you try to forgive them too because they are ignorant of life'.

As part of his teachings Jesus had advocated that:

The dead bury the dead.[xi]

What on earth did this phrase mean? Could it be that his last words on the cross were the explanation to this puzzle. Could the answer be that those who choose not to learn anything about the art of living, and giving, should stay together in ignorance. He had taught too:

Be merciful as your Father is also merciful. [xii]

Did his last words also embrace this example of forgiving other people's faults in the same way that we expect God to forgive our wrongs?

Forgiving other people for the wrongs they commit against us is the ultimate task given us. Jesus, the man, reached this final stage of spiritual perfection. If you do believe that Jesus did exist then, try to think of him as just a man. A man with the same inadequacies as us all, the same faults, the same fears. Try to forget the legends of Jesus the God – Jesus the Saviour. Ask yourself, if he were more than a mere human being, a God, an alien, would he have needed to suffer such a cruel death. Wouldn't a God merely have evaporated, or at least felt no pain? Wouldn't an alien from another planet merely have 'beamed up', or at least have been rescued by his own people? During the very short span of his infamous life, Jesus was a teacher of living. He told of ways to acquire personal happiness. He did not say, 'I am a God who will make everything right for you' and he did not ask to be worshipped. His words conveyed only the strong message of how to gain one's self-esteem. He wanted us to know that it was up to us what we made of our lives – pointing out that there is a wrong way and there is a right way.

Knowing that his life would be short-lived he had recruited the twelve men, known as his disciples, to learn the lessons that he had learned. What he wanted of them was to spread his words so that they would be known in all corners of the world. He did not advocate that they go out and construct buildings where people could gather to hear the words. Nor did he spawn the idea of their erecting places so that groups of folk could pray together. On the contrary. When he taught his followers the prayer, commonly known as the Lord's Prayer, he said:

> *When you pray, do not be like the hypocrites who pray in the synagogues or on the corner of streets, so that other people can see them. When you pray, go to your own room and when you have shut the door, pray to your 'father' in secret. When you pray do not use vain repetitions like heathens do. They think they will be heard because they are saying a lot. Don't be like them, because your father knows what you need before you ask him. These are the words that you pray.*
>
> *Our father, which art in heaven, hallowed be your name. Your Kingdom come, your will be done, on earth as it is in heaven. Give us this day our daily bread, forgive our debts as we forgive our debtors. Lead us not into temptation but deliver us from evil.*[xiii]

As a child Jesus visited the synagogues of the day but he did not go there to pray; he went to listen to the words of his elders to learn from their wisdom of life and its meaning. Now here as a man he was asking his followers to pass on *his* words. He wanted people to experience the personal effect they might have on their lives, and was asking them to give it a try. The wishes of Jesus did reach fruition for his disciples did go to different parts of the world to spread his words. In a movement called Christianity people gathered together in great numbers. The disciples, and many Christian followers, lost their lives advocating the cause; many of them suffered deaths more agonising than Jesus did. After this came the first 'Christian' Church which was founded in Rome, Italy by Peter – the disciple who denied knowing Jesus three times. Figures at the end of the twentieth century estimate that one third of the world's population is 'Christian'. But is this so? How many of this number follow the teachings of 'the Christ', and how many of that number earn the title 'Christian'. Has the word – like God, become commonplace and meaningless? Do we say the word in the same way we would say 'God Almighty', 'Christ', 'Jesus', or 'Good Lord'? – a series of catchy phrases that trip easily off the tongue. Hordes of us scramble off to church, week in week out where together we mumble choruses of words. We kneel with eyes closed and chant the prayer that a very wise man taught us to say in private, some two thousand years ago. Many of us know the words so well; we have been hearing them since the day of our birth. The prayer is our heritage and we believe that by chanting it, we are securing a place for ourselves in that destination known as heaven. But what of this heaven, where is it? When Jesus preached:

> *Do not accumulate treasures on earth where moths and rust consume and thieves break in and steal. Instead, accumulate treasures in Heaven, where the moths, rust and thieves can't get at them. That's where your heart will be*[xiv].

was he not telling us that the only treasure that cannot be stolen from us is the inner happiness which constitutes the heaven in our lives? And more vigorously encouraging, and positive suggestions followed:

> *Do not be anxious for tomorrow for tomorrow will take care of itself. Let the day's own trouble be sufficient.*[xv]

I take this to mean don't worry about the things that might never happen. Use all the strength you have to make the most of today. Indications of the 'boomerang' aspect of our lives was made when Jesus said:

> *Give and you will be given.*[xvi]
> *Forgive and you will be forgiven.*[xvii]
> *Do not judge others and you will not be judged.*[xviii]
> *Do not condemn others and you will not be condemned.*[xix]

Do these statements not tell us that whatever we put into our lives, we will get back? From personal experience, I would like to add my own comment here which is – whatever we put into our lives we get back *eventually*. Nothing happens overnight, we have got to be prepared to wait till the time is ready. Even if we cannot believe in having to live more than one life, surely we can see the logic of making the most of the life we have now. Before we can begin to feel happy we must first try to make others happy. Everything comes back – especially a smile. Have you ever smiled at someone without their returning it? And so it is with everything else too. All of us might verify that if we shout at someone, they'll shout back. If we're nasty to someone, they'll be nasty back and so on and so forth. My dad always used to say, "it costs nothing to be nice". But then, it might take us many years of living to recognise that what we give we'll receive. Many years, because we can't see the light of day through the mist that hovers over us. The mist that is made up of our own hang-ups, our own misgivings, our own suffering, which are the tests we have to overcome before the light will shine in. With compassion in his heart, Jesus offered words of consolation and encouragement for those carrying a heavy burden. He said:

Blessed are the people who are hungry because they will be filled.[xx]
Blessed are those of you who cry because you will laugh.[xxi]

What about this promise, that all would be well? Was he saying that once we overcome the suffering that we experience, we will be better beings? Might it be that our suffering makes us happier with ourselves and those around us – might it not even inspire us to become contented with what we have going for us? Jesus was against wealth and stressed that the only road to happiness is by way of adversity. He said:

Blessed are those of you who are poor because you will make it to the kingdom of heaven[xxii] *(heaven in the sky? Or heaven on earth?).*
It is harder for a rich man to reach the gates of heaven than it is for a camel to squeeze through the eye of a needle.[xxiii]
What shall it profit a man if he gains the whole world and loses his soul.[xxiv]
Misery to those of you who are rich, because you have already received your consolation.[xxv]

Might these statements suggest that money cannot buy the happiness that comes to us only when we have learned to measure our riches through the fewness of our desires?

Yet the Christian church is dominated by wealth. Church buildings are adorned with gold effigies and valuable art treasures. The risk of theft of these items is so great that the buildings have to be secured against thieves. Alarms are fitted to the walls, metal grids to the windows, and padlocks to the doors. At the end of every church service collection plates are passed around and the congregation is asked to fill them with money. Monetary investment is paramount to the establishment. In its early stages one could only become a church member if one had land to bequeath to the cause. Now the church is the proud possessor of thousands and thousands of acres of valuable land, on which is built churches, and massive houses to home the clergy. The site of the first Christian church, built by one of Jesus' disciples, has now become a city which bathes in wealth. There, in the name of God, reigns an empire of money collectors who sport their own bank and law enforcement, etc.

Something very alien to Christianity is practised in some churches too – this is confession. In a two-way box sits a priest on one side, and a sinner on the other. With a partition between the two, the sinner reveals his wrongdoings, whilst the priest forgives him for these. The priest blesses the sinner and suggests that he doesn't sin again. The sinner goes away happy with the thought that his wrong doings have successfully been wiped out. How can one human being believe that he or she has been endowed with such superiority, that he is empowered to tell another human being that his sins are forgiven? Even Jesus (who was supposed to be God) never assumed that he could take people's misdemeanours away from them. Never did he encourage anyone to leave it to him to solve their problems. He suggested instead what they could do to create happiness for themselves. Never did he say to anyone, 'Tell me what you have done wrong and I will forgive you for it'. Jesus was very aware that every soul is responsible to itself. He was very much in tune with the fact that only souls can correct any faults that occur. Jesus taught us a prayer, which embraces the words 'forgive us our sins'. He told us to say this prayer only when we were alone with the thoughts of our own space. Why? Was he perhaps advocating that we appeal to the good inside ourselves to support us through life? Was he not suggesting that, if we recognised our misgivings, we might be nearer to overcoming them? Was he not telling us that the good inside ourselves is the God inside ourselves? Never in his capacity of leader of man did Jesus ever say, "Off you go, do exactly what you want even if it means hurting someone else, then come back and tell me about it so I can forgive you". He did recommend that thought and kindness be given to others and suggested that, if this could not be achieved, we look to ourselves for forgiveness. So what gives the church the right to the supremacy it assumes? No one human being can manipulate the soul of another human being. One man cannot remove the responsibility of living from another. Souls are responsible for themselves and to themselves with the exception of none. No matter how many reassuring words are spoken to us by vicars, priests, rabbis, monks and nuns etc., our misdemeanours will live in our souls until *we* learn to correct them.

We humans have a need – one that requires us to hold onto something to stop us drowning in the whirlpool called life. God, Christ, Buddha, Jehovah, Mohammed, Krishna, the church – all offer the lifeline which eliminates us from learning to swim. The fear of oneself is the one which sends us scurrying into the arms of religion looking for protection from ourselves. Jesus, the man, the teacher, lost his life whilst endeavouring to educate us into believing that we are the masters of our own destinies. He tried to impress that God is the love which exists in a soul. He spoke with wisdom, knowledge, courage and sheer common sense. For his 'crimes' of speaking aloud, he was first crucified and then immortalised. Whilst churches continue the immortalisation with messages on their billboards saying, *'Christ is risen,' and, 'Christ is with you,'* the truth is that Jesus the man, the philosopher who died nearly two thousand years ago, did not ask to be worshipped. What he did ask was that his words of hope be heard. Words that told that happiness is achievable through oneself.

---

i Dave Allen (1936-2005)
ii John 14:12
iii Luke 6:31
iv Matt. 17:20
v Matt. 9:22
vi Matt. 7:13-14
vii Luke 4:8
viii Matt. 5:39
ix Matt. 27:46
x Luke 23:34
xi Matt. 8:22
xii Luke 6:36
xiii Matt. 6:5-13
xiv Matthew 6:19-20
xv Matt. 6:34
xvi Luke 6:38
xvii Luke 6:37
xviii Luke 6:37
xix Luke 6:37
xx Luke 6:21
xxi Luke 6:21
xxii Luke 6:20
xxiii Luke 18:25
xxiv Matt. 16:26
xxv Luke 6:24

CHAPTER THREE

The Purpose

In the weakness of human frailty and lack of imagination, power has always been acknowledged as strength throughout mankind's existence. When philosophers (like the man Jesus) have come along to inspire the human species with visions of hope and well-being, they have too often met with execution. For this is the resolve that powerful leaders have taken to silence those whom they fear will incite the populace into revolution against their ruling, should they reveal simple truths to them. We talk here of the superpower which belongs to those who control fellow humans en masse to gain their own ends. However, power-seeking has an abundance of followers outside this realm, and in every walk of life there are those who wish to dominate many, are happy to rule the few, or are satisfied to dictate to just one other person to achieve what they believe to be strength. If we are to try to forgive the wrongs which are committed man against man in the cause of power, the belief in multiple lives is essential, for to have this is to recognise that those who inflict suffering this way are in the early stages of learning. Also, to have this is to be aware that we all have practised cruelty by power at some stage of our evolution. As souls who incarnate on Earth to learn the lessons that teach how to reach perfection in human form, we have to get it wrong before we can get it right. Therefore when we exercise the evil of power or any other negative human trait, in one lifetime, we will become the recipients of same in our next, or future, incarnations. For only by experiencing the negative and positive aspects of humankind can souls determine which of them will develop the inner happiness that will carry with them life to life. One day we will all graduate to human perfection through our learning.

Apart from those we know who have lost their lives because of their humane beliefs, there are millions of others who do not make the headlines but are reaching the 'Jesus standard' daily. People who have acquired spiritual perfection by learning firstly, how to forgive themselves, then how to forgive others. They won't be shouting the odds about themselves or even desiring to let others know how they have done it. In fact they probably won't even know that they have. Their spiritual perfection will have happened to them because it was ready to happen. Have you ever met someone who makes you feel inadequate because of their abundant tolerance? I know I have and have always wondered at that person's tranquillity and capacity to forgive. This person never has a bad word to say against anyone. He or she is happy with their lot and feels nothing but love for the rest of mankind.

Some time ago I was listening to a radio programme about drink drivers. Three mothers, whose children had been killed by people under the influence of alcohol, were being interviewed. Two of the women voiced their opinions with anger and full-blown bitterness. Every mother listening to the programme would have understood their feelings and joined with the two to campaign for the execution of people who killed other people whilst drunk. My whole being fell into peace as the third lady began to speak. With love, tranquillity and compassion, she told the story of her five-year-old daughter who had been run down and killed by a young man who was driving his car after consuming too much alcohol. What's more, the lady was not able to bear any more children – her daughter had been a long awaited miracle. When she heard the news of her daughter's death she was devastated. She said that she died an agonising death herself. When the court case was due to be heard she duly attended. Reaching the courtrooms she saw the young man and his wife outside. They looked so anxious and very sad as he stood there waiting to be called. She felt so much compassion for them that she went over to them and embraced them both. The man started to cry and said that he would never forgive himself as long as he lived. She comforted him as best she could by saying that she wished him love and hoped that one day he would learn to forgive himself. The lady went on to explain to the interviewer that she felt sorry for the plight of the young of the day because the pressure and stress of modern day living was enough to turn people to drink in order to forget life for a while. With job insecurity as it was, who knew who was going to be out of work next? Then what would happen to them; they would not be able to keep up payments of their large mortgages and could risk having their homes repossessed. On top of this worry the young were continually hearing that the planet is 'burning up'. The lady's interview concluded by her saying, 'Their world is one which portrays no hope for the future.' How more spiritually perfect could one be than this? This lady had lost the only child she would ever have, but found it in her heart to forgive the child's killer and wish him well. No world headlines – no television coverage – no god-like worship for this lady. Yet, like Jesus, she had reached perfection with flying colours, with the likelihood of never having to return to Earth for any more lessons. The survival of our species depends on the influence of the more developed spirits – like the lady I have just mentioned who generate love and forgiveness. Without these spirits our species would become extinct.

The purpose of our lives is to build strength for our souls but as with any building, this depends on the quality of the foundations. One course of bricks would not be sufficient to support a building, so, a second is laid then a third and a fourth and so on, until the foundations are solid enough to take the weight of the structure. So it is with our lives. As mere human beings we are not able to house our souls properly until the foundations are made ready. However, the building materials for this purpose are not as readily available as bricks and mortar, for there is only one supplier of the commodities we require, and that supplier is us. We need to build up a stock of unselfishness, thoughtfulness, kindness, tolerance, compassion, self-esteem, humility and love, and then mix these together with a generous helping of suffering.

Why suffering? Isn't this something that represents injustice in our lives? Why should we have to suffer, and why should we try to comprehend the diseases, bodily imperfections, poverty, cruelty, heartaches, etc. that are inflicted on us? Only by believing that we are souls with bodies, and not bodies with souls, could we begin to understand that the karma we live now is dictated by our souls. They are the ones who have to make amends for mistakes made in previous lifetimes, and the source they choose for the purpose is the suffering that *we* now know. However, we can't sit around worrying about past lifetimes and wonder what our souls did wrong then, can we? After all, they occupied another body then and lived in a different time. All that we can do is to try to accept that suffering is an aid to our soul's human perfection. From here we must try to harmonise with them to overcome current pain (without bitterness) by summoning all the strength we can find. Another theory which may be worth a thought is – could it be that during incarnations our souls choose to undertake challenges without an atonement plan afoot? Might they do this just to examine the emotion of the experience in an endeavour to learn from it?

We have to consider also that we humans often create our own misery as we trundle along life's paths. When we make mistakes and they cause us to be unhappy the simple resolve would be for us to correct these errors. However we don't apply this method, but instead continue to do the same things over and over again. Each time we err we might find our unhappiness deepening, and our health deteriorating, but still we don't submit to the pressure of it all. Only when our self-manufactured suffering reaches its peak and tells us that enough is enough will we mend our ways and put an end to our pain. Suffering, I believe, is the master teacher whose fees are exorbitant but is as essential to us as the air that we breathe, for without it we would learn nothing of life. In the following prose I offer my impression of the subject:

Without suffering there would be no compassion or understanding in the world.
Without suffering mankind would not explore the depths of its soul, or the extent of its talents. Suffering is hard to bear – it appears futile and Godless.
Yet it develops character, strength and an understanding in human beings.
The qualities, which enable the human race to survive.
The gains, which are a deterrent to complete selfishness.
How can the most selfish of people retain their self-pity when they come to face another who is less fortunate than themselves? Another human being who is without eyes, ears, limbs, senses or who suffers an incurable disease. Do they not feel compassion for that person and forget their own ego, if not for more than minutes, hours, days or weeks? The feelings of unselfishness appear and those of self disappear. The sufferings of the sufferers are never in vain.
We ask ourselves why we are born – to what purpose? Is the reason to travel through life in an oasis of self-indulgence? Or is it to learn to be unselfish despite the gruelling tests we face? To give, to love, to feel, to understand – above all to be tolerant of others, to recognise their qualities regardless of their aims. Only through the suffering of our own existence will we appreciate the needs of others.
Day by day the atrocities of evil beset us and a cry goes out against God. But is it God's world? Or is it man's world? Does God create suffering, or, does it support our moral strength? Can it prevent the actions of man against mankind, or is it not the epitome of compassion? If it were God's world there would be no need for man. No aims, no purpose, no reason to conquer selfishness in our own being. The sufferings of the sufferers are never in vain.
Only because of them can mankind continue to live. And when we realise the good, which is done in the world we can relate to them. We have them to thank for the benefits, which many are able to enjoy. We have them to thank when we try to correct our own misgivings. Them to thank when we learn to offer love and understanding to our fellow men.
Without suffering there would be no music. No book or poem would ever be written – no painting ever painted. Without the suffering of the few there would be no freedom from suffering for the masses. No gentle blessings to appreciate, no great heights to explore – no feelings. Our thirst for the knowledge of living would wane. Our appetite to learn the answers would evaporate. Without suffering there would be no eternal happiness for anyone.

Many times I have heard it said that it takes different things to make people happy. Of course it does, because all people are on different levels of learning. Mrs Rumouroid is happy when she is spreading gossip. Mr Wantalot is happy when he is talking about his possessions. Mr and Mrs Powerseeker love to portray their control over others. Young bully Jim is not happy unless he is knocking someone's block off. Some people even seem to derive happiness from torturing or killing others. The question is – do the things they do make these people happy or, is it just kindergarten happiness? Are they not the scholars in the infancy of learning and might further lessons prove to them that what they used to do does not make them happy anymore?

What is happiness? It's a similar question to 'What is God?' isn't it? There is no definition, there is only the explanation that you either are, or you are not. My own observation is that only happy people can, or want to, promote happiness for others. I feel that happiness comes when we are content with ourselves, content with who we are and what we are, leaving no room in our minds for guilt or self-remorse, hate or bitterness. This frame of mind cannot be achieved by waving a magic wand – so how does it happen? Well, how many years does it take to become proficient at anything? Life is rather like a garden. We can plant a flower or a shrub in one position but come to realise that it does not flourish there. Perhaps there is not enough light on the spot, or there is too much sunshine. So we decide that we must move it to another part of the garden where it will grow better. It might take us many, many years of making mistakes and correcting them before we create a garden which satisfies our own standards. So then, how long might it take to perfect something as delicate and intricate as a human soul? Perhaps many, many lifetimes, eh? As human beings, all we can do in any one lifetime is our best. Advancement in our development will happen only when the time is ready. However, as we are earthbound so many times, the sooner we consciously try to learn our lessons the better. The most important one we should know, regardless of the level we are on, is that life is an investment. Therefore the sooner we recognise that we get out of life what we put in, the better it will be for us. If we look at the words of every philosopher who has walked the earth, we will note that their messages have said quite clearly, 'every soul is responsible for itself and to itself'. The despatch given to us throughout history has been 'what you sow you will reap'. Really it takes only a little common sense to realise that all happiness stems from ourselves. Only we can determine what makes us happy – not socially happy, agreeably happy, or outwardly happy – but inwardly happy. Throughout our lives all we can do is to ask ourselves, "Does what I do make me happy? Am I happy with who I am? What am I?" How many of us know what we are or who we are? We are on a mystery tour where we won't know what makes us do this, or why we feel that. Life is not easy, but then, never was it intended to be. That's the test. The test is to strive to know ourselves as we truly are. It is to triumph over fears, clamber over obstacles and conquer suffering by forgiving its source. Regardless of our level of learning, we all have the capacity of thought and are able to measure the results of our actions. Whether they have good results or bad, whether they promote happiness or unhappiness. And, at the end of the day, whether what we do makes us feel good inside.

Being aware of multiple lives can stimulate the state of acceptance of life itself and make living more bearable. We can learn to believe that our lives are ordained and therefore there's not much point in worrying too much. With luck, we might stop worrying at all; knowing that 'what will be will be'. If this happens then all that is left for us to do is to get on with our lives and make the most of them. We have to forget previous lives and future lives. We have to stop thinking about heaven and other planets. We have got to come to terms with the fact that this is the life we have now, and this is the world in which we have to live. After this, all that is left is to make the most of ourselves, and aim towards self-worth. Don't forget, life is an investment where we get out what we put in. If we dole out love, happiness and giving, then that's what we will eventually get back. If we spread hate, aggression and selfishness, then this too will come back to us – sooner rather than later.

'Self-worth' is defined by the view we have of ourselves. We can profess to have this commodity if we *are* contented with what we are. It does not matter a dot what other people think of us – it's what we think about ourselves that matters. If we are happy with us, if we silently love ourselves - then we can say that we love God. If we love God (which is the good inside ourselves) we are well on the way to promoting love itself and developing an inner happiness which is indestructible. Then, from here on in, there will only be room left in our lives for the advancement of our own spirits – all else will be unimportant.

Because I am neither a 'God botherer' nor religious in any way, I offer my apologies for continuing to quote the words of Jesus. But as you know I regard him only as a wise philosopher. He was speaking about self-worth when he said;

Love your enemies and try to do something good to the people who hate you.[i]

Love your enemies and do good for them without asking for anything in return. Your reward will be great.[ii]

The words are simple enough to understand aren't they? They convey the message that you would feel good inside if you did either of these things.

We always need to remember that if we do something good, then we will feel good. If we do something bad then we will feel bad – if we do nothing at all then this is what we will feel. Our happiness depends on us.

In all our lives there is an ever-appearing deadly dragon which signifies our most dominant fear – the one of ourselves. When Mr Dragon appears we run to hide until he has gone away. We have to learn that he will never go away completely, unless we go out there and conquer him. We are constantly running away from ourselves; always blaming others for the negative parts of our personalities. The most popular victims of our blame are parents or birthright. There are those who believe that our souls choose who our parents are going to be before we make our re-entry into the world. I can feasibly go along with this theory, knowing that what we think of ourselves depends very much on our upbringing. Therefore, our birthright can be one of the most paramount tests of our lives.

Every child born to the earth seeks love and security to promote well-being. If a child knows these assets then he or she has a head start and can come to terms with themselves as adults, without having to fight for love and attention. The child who has been unloved (or even imagined that he or she has missed out on love) might spend a very large proportion of life looking for that love. The pursuit to find this might be so intense that progress will be stunted. The chance is that these people will remain in the state of childhood for either a long period of their lives or, for the whole of them. They might be lucky enough to meet other people who are strong enough to steer them away from their constant demands for love and attention. Through them they might discover the path to self-esteem and maturity. If not, they will have to suffer the misery they will cause themselves by not knowing that no one will love and respect them until they love and respect themselves. For the child who suffers either abuse or total rejection at the hands of parents, a really tough task lies ahead. These children have a thousand mountains to climb before they can get started on building their own self-esteem. They are of a mind that they are bad; that they have done something terrible to be punished like this. They will probably continue to punish themselves unmercifully. They might live in an abyss of confusion – where other people's nightmares are their reality. Their burden in life could be so heavy that the only thing they would be able to carry with them would be their own survival kit. There would need to be an army of understanding and compassionate people, to guide these people to the path of self-esteem.

So then – our birthright can either be our building block, or our stumbling block, depending on our soul's choice of parents. Karma has begun. To outwit our soul, and advance in our own progress, we need to learn quickly that our parents were only the vehicles of our birth and not the reason for it. Once we have recognised this very simple fact, then we can begin to look for the reason itself.

Only then can we start to take a good look at ourselves, to observe what we've got going for us. Time to move Mr Dragon away, he's blocking our view.

If we have experienced a handicap in our lives which we feel has been caused by our parents, it is more than likely that this is what our karma intended for us. Then as we embark on our quest for adulthood, with plans to overcome this hurdle, our relationship with our parents should be allocated to perspective accordingly. There are lots of things to be considered when we assess our folks. Firstly, they are mere human beings, the same as ourselves. When we were born, nobody waved a magic wand over them to transform them into perfect parents. The only way they could raise us was their way. They had their own beliefs, standards and morals. Most important too: they had their own deadly dragons to deal with. When we contemplate the worries in our own life, let's not forget that they probably had the same concerns. They were only able to pass onto us what they knew themselves. Therefore, we need to learn to accept them for what they were, and to forgive them for what they were not. Then, to appreciate that the love our parents gave us was given in the only way they knew how. We should not go on blaming them because they did not love us in the way we wanted to be loved. If we feel that the only thing our parents gave us was life itself, then we must be grateful for this. Our life is important, it is precious. Our parents gave us this life. No person on earth is perfect, so why did we expect perfection from our parents? Until we learn that we cannot go on blaming our birthright for our own inadequacies, we cannot go forward. If we respect our parents for what they gave us, if we feel love for them, this is as near perfect as we can get. If we cannot respect them, and feel only hate and anger towards them, we have to try to forgive them for their wrongs against us. This is the only way that we will move forward.

At some point in our lives we have to become responsible for ourselves, regardless of our birthright. We cannot travel through life forever blaming our parents, or others, for what we are ourselves. We are the ones who affect our thoughts and actions; we cannot shift the blame for our failures, or our wrong doings, to anyone other than ourselves. The more we shift the blame, the bigger the hiding place we create when that dragon comes along. Learning to face the dragon requires strength; learning to defeat him requires self-acceptance. Accepting oneself is the emotional beginning of happiness and contentment and once we learn this we can stop jumping into the dragon shelter. In fact we won't know where to look for it anymore because we won't need to use it. All that is left is the massive recognition of oneself, and the mammoth responsibility of controlling our own happiness. With the dragon dead we can come to terms with the cause and effect syndrome in our lives. We will begin to see that our actions – be they good or bad – bring about our own ends.

There is the reverse side to parenthood to think about also. After clambering over the painful bridge to adulthood we are faced with becoming parents ourselves. As parents can be the source of challenge for a child, so too can children be the instruments of suffering to parents. Regardless of how well we as parents guide and love our children, it doesn't mean that they will automatically develop into trouble-free human beings. On the contrary, they will have the same climb as we did. Very few parents escape the hate and resentment hurled at them as children face the painful task of growing up. However, they allow the love that they have for their children to override the hurt they cause them. Can parenthood therefore be the first lesson in the art of forgiveness? If parents of children who commit crimes forgive them because it is felt that they have not yet learned enough to control themselves, could this gesture not be extended to the rest of mankind? The supreme test of parenthood is to be chosen by a soul who has undertaken to carry a heavy burden in this lifetime. For example, to be the parents of a child with a handicap of any kind asks for devotion beyond limitation. All thoughts of 'self' must be annihilated by them as they commit themselves totally to the well-being of their child. Somewhere in their hearts they will discover a courage they never knew they had. A courage which will carry them all through.

Another 'birthright' to be considered is that of the time of our birth. Whilst I do not believe in horoscopes and the like, I do believe that our characteristics are governed by the time of year we are born. My family and friends jape my attempts of predicting other people's star signs. However I would say that even the most sceptical of people cannot deny that those born at the same time of year often show similar characteristics. Obviously there are going to be differences of attitude, depending on the circumstances of each person's lifestyle. However, the main characteristics will still be there. Even in small children, likenesses to other children, or adults, can be spotted and compared to the fact that they were born under the same sign.

I have my own pet theory on the subject. I feel that when human life expires, the soul holidays for a while in a quiet and peaceful sanctuary, and that it is here that they reflect the efforts of their lifetime. Some may be happy with the way they conducted themselves, and decide that in the next lifetime they will learn further lessons on life just from unplanned experiences. Others however will recognise some of the mistakes they made, and will want to correct them. For this purpose they will undertake to carry an obstacle with them when they are reborn. As all souls are aware that they need to undergo all aspects of suffering in order to achieve human perfection, the weight of the obstacles will depend on the degree of atonement they wish to make in any one lifetime. When they leave the sanctuary, they choose to go to the planet they believe best suited to prepare them for their next lifetime. And, on these planets there will be other souls who have chosen likewise. Therefore, the beliefs and the plans that have carried them to their transient 'workshop' render their outlook on a par. When graduation day comes, and the souls are ready to be born again to Earth, off they go bearing similar achievement gradings. Then, at some time during the course of their new lifetimes, souls will need to execute the plans they have made. Those who opted for the 'learn as you go' method of living may be faced with life traumas that they find hard to tackle. But, this might also apply to the souls who took it upon themselves to carry a burden with them through this life, being born into a country of famine and disease where cruelty might be practised; being born with a handicap, or disease; having cruel, or difficult parents; developing an illness; losing a limb; losing a loved one; having to watch a loved one suffer; loneliness; alcohol or drug dependency, and so on and so forth. And why? Because it may be one thing for souls to sit on some planet or another making plans for their next visit to Earth as human beings, but another when as human beings they are oblivious to their own intentions! However, the test for them as humans is to muster as much courage, strength, tolerance and forgiveness as is needed to bring their plans to fruition. At the end of yet another lifetime, these souls will return first to the sanctuary and then to the planet of their choice. If they have proved successful in their aim to correct previous mistakes, and have had to pay a high atonement fee, then the planet that they choose for further preparation will be of a higher grading. If they have proved unsuccessful, then in all probability they will choose to return to the planet from whence they came. So, the basis of my 'star sign' theory is that people born at the same time of year have similar characteristics because their souls have a uniform grading. Perhaps when that very wise philosopher said, *'My father's house has many mansions'*[iii] he was attempting to indicate that the universe is made up of many planets where souls are housed.

You may now be tempted into believing that there is more to life than just being born, living and dying. You may connect with the well-founded assumption of multiple lives. If you do, you will recognise that all people born to the Earth are born with a purpose. The purpose is to prove ourselves to ourselves despite the mammoth tests we have to face, then to overcome.

i Matt. 5:44
ii Luke 6:35
iii John 14:2

CHAPTER FOUR

Discipline

What we humans are looking for is happiness, but without there being discipline in our lives we will not find it. As souls with bodies, as against bodies with souls, we incarnate on Earth to learn how to develop this precious commodity within ourselves. However because all learning is established through a procession of mistake-making, it follows that before we can get things right we will first have to get them wrong. So, what we need is guidance from those who have perfected the art so that we might follow their lead. As an example, if parents did not admonish us when as young children we broke the rules they had set down, we wouldn't know how important it was to adhere to rules. In later years if tutors failed to reprimand us for not toeing the line as far as school regulations went, we wouldn't have a clue where to stand in life. If, by the time we enter the world as adults we are still not sure which is the right way to act and which is the wrong, without work colleagues to tell us what will and won't be tolerated by them, we would spend our days in alienation. Should we fail to adopt the conventional lessons of discipline development and go on to break the rules of the land to which we are born, without there being a severe punishment imposed on us by governing bodies, never would we ponder if breaking rules really was the way to earn self-respect.

When the rules of discipline have been established, with our souls more developed, our mental and moral training will continue by way of the guidance we receive from spirits who are in a more advanced state of being. They are the ones who generate the love, compassion and unselfishness that fills the atmosphere with the good that prevents the growth of bad. They can be the inspiration we need to stop us stumbling as we fumble to find our bearings in the battle of our own existence. Whilst these people can inject us with examples of love, most of them live their lives to be unacknowledged or unnoticed. Others of them choose to pen their wise observations of the road to happiness to leave as the gift which might bring courage and comfort to others. One such inspirational piece of prose, written by Max Ehrmann, follows and is entitled *Desiderata*:

Go placidly amidst the noise and haste, and remember what peace there may be in silence. As far as possible without surrender, be on good terms with all persons. Speak your truth quietly and clearly; and listen to others, even the dull and ignorant; they too have their story.

Avoid loud and aggressive persons; they are vexations to the spirit. If you compare yourself with others, you may become vain and bitter; for always there will be greater and lesser persons than yourself. Enjoy your achievements as well as your plans.

Keep interested in your own career, however humble; it is a real possession in the changing fortunes of time.

Exercise caution in your business affairs, for the world is full of trickery. But let this not blind you to what virtue there is; many persons strive for high ideals, and everywhere life is full of heroism.

Be yourself. Especially, do not feign affection. Neither be cynical about love; for in the face of all aridity and disenchantment it is as perennial as the grass.

Take kindly the counsel of the years, gracefully surrendering the things of youth. Nurture strength of spirit to shield you in sudden misfortune. But do not distress yourself with imaginings. Many fears are borne of fatigue and loneliness.

Beyond a wholesome discipline, be gentle with yourself. You are a child of the universe, no less than the trees or the stars; you have a right to be here. And whether or not it is clear to you, no doubt the universe is unfolding as it should.

Therefore be at peace with God, whatever you conceive him to be, and whatever your labours and aspirations, in the noisy confusion of life keep peace with your soul.

With all its sham, drudgery and broken dreams, it is still a beautiful world. Be careful. Strive to be happy'.

When primitive man was born to the Earth his only teachers were the plants, animals, the soil beneath his feet and the sky above his head. Quickly he learned that the Earth was his creator and as such should be treated with the emotions that we now call love and respect. He studied the animals' activities to note their survival strategy and copied their rules accordingly. He watched how the plants formed and did nothing that would hamper their growth. He listened to the wind and watched the skies for indications of weather conditions. Like all other life forms primitive man walked hand in hand with nature. However, he was not averse to acquiring knowledge first-hand too. He learnt how to make the fires that would cook his food and keep him warm. Tools were made to enable him to make clothing from the skins of the animals he had slaughtered to provide food, and to cut the vegetation required to make shelter for himself. Weapons were made to enable him to hunt his prey and defend his family from possible attacks on their lives. By chiselling wood to form a circle he realised he had become the inventor of transportation. Either two circles, or four, held together with twine and topped with pieces of wood proved a successful way of moving items from A to B. As primitive man grew in knowledge he also learnt that he could utilise the more docile members of the animal kingdom. Horses for instance were used for transportation; so too were other hoofed animals. The art of milking uddered beasts was also perfected. Regardless of his progression, primitive man still walked hand in hand with Mother Earth and respected her rules. Even up to a mere five hundred years ago in man's calendar, one such species of 'primitive' man existed on one of the largest continents of the world.

It was in 1492 that an explorer sailed across the ocean from Spain and discovered this continent and the people there. He named them 'Indians' and dubbed them savages. He rushed back to his homeland to spread the news of his miraculous discovery. Before long his ship returned to the land, but this time he brought other ships with him. These ships were filled with people eager to make their home in this 'new land'. Despite the fact that the explorer, his crew and the pioneers had known nothing but hospitality and helpfulness from the natives, they now began to kill them by the hundreds. Not only were the 'Indians' killed en masse, hundreds and hundreds of them were taken as slaves to be bound and herded together to wonder their fate. In the ensuing years many more hundreds of settlers arrived at the continent now named America, all eager to be granted a piece of the new land. At first the newcomers came from Spain, but it wasn't long before news travelled to other corners of the world. More and more people started to arrive, firstly from France and then from England. As the settlers moved further and further into the country, the vastness of the newly discovered land was revealed to them. And wherever they travelled, they found indigenous people of the continent living there. Those who were not slaughtered or taken as slaves were enlisted to be guides to the settlers. Whole cultures of people were being eradicated from the land that they loved. With weapons of bows and arrows, the 'Indians' started to fight off the invaders in attempts to safeguard their land.

As the armies of the new Americans grew, so too did the determination of the natives who were prepared to fight to the end. They loved their land and their culture and did all that they could do to chase the white man away. Many of their numbers died during the raging battles against the American armies, but so too did many of their aggressors. History tells that the native showed his savageness by his ritual of scalping the victims of his slaughter and hanging these scalps on his wigwam. It is not generally known that the native American was taught how to scalp by the white man.

It soon became obvious to the leading powers of the new nation of Americans, who had claimed complete ownership of the land, that the natives were no longer going to be the innocent victims of their violence, so treaties were offered to coax them from their land. The American nation wanted this to extend their penetration into the country but the natives were sitting right in the middle of that which was designated as railway track. As well as being offered cash for giving up their land, the natives were told that they would be rehoused in settlements of their own. They were informed that their standard of living would be improved and their culture maintained. Some tribes succumbed to the offer in the belief that they could not win any more battles. Reluctantly they moved into the reservations where many of them died out of sheer despair and unhappiness. Their lives had been shattered – their culture annihilated.

An illustration of the advancement of the native American culture was the fact that these people could will their own deaths. The old people of their tribes always knew when they were ready to die. They would say their farewells to their loved ones and then ask the eldest son to go with them to a chosen place of death. There the two of them would sit and talk until the old one decided it was time for his spirit to depart his earthly body. This is how it was when the tribes moved to the reservations – they willed themselves to die, rather than to live the new lives that had been forced upon them.

It took up to the end of the nineteenth century to remove the natives from their reservations with the Duwamish Tribe being one of the last clans to remain. In 1854, during treaty negotiations with 'the aggressors', the chief of this tribe, Chief Seattle, recited a speech which is regarded as one of the greatest statements ever made concerning the relationship between a people and the earth. However, as his words were spoken in the language of his people, it was only they who understood the content of the speech. Present at the event however was an early settler who, because he was an amateur writer, took notes of the chief's words. Then, thirty years later he rendered what he claimed was the chief's speech of 1854. Since this time it has been said that the words as quoted are not authentic, but those of the writer himself. Sceptics never pondered that it might have taken all of those thirty years for the presenter of the speech to research the material and to grow familiar with a language he did not understand. Perhaps also during these years he turned his attention to the study of Native American culture, and developed the respect and love which inspired him to pen a tribute of admiration to it. Although the words that follow are a version of the original tribute, and were those used in a film, I quote them as they are so beautifully written that they will live in my heart always:

The great chief in Washington sends word that he wishes to buy our land. The Great Chief also sends us words of friendship and goodwill. This is kind of him since we know he has little need of our friendship in return. But we will consider your offer, because we know if we don't sell the white-man will come with guns and take our land. How can you buy or sell the sky, the warmth of the land, the idea is strange to us. If we do not own the freshness of the air, and the sparkle of the water, how can you buy them.....

Every part of this earth is sacred to my people. Every shining pine needle, every sandy shore, every mist in the dark wood, every clearing and humming insect is holy in the memory and experience of my people. The sap, which courses through the trees, carries the memory of the red man. The white man's dead forget their country of their birth when they go to walk amongst the stars. Our dead never forget this beautiful earth, for it is the mother of the red man. We are part of the earth and it is part of us.

The perfumed flowers are our sisters; the deer, the horse, the great eagle – these are our brothers. The rocky crests, the juices of the meadows, the body heat of the pony and man, all belong to the same family. So when the great chief in Washington sends word that he wishes to buy our land, he asks much of us. The great chief sends word he will reserve us a place so that we can live comfortably to ourselves. He will be our father and we will be his children. So, we will consider your offer to buy our land, but it will not be easy, for this land is sacred to us...

This shining water, which moves in the streams and rivers, is not just water, but the blood of our ancestors. If we sell you our land, you must remember that it is sacred, and you must teach your children that it is sacred, and that each ghostly reflection in the clear water of the lakes, tells of events and memories in the life of my people. The water's murmur is the voice of my father's father. The rivers are our brothers, they quench our thirst. The rivers carry our canoes and feed our children. If we sell you our land you must remember, and teach your children, that the rivers are our brothers and yours, and you must henceforth give the rivers the kindness you would give any brother.

The red man has always retreated before the advancing white man, as the mist of the mountains runs before the morning sun. But the ashes of our fathers are sacred, their graves are holy ground and so these hills, these trees, this portion of the earth is consecrated to us. We know that the white man does not understand our ways – one portion of land is the same to him as the next, for he is a stranger who comes in the night and takes from the land whatever he needs. The earth is not his brother but his enemy and when he has conquered it, he moves on. He leaves his fathers' graves behind and he does not care. He kidnaps the earth from his children, he does not care. His fathers' graves and his children's birthright are forgotten. He treats his mother, the earth, and his brother the sky, as things to be bought, plundered, sold like sheep or bright beads. His appetite will devour the earth and leave behind only a desert.

I do not know – our ways are different from your ways. The sight of your cities pains the eyes of the red man, but perhaps it is because the red man is a savage and does not understand. There is no quiet place in the white man's cities; no place to hear the unfurling of leaves in spring, or the rustle of insects' wings. But, perhaps it is because I am a savage and do not understand. The clatter only seems to insult the ears, and what is there to life if a man cannot hear the lonely cry of the whippoorwill, or the arguments of the frogs around the pond at night. I am a red man and do not understand. The Indian prefers the soft sound of the wind darting over the face of a pond, and the smell of the wind itself cleansed by a midday rain or centred with a pinnon pine. The air is precious to the red man for all things share the same breath – the beast, the tree, the man – they all share the same breath. The white man does not seem to notice the air he breathes. Like a man dying for many days, he is numb to the stench. But, if we sell you our land you must remember that the air is precious to us, that the air shares its spirit with all the life it supports.

The wind that gave our grandfather his first breath also receives his last sigh. And the wind must also give our children the spirit of life. And if we sell you our land, you must keep it apart and sacred, as a place where even the white man can go to taste the wind that is sweetened by the meadow flowers. So, we will consider your offer to buy our land.

If we decide to accept I will make one condition – the white man must treat the beasts of this land as his brothers. I am a savage and I do not understand any other way. I have seen a thousand rotting buffalo on the prairie, left by the white man who shot them from a passing train. I am a savage and I do not understand how the smoking iron horse can be more important than the buffalo that we kill only to stay alive. What is man without the beast? If all beasts were gone man would die from a great loneliness of spirit, for whatever happens to the beasts, soon happens to the man – all things are connected...

You must teach your children that the ground beneath their feet is the ashes of our grandfathers. So that they will respect the land, tell your children that the earth is rich with the lives of our kin. Teach your children what we have taught our children – that the earth is our mother. Whatever befalls the earth befalls the sons of the earth. If man spits upon the ground they spit upon themselves. This we know – the earth does not belong to man. Man belongs to the earth – this we know.

All things are connected – like the blood, which unites one family, all things are connected. Whatever befalls the earth befalls the sons of the earth. Man did not weave the web of life – he is merely a strand in it. Whatever he does to the web, he does to himself...

But we will consider your offer to go the reservation you have for my people. We will live apart and in peace. It matters little where we spend the rest of our days. Our children have seen their fathers humbled in defeat. Our warriors have felt shame, and after defeat, they turn their days in idleness and contaminate their bodies with sweet food and strong drink – it matters little where we pass the rest of our days.

We are not many. A few more hours, a few more winters and none of the children of the great tribes, that once lived on this great earth, or that roam now in small bands in the woods, will be left to mourn graves of a people once as powerful and hopeful as yours. But why should I mourn the passing of my people, tribes are made of men – nothing more. Men come and go like the waves of the sea. Even the white man, whose God walks and talks with him as friend to friend, cannot be exempt from the common destiny.

We may be brothers after all we shall see.

One thing we know which the white man may one day discover. Our God is the same God. You may think now that you own him as you wish to own our land, but you cannot. He is the God of man and his compassion is equal for the red man and the white. This earth is precious to him and to harm the earth is to heap contempt on its creator.

The whites too shall pass, perhaps sooner than all other tribes. Continue to contaminate your bed and you will one night suffocate in your own waste. But in your perishing you will shine brightly, fired by the strength of the God who brought you to this land and for some special purpose gave you dominion over this land, and over the red man. That destiny is a mystery to us for we do not understand when the buffalo are all slaughtered, the wild horses are tamed, the secret corners of the forest heavy with the scent of many men, and the view of the ripe hills blotted by talking wires. Where is the thicket? – gone. Where is the eagle? – gone. And what is it to say goodbye to the swift pony and the hunt. The end of living and the beginning of survival.

So, we will consider your offer to buy our land. If we agree it will be to secure the reservation you have promised. There perhaps we may live out our brief days as we wish. When the last red man has vanished from this earth, and his memory is only the shadow of a cloud moving across the prairie, these shores and forests will still hold the spirits of my people. For they love this earth as the newborn loves its mother's heartbeat.

So, if we sell you our land love it as we've loved it, care for it as we've cared for it. Hold in your mind the memory of the land, as it is when you take it. And with all your strength with all your mind, with all your heart, preserve it for your children and love it – as God loves us all.

One thing we know – our God is the same God. This earth is precious to him. Even the white man cannot be exempt from the common destiny.

We may be brothers after all. We shall see.

Irrespective of who wrote these wonderful words, from them I can conclude that the Native American Indians revered the earth and respected that they were a part of it. There was nothing they would do to harm any aspect of nature. It might be argued here that they killed buffalo for food and clothing, and that they executed their slaughter in a barbaric fashion. However, in answer I would point out that Native American Indians were, after all, just mere imperfect human beings who utilised the killing methods of the day. It has to be appreciated that they killed only for survival and, therefore, never slaughtered more livestock than they needed for this purpose. In fact, like other animals they would move onto another settlement after killing to give the buffalo herds time to replenish. Something else they did was to honour the buffalo before they killed them. They would thank them for the sacrifice of their lives given in order to sustain their own. And, whereas the speech of 1854 stated that 'our God is the same God' the 'red man's' name for that something we cannot define was the 'great spirit'.

Can we not wonder just how many years these native Indians had occupied the continent now known as America? Had they been in existence there since the birth of the planet? Whatever, they certainly fulfilled their obligation to honour the ethical laws of the earth, and in doing so retained the discipline to preserve their species. This is, until the white man came along to render their advanced culture extinct.

Whereas, by obeying the disciplines of life and nature, Homo sapiens have survived on Earth for millions of years, have they not, in a mere century, put their species at great risk by defying the rules? Was it the 'white man' of the twentieth century that a wise Native American chief spoke of in 1854? Let us look at the hundred year history of one country's people to ponder his predictive words.

PART TWO

Twentieth Century Britons

CHAPTER FIVE
Where We Began

The twentieth century began no differently from its predecessors: there were good people and there were bad; there were the rich and there were the poor. The power-seeking rich pursued their wealth in accordance with the tradition of exploiting the poor.

As the century began, the boast might have been that the country was completely slave free, but was it? For, as through the whole of the nineteenth century, the people recruited to enter into service were regarded as extremely inferior and treated no better than slaves. As most of them lived in, they were expected to be on call twenty-four hours a day, if need be. Their normal working hours started at the crack of dawn, and ended at sunset. Duties for them embraced cleaning out and resetting coal fires; remaking and changing beds; washing the household's clothes by hand; helping the master and mistress dress (and undress); polishing shoes; polishing floors (on hands and knees); cooking and serving; washing dishes; bowing in and out of rooms; grooming and feeding the horses; cleaning out the stables, etcetera, etcetera. Sometimes young lady servants, or young men, were even required to administer sexual 'comfort' to 'the Master' during his periods of woe. Should any member of the household staff fail to create perfection from their toil, they would expect to be punished.

Then children, as young as six or seven, were compelled to work in early twentieth century Britain in the status of slavery. These children worked in cotton mills, woollen mills and coalmines, from six in the morning till seven at night. Their workload in the mills was so strenuous that many children died because of the accidents that occurred through tiredness. In coal mines particularly, children proved very useful as they were able to squeeze through the tiny tunnels and crevices not accessible to fully-grown men. Their size was of paramount importance too when it came to chimney sweeping. Here they would be pushed up chimneys, armed with brushes, where they would clean away collected soot. Though it may have been protested that children did not work in a slavery capacity, because they were paid for their toils, the money they received was no greater than the pittance that might be thrown to beggars.

All this was going on despite an Act of the 1870s that stated that it was compulsory for all children to attend school. However, there was a clause in the Bill that all employers knew about. It said that if a child had attained a good standard of education, that he or she would be allowed half-time schooling. This meant that a child could work for half a day but must be schooled for the second half. For the kids who worked from six in the morning to seven at night, the protection of the Education Act escaped them entirely, with the law turning a blind eye to the situation.

The poorer working classes were not only at risk of exploitation by industrial capitalism, there were some of their own kind who sought to profit from them. Unscrupulous crooks would abduct women and young girls from streets they walked to force them into lives of prostitution. They would lock them away in houses where their bodies would be used by 'gentlemen of means'. The pimps grew rich from the fees they collected, whilst the enslaved women grew weary. However, they had to suffer their torment in silence because their owners would kill them if they became troublesome or escapist.

Another crook who was still operating in the early twentieth century was the master thief. He would collect orphaned or abandoned children and house them together under one roof. Here he would teach them the art of stealing, then send them out to prove their learning. All he had to do was sit back and wait for the children to return with their pickings.

The practice of exploitation was nothing new to the populations of people who had been born to poverty and strife. Whilst learning to survive their plight as best they could, their unspoken law was to 'make the most of the life that God had given'. The working classes of the early twentieth century were no different from their ancestors when it came to their attitude towards life. They got on with it and appreciated any morsel of good luck that came their way, especially if it were food or clothing. They thought themselves fortunate to have the facility of a cold water tap. This had been brought to them courtesy of early 19th Century people who had laid mains water pipes.

Regardless of the water, conditions for them remained squalid and there was no proper sanitation. Poor working class homes did not have the luxury of lavatories for people to use. In the poorer dwellings, known as back-to-back, the inhabitants shared the WC facilities that were situated in open yards adjoining the properties. Some of the terraced working class properties did have their own lavatories and they were housed at the bottom of private yards. For the many hundreds of people who lived in the cellars of houses, even the installation of cold water taps was denied them, let alone the use of a lavatory.

Whatever the privilege of early twentieth century lavatory status, chamber pots were favoured when bedtime came around. After all it wasn't much fun having to rush outside (if taken short) in the middle of the night. Next morning the contents of bladder or bowels would need to be emptied from the pot into the WC. This would mean having to queue with the rest of the neighbourhood to perform the task. Not everybody could be bothered to do this, so the odd few retained the habit of earlier centuries of tipping their waste where they would (most times through a window onto the street below).

The installation of piping to carry sewage came about between the period of 1847–1864. Before this time it used to lay in foul-smelling cesspools, or middens, where it created much disease. In an attempt to rid the environment of disease, the government of the day declared that sewerage must be confined underground, hence wooden piping was laid.

However because of inadequate sanitation, disease remained prevalent in the early twentieth century. The people of the time accepted early death amongst their numbers as readily as they received death itself. They might have thought that 'life's a bitch and then you die' but they got on with the task of living. When a loved one was taken from them in demise, it was naturally assumed that that person had 'gone to a better place'. They carried their loss in their hearts but were happy to feel that 'God' had chosen their loved one to live in a world that was free from strife. 'Heaven' was the name that was given to that world, and their God was the one 'who knew best'. There was also the stoic determination that one must get on with life and not go around moaning about it.

The working classes rented their houses from landowners, or their homes were let to them on a tied property basis. This meant that the house went with the job as part-payment for work carried out by the tenant. The mining industry was the main provider of tied property during the whole of the nineteenth century, and into the twentieth century. The downside of living in these properties was that if you lost your job, you would lose your home also.

During these days people were sacked from their jobs for the flimsiest of reasons – perhaps for spending too much time in the WC; being considered a slow worker, or disagreeing with the pit owner's orders. The dismissed employee would not be given any grace to pack his family belongings, in readiness to vacate his house. Instead he would arrive home from work to find the contents of it strewn across the pavement. He would see his sobbing wife, and children, sitting atop of furniture whilst they watched the new occupants moving their belongings into the house. The homeless family would then try to find neighbours who might have an odd corner available to house their pieces of furniture. From here they would have to look for shelter for themselves. If the eviction had come in the winter months when snow, ice and blizzards were the order of the day, the family would have no alternative but to take refuge in the dreaded workhouse.

Workhouses were established in the 1830s and they were administered by a body of people called the Board of Guardians, whose funding came from the parishes and the Church. These establishments were introduced in accordance with the Poor Law of the time. This law stated that every parish look after its own destitute population. Children who were orphaned, or whose parents could not support them, were taken to the workhouses where they were bonded by apprenticeship. The bonding lasted until their twenty first birthday.

Adults with nowhere to live also headed in the same direction. Here they were housed in dormitories where beds, numbering forty to sixty, stood side by side. Should a whole family be rendered homeless, then their lives together would be no more. The workhouses operated a ruling of segregation. Hence, the ladies of a family would be sent to the female wards, whilst their menfolk were herded to the male wards.

As well as being responsible for its own destitutes, the parishes also had to look after the sick and aged of the community. Hence wards in workhouses were set aside for this purpose, and here doctors and nurses administered a minimum of attention to those with no one else to care for them.

Like any institutions of this magnitude, the workhouses had their own kitchens, bakehouses and laundries. Both inmates and paid staff toiled endlessly in the dark and depressing atmosphere of the buildings. Even the tramps, who took a night's refuge there, would be made to pay for their shelter by working for a day in the kitchen, the laundry or the bakehouse.

The establishments' rules for both inmates and staff were very rigid. The keeper of the rules was the man who operated the institution and he was called the Master (and we thought that slavery had been abolished!). Not surprisingly the working classes feared the place known to them as the Bastille because prison could be no worse.

The poorer working classes were at the mercy of their employers, as they always had been. Throughout history however, tiny minorities of people were brave enough to seek justice for their kind. For example, in 1811 a group of workers banded together and called themselves the Luddites. Their fight against their employers was about the machinery that had been installed in the woollen mills they owned. It was feared, by the workers, that these newly-invented machines would rob them of their jobs by demonstrating they could work faster than man. The Luddites protested and rioted by trying to smash the machines, but they lost their fight. Then in 1824 a handful of workers banded together and formed a secret group which they called a union. They pledged to fight for better working conditions and higher wages. Sick were they of the dangers in the workplace that robbed them of their lives. Also, they were weary of trying to survive on the small amount of money their employers deemed fit to pay them for their hard toil. Alas the effort at this time was of no avail. Talk of workers standing together and demanding rights was mutiny in the ears of the industrialists – it was not to be tolerated. This message was made so clear that the movement died a natural death. It seemed that men would rather work in poor and dangerous conditions for very little pay, than not to have any work at all. However, as the century progressed more groups were formed despite the fact that men had died for being the instigators of unions. In 1888 even the poor little match girls refused to work any more, unless their employers increased their wages. For standing on street corners in all kinds of weather, and running the risk of developing an illness called 'phossy jaw' (a form of gangrene caused by the sulphur content of the matches they sold) these children were not paid enough to buy food to sustain them. In the following year a mass strike was held by the men who worked in the dockyards. Not one man defied the 'down tools' plan and, because of this, the action earned the title 'The Great Dock Strike'.

Because of the militancy of nineteenth century people, the twentieth century began with industrialists recognising that unions, representing the rights of workers, were well-established.

Machinery was also well-established in Britain as 1900 was born. Most of this was operated by horse power, with others driven by gas. Less powerful machines were operated, as they always had been, by the hand or foot of man. The most pronounced success of machinery was the steam train. The first train took to the tracks in 1825 and ran between Stockton and Darlington. The next track to be built was the one that ran between Liverpool and Manchester and this was opened in 1830. The train ideal was born through industrialists who sought to ferry their wares from town to town. The eighteenth century practice of transporting goods by way of canals (the first of which was cut and financed by Josiah Wedgewood, the owner of a pottery factory) proved to be too slow for nineteenth century businessmen. They wanted their goods to travel from town to town as quickly as possible, so that they might sell them the same way. The building of both waterways and railways was carried out by Irish workers, who had been brought to Britain to be employed as cheap labour. Other ways of transportation were also being explored in the 1900s. Eighteen years before the start of 1900, two German inventors Karl Benz and Gottlieb Daimler independently discovered that they could propel a machine by means of an engine fuelled by petroleum. Then in 1897 an American, Henry Ford, built his first petrol-fuelled vehicle and called it an automobile. By 1900 this vehicle had made its mark on Britain under the banner of motorcar. There were thirty-two thousand such vehicles on the country's narrow roads at the time and, their speed was restricted to twelve miles per hour. To warn people of their approach, a man walked ahead of the vehicles waving red flags. The only people who could afford to buy one of the new-fangled machines were the rich. For them the vehicles replaced the horse-drawn carriages that had previously conveyed them from place to place.

The wealthy were also the privileged possessors of yet another machine – the telephone. This device had been invented in 1876 with the first telephone exchange being opened in 1879. At this time only the likes of the aristocracy were able to talk to each other by way of telephone communication. However, in 1900 there were three thousand telephones in use in Britain, suggesting that both the royal and the rich were telephone beneficiaries.

Gas lighting had been in use all through the nineteenth century but this was only used to illuminate streets and factories. Home lighting depended on the burning of candles and oil and kerosene lamps. Although the first gas company had been opened in 1808, it was only commercial outlets that used the commodity seventy years on. In an endeavour to spur the public into using gas, the company decided to drop the charges for installing gas piping in people's homes. To compensate for their loss of profit here, they chose to increase the price for gas consumed. The result was, by the start of the 20th Century, gas lighting was installed in most urban houses. In some of these privileged homes the occupants even possessed gas rings on which they cooked food.

In the poorer areas, working class families still depended on burning coal to provide their means of cooking. Great black iron ranges, that stood five feet high and five feet wide, were a feature of their homes. These constructions housed a grate on which to burn coal, and one or two ovens. In better off houses the fireplaces were fitted with back boilers to produce hot water. When people could afford the precious commodity of coal they could enjoy the many functions of the fireplace. In winter the fire brought them warmth. Wet washing was draped over wooden 'maidens' and left to dry there overnight. On icy nights the hot trays from the oven were wrapped in pieces of cloth, and then placed in beds to air them. Stews slowly cooked in fireplace ovens, filling the air and nostrils with pleasurable aromas. Kettles of water were placed on the pivots of the grate that swung over the fire to boil. Hot water was the luxury that everyone enjoyed, especially on Friday nights. This was the time when the family would indulge themselves by bathing. The bath, which was made of tin and was hung in the back yard, would be brought in and placed in front of the fire. Kettles of water were boiled, and then poured into the waiting receptacle. When there was enough boiling water in the bath, cold water would be added to adjust the temperature in readiness for its first occupant. The man of the house would be the first to shed his clothing and step into the welcoming hot water, after him came the children in order of age. As bathing continued, and the water grew colder, further kettles were boiled and tipped into the now murky liquid. Bath night was the time when hair was washed too and a powdered substance, called borax, was the commodity used for this purpose. For those who wanted a shiny head of hair, a couple of spoonfuls of vinegar would be added to the last jugful of rinsing water. Washing faces in cold water would be the order for the other six days of the week, unless of course the coal lasted for a whole week, when water could be boiled over the fire. Mother would be the only one who didn't take a bath on Friday nights. Instead she would have an all over wash, taken in the privacy of her own company, when the rest of the family were out. Many working class houses had boilers built into the corners of the kitchens. Middle class households had theirs built in small brick buildings next to the properties and, these were called wash houses. The purpose of the boiler was to heat the water that would be used to wash clothing. The receptacle was filled with water and, a fire lit beneath it. As it took hours for the water to heat up, it was imperative that the fire be lit as soon as possible on 'washing day'. As coal was too precious a commodity to be wasted on the boiler, the fire was set with wood and clinkers from the firegrate (perhaps an odd piece of coal might be thrown on for good measure). It took a whole day for the lady of the house to complete the washing procedure. She would constantly 'punch' the clothes in the boiler, using an implement that looked like a three-legged stool with a handle. With the aid of a pair of wooden tongs, she would then remove the hot clothes from the boiler and take them to a table. This is where they would be scrubbed with a brush, and soap, until any traces of dirt vanished. From here the washing was carried to the sink to be manually rinsed clear of soap. The last step was to put the clothes through a mangle (an iron frame housing two large rubber rollers) to remove the water. Phew! And even then washday chores were not over, for when the clothes were dry the lady of the house would need to press out the creases. For this purpose she used a hot iron – a piece of moulded iron with a handle which was heated by placing it on the pivot of the fireplace.

The acquisition of coal was achieved by two methods. The occupants of middle class homes ordered their coal from a merchant and had it delivered to the door. The poorer working classes went to the railway sidings, where it was housed, to collect it for themselves. They used old perambulators, or home-made carts, to carry home their precious cargoes.

Blankets were a luxury early twentieth century working classes could ill afford. Instead overcoats would be thrown over the bedding sheets to bring warmth to sleepers. Overcoats proved very versatile, as during the day they were a garment, at night a blanket, and for years to come – a rug! When the coats were past their best they would be shredded into little pieces and made into colourful rugs. This was achieved by weaving the cloth into pieces of sacking. As the instrument used to accomplish this task was called a peg, these floor coverings were known as peg rugs.

The average diet of early twentieth century working people consisted mainly of potatoes, bread, cabbage, jam and cheese. Very rarely were there funds enough to buy meat, and when there was, only cheap cuts were purchased. Neck ends, boiled with barley provided nourishing broth. Shanks of ham or bacon proved very wholesome too. These meats could be used either to concoct a panful of pea soup, or cooked in the oven to be served with potatoes and cabbage. Fish was a delicacy which was enjoyed also, but here again it was the cheaper variety, like mackerel and kippers, that were consumed. No matter which meals were served at the table they were appreciated to the full, for the poorer working classes of the early 1900s were no different from those throughout the ages. They knew that if they didn't have food they could not survive so this, together with shelter and clothing, was their priority. They did not bemoan any dish which was set before them because they felt lucky to have any food at all.

As employment had increased by 1900 so too had the population. The peoples of the British Isles numbered twenty-five million in 1838 whereas now, sixty-two years on, the count was forty million. Permanent employment therefore was not easy to obtain. Working class men needed to be up at the crack of dawn each day if they were to stand a chance of acquiring work for its duration. If they succeeded in gaining employment that would last for a whole week, or even a number of weeks, there was much rejoicing for all the family. This would be the time when rent arrears were paid and homes secured for a little longer, and it was a time when food could be bought to fill bellies. It was not only the man of the house who provided for family needs. If employers offered work suitable only for children, then the kids of the family became the breadwinners. Mother played her part too. As if she hadn't enough washing and ironing of her own to do, she would earn the odd copper or two by undertaking other people's laundry tasks. She would collect dirty clothing from the 'posh' ladies who lived in the big houses streets away. Then, washed and ironed, she would deliver the load back to them. Even little girls were not free of the responsibility of earning money. Apart from having to help Mother in her chores, they were sent to earn cash in their own right. They would knock on doors, in the better off areas, to ask the lady of the house if she wanted her front step 'stoning'. This procedure involved wetting the step with water then, rubbing something called a donkey stone over it. When it dried out it looked as if it had just been painted with whitewash (emulsion) and gleamed with cleanliness as well as giving an anti-slip finish. These cleaning stones could be bought in shops or obtained from the rag-and-bone man. He was the fellow who wandered the streets either trundling a handcart before him, or perched on the edge of a cart being pulled by a horse. His mission was to seek out old clothes and unwanted articles. As he travelled the streets his call of 'rag bone' echoed the area and, people would rush out to meet him. In exchange for their obsolete clothing etc. he would give them a donkey stone.

Although the poorer working classes of the early 1900s did not have many possessions, what they did have was lots of pride. To the people who had 'nowt' it was important to portray that at least they had their dignity. They demonstrated this by showing their belief that 'cleanliness was next to Godliness'. Hours would be spent polishing fireplaces until they shone to mirror reflection. Floors would be scrubbed until they gleamed. Peg rugs, or cheap coconut matting, would be slung over washing lines outside and beaten until every speck of dirt took flight. Windowsills were wiped, windows washed and steps stoned. These people even needed to be proud of the area in which they lived and took to the streets and passageways with brushes and shovels, to render them 'spotless'. The epitome of pride shone most brightly in the bed sheet department. No matter how little money there was in the household kitty, sheets were sent to be professionally laundered every two weeks. To prove one's worthiness to one and all, it had to be seen that the laundryman visited the house regularly. Mother's pride would really sink to her shoes if she had to go along to the workhouse and beg for charity. For not only did workhouses serve to house the homeless and sick, they handed out food to those who could prove that they were starving.

Recycling was a natural instinct in these times so there was very little that went to waste. When a child grew out of its clothes they were handed down to a younger member of the family. This child would be expected to grow into the clothes eventually. Meantime there would be lots of little girls wearing dresses that reached their feet, or little boys whose pants reached their calves. Then, when a whole family of children had outgrown the clothes, they would be passed to another family for use. When the garments were beyond wearing, they would be traded in to the rag-and-bone man who, in turn, would trade his bounty with the rag merchant who would recycle the material. Shoes and boots were the precious commodity to be treated with the utmost respect. Every night they were polished and buffed for maximum protection (after all, if you didn't have a pair of boots for your feet then you couldn't walk outside). Most households possessed a last (this was an iron frame in the shape of a boot). As well as being the breadwinner, the man of the house was also a cobbler. When his boots, or his children's' were in need of repair, he would get out the last and re-sole the footwear with new pieces of leather. If a family was last-less, there would be a neighbour nearby who would be prepared to lend one. No possession was ever discarded – if a chair was broken, then it would be repaired; if a bed leg fell off, it would be replaced with a piece of wood. String was a constant companion, for it had so many useful functions when there was mending to be done. Even the peel of potatoes and carrots was put to good use. This was thrown onto the back of the fire at night to make the coal last longer. And of course, when the firegrate was cleaned out, all the clinkers were gathered together to be used again.

Mankind's obsession to discover the intricate mechanisms of his own body meant that medicine had always been a feature of his evolution. Even the early cavemen were eager to find cures for illnesses. Believing that sickness was caused by the penetration of the Devil into the body, they devised an operation to release the demon. Using pieces of pointed stone, they would bore through the skull of a 'patient' until a hole appeared. To them this was the Devil's door of escape and they thought that once he had departed through the hole, the sickness itself would follow. The theory, and practice, continued throughout the centuries gathering momentum along the way. Then, other experimental 'operations' were used when the hole-boring practice proved an inadequate way of curing illnesses.

The men with learning and ambition to cure the sick were called physicians and they, in early days, practised their medicine in monasteries and on the battlefields. As time went by, and more and more men were drawn to the field of medicine, hospitals came into being. These were operated on a charity basis and were funded mainly by donations from the rich. Needless to say the rich did not use these facilities themselves. Instead, when illness occurred, they were treated in the luxury of their own homes by physicians of the highest calibre.

Hospitals were places of learning where life-saving techniques could be practised. If a remedy proved useful then it would be written up and used again when a similar illness occurred. If a patient died, the cause would be better established if the body itself was investigated. For this purpose it had to be cut open so that internal organs, and possible malfunctions, could be observed. It is not surprising therefore, that the type of patient admitted to hospitals in the early days were those without families. After all, the lack of a body would be difficult to explain away to grieving kinfolk. Indeed bodies (preferably dead) were in great demand during the latter half of the nineteenth century. Enterprising entrepreneurs, who recognised the handsome payment for body supply, didn't miss out on the body-snatching boom. In the quiet of the night, they would visit cemeteries to dig up bodies deposited in the ground. If this proved too hard a task, they were not averse to murdering an odd passer-by in order to acquire flesh. The medical scientist paid well for illegally-supplied bodies and, the fresher the better, so why miss out on the opportunity of making a few bob. Although hospitals for the sick had been a feature of society for hundreds of years, they were only made available to the public in general at the end of the nineteenth century. Even then it was only the chronically sick who warranted admission.

For the rest of the working class population at the start of the twentieth century, healthcare was of their own making. Popular medications came in a variety of colours. There was a green ointment (name unknown) that was used to treat skin conditions. It was rubbed onto rashes, cuts and grazes until they healed. In another shade of green came comfrey, which was a plant which could be grown in the garden. The leaves of the plant were bound to joints of the body, to heal muscular strains and rheumatic problems. Then came the red flannel which was bound to the chest or back. Its function was to ease lung or back pain by extracting inflammation. Yellow was the shade of the ghastly castor oil that was forced down throats by the spoonful. This dreaded, but versatile, agent was relied upon to cure digestive and bowel problems. Consumption, bronchitis and all breathing problems were treated with boiling water, to which was added a brown substance called balsam. The patient would lean over the bowl that held the concoction, with his or her head covered by a towel. This would allow the steam to be inhaled without being lost to the surrounding air. Then there was the browny-yellowy mustard powder (also used to make mustard!). This was sprinkled into a bowl to which hot water would be added. Sitting with one's feet immersed in this liquid induced a shivering cold to be 'sweated out'. Yet another brown was Indian brandy which was drunk, with a little hot water, to ease stomach cramps and pains. White was the shade of the salt which had many medical uses. When added to a bath full of water, it became an antiseptic and cleansing agent and was said to promote healing of the flesh. Salted water was gently sniffed through the nose to relieve sinus congestion. When earache or toothache were present, hot salt would be used to bring relief. Here a few spoonfuls of salt would be placed onto a metal container to be warmed over a fire. Then the hot salt would be tipped into a piece of material (usually a sock), to assist its transfer to the infected area.

In dire circumstances of bad health a doctor would be summoned and he would use hospital techniques in his administrations. His method of healing might involve the skills of blood letting or cupping. Bloodletting involved slitting a patient's arm with a knife to allow blood to escape. Alternatively, a live leech would be placed on the patient's body. This little fellow would merrily suck from the flesh, without even knowing the advantages his appetite was providing. For instance, extraction of blood was believed to relieve high blood pressure and, reduce the possibility of an infected wound turning gangrenous. Then there was the ever-popular notion that 'bad blood' was the cause of many illnesses. So ridding the body of some of that blood was said to be a cure. Cupping was a more determined approach for combating lung diseases and other serious pain. A glass would be heated and placed on the body at the point of discomfort. As the glass cooled it was thought to induce pain-causing inflammation to leave the body.

Doctor's fees were a burden the working classes could well do without. But then, they had the services of the 'doctor's man'. He was the person who called to the door every Friday night and collected sixpence from each household (if there was sixpence to spare), on behalf of the doctor of the neighbourhood. This was done because no-one could afford to pay his fees in full, therefore his administrations were given on a credit basis. The sixpence per week was collected until the fee was cleared (which in most cases it never was). Amongst the working classes, however, there were those who were fortunate enough to be employed by the large industries that had their own doctor. Hence these employees, and their families, had the opportunity of receiving medical attention from this man. However, his services were not given freely and employees had to make regular payments aligned to their earnings. Nevertheless, having the facility of a 'company doctor' was recognised as a perk of the job.

The working masses of the early twentieth century had little to promote happiness and contentment in their lives. However, when compared with the matter of survival, these assets were of little consequence. Because, like their ancestors before them, these people recognised that they had to 'get on with it'. They'd been given the task of living and their duty was to make the most of what they had. In this society there was no need for doors to be locked to secure possessions, because people had nothing to steal. Even if they had, the temptation to barricade their homes would not have arisen as there was a code of practice that was silently honoured. This was that you must not steal from your own kind. Though disease or ill-health, due to the lack of sanitation and under-nourishment, took the lives of many at an early age, early twentieth century working people were tough and hardy while they lasted. This was because the physical effort they put into their everyday living developed bodily strength. They used their legs, feet, arms, hands, fingers, backs, eyes and ears to capacity, and certainly made full use of their gumption. They appreciated that their lives depended wholly on their own efforts, and therefore exercised commonsense to its fullest. In general, as far as their lot in life was concerned, their attitude was to stoically battle their downfalls as best they could and cherish any blessing that came along (however small). Perhaps the most precious asset in their lives was the care and support they shared as comrades.

CHAPTER SIX

The First Forty Years

1901 heralded good news for children when the government announced that the minimum working age was to be raised to 12. Whilst young children had always been made to work, and had learned good lessons from the experience, their exploitation in the workplace was out of order.

The coming of the twentieth century was bringing a feeling of 'let there be light'. For, as well as having established gas lighting, more electricity power stations were beginning to open. Electricity was something that had been discovered in 1880 when an Englishman, J.W. Swan, and an American, T.A. Edison, had both invented carbon lamps which were produced commercially. Before that time, electricity was obtained from batteries or steam driven dynamos. After this came the opening of small electricity generating companies that sold the commodity. Then, in 1888, the first major power station opened to supply electricity to the capital city, London. It was two years after this that the London underground train track was electrified.

However, the poorer working classes were oblivious to the progress which was taking place. They were too busy trying to survive the burden of making their living. In fact, they had not even yet become acquainted with socialism, let alone the definition of it, which was: 'the collective ownership and control of the resources of life'. Mind, some of them did have the bonus of the Co-op to aid them on their way.

The Co-operative Wholesale Society was started by twenty-eight working Lancashire men (who later became known as the Rochdale Pioneers). These men decided that if they bought goods in bulk, it would enable them to sell them on to the poorer general public, at less than shop prices. (It was known that private shops charged excessive prices for their goods, and were not averse to adulterating them into the bargain. For example shopkeepers had been known to mix sand with oatmeal, and plaster of Paris with flour. To add to this they occasionally gave false weight and measures.) The pioneers' idea was that a shop owned by its customers was the best way to achieve consumer protection. It would also be of benefit to the customer/member, if the excess profits of the business came back to them. Becoming a member of the Rochdale Equitable Pioneers Society (as it was then known) involved paying a membership fee of £1. As no one was the proud possessor of one full pound, subscriptions from members were collected weekly. At first two pence a week was collected. Then, to raise funds more quickly the amount was raised to three pence. The pioneers' idea worked well and, in 1863, the Co-operative Wholesale Society (CWS), small as it was, began. The twenty eight men, who pioneered the Co-operative Society and Co-operative shop, did not profess to be the first in this field. There had been others before them who had tried to install the principle. However, many had failed because they operated under-price selling, or gave excessive credit facilities to customers.

Those fortunate to be members of the now successful CWS, at the beginning of the twentieth century, had the luxury of 'Divvy Day'. This was the day when the dividend of the year's profits were shared. The amount depended on how much the member had spent throughout the year. To calculate spending, a tiny slip of paper was given to the customer every time purchases were made. The paper, which showed the total amount of purchases, was then taken home and stuck onto a piece of gummed paper. When 'Divvy Day' arrived, the papers were taken to the CWS offices where they were exchanged for hard cash. It was the day of rejoicing as people rushed out to buy essential items otherwise unavailable to them.

Another early twentieth century 'co-operative' facility was the one dealing with healthcare. The 'Co-op doctors', as it was known, comprised groups of doctors, dentists and nurses. Their aim was to administer medical attention to the working classes. That is, to those who could afford to pay a small contribution. These 'Co-op' practices were established through voluntary sources. Once again, the rich donated to the cause, but the bulk of the money needed to operate the service was raised from 'flag days'.

For many, many years before 1900, ordinary working class people tried to save money to cover the funeral expenses of family members who died. They deposited their savings with groups of people who operated 'friendly' and 'burial' societies. Although insurance companies had been in existence for a hundred years or so, their services were provided only to the rich. Insurance facilities did not extend to the working classes. However, it was observed that the public in general did endeavour to set aside monies for the event of death. The opportunity of collecting weekly sums of money was one not to be missed. The chance was seized upon by a leading insurance company, which chose to amalgamate with a series of collecting societies. In 1852 the company, which now dominated the field, proposed a scheme of insurance called Industrial Life Policies. So, at the start of 1900, there were ten million working class families who didn't have to worry any more about burial expenses. If a member of the family died, then money would be available for the funeral. Also, when a child was born to a family it was insured for the sum of one penny against death.

Recalling that the species of man is a mixture of good and bad, it is not surprising to realize that wars have been fought since his birth. Great Britain in 1900 was no different – in fact it was in the full throes of conflict. The war of the day was called the Second Boer War and had begun in 1899. The fighting came about when Britain tried to extend her rule to include the independent African republics of the Transvaal, and the Orange Free State. This is when the discovery of vast gold mines had made these states powerful overnight. So the prize for the victor of this particular war was gold. Up to the end of the war in 1902 the rich and mighty sat back awaiting their bounty, whilst Britain's working husbands and sons, fathers, brothers and cousins, were being slain in the name of the cause. The determination of the British to win the farming land of the Boers was such that serious ills against their enemy were committed. In a campaign to reduce the peoples to starvation, not only were farm animals slaughtered en masse, but every other living animal in the area was killed. The other atrocity was that concentration camps were created. These were places where prisoners of war were housed in appalling conditions then made to suffer torture.

1902 Although the need for education was acknowledged as early as 1839, and school boards were formed in 1870, working class people received only a minimum of learning in their childhood. As well as the compulsory education brought by the 1870 Act, there were also the voluntary schools run by churches. However, the need for children of the poor to work had always overridden the need to be educated. But now in 1902 education was again being re-assessed by the government. The body of people whose job it was to recruit working class children to the schoolroom, and was referred to as the 'school board', was being abolished. In its place town councils were to be responsible for the compulsory education of all children. For this purpose local education authorities were formed.

1903 With the motor car, the steam train, electrified trains and motorbuses well established on the ground, it was not surprising to find man looking to the heavens for new ways of travel. After many, many years of failure at trying to make machines defy gravity, success was now at hand. For in 1903 two American men, Orville and

Wilbur Wright, made the first ever powered air flight, heralding that life was about to start moving faster. In support of this forthcoming event the speed limit for motor cars was increased from 12 mph to 20 mph.

Although a parliamentary voting system was in operation in Great Britain, it was only for the privileged few. An electoral register was introduced under the Reform Act of 1832 – however, the vote had to be bought. It was only the rich who could afford the one shilling fee, which entitled them to elect a candidate of their choice to sit in parliament. The government of the nineteenth century was one that made the rules to suit the wealthy (what's changed?). In fact, all parliamentary members were rich, wealthy landowners. And, even though votes could be bought by those with money enough to make the purchase, women were denied this privilege. Now though, an organisation called the Women's Social and Political Union was formed to press for female suffrage. The pioneers of the movement, Emmeline, Christobel and Sylvia Pankhurst, were ladies of good education who came from a family of financial means, and who recruited others of similar background to join their fight. Together they began to cause nuisance so that they would become noticed. They chained themselves to railings, broke windows, set fire to post-boxes and heckled the speeches of government spokesmen. These women, who had become known as suffragettes, soon began to learn the force of governmental powers. Every day women were arrested and thrown into prison. Whilst they were under lock and key some of the women went on hunger strike. Their punishment for this action was to be force fed. This involved a piece of tubing being pushed down the women's throats, and then into their stomachs. Then, pulped food would be fed into the tube and poked along the gadget. The women had to be held down by many pairs of hands whilst this ugly procedure was carried out. It was not long before details of this cruelty reached the newspapers. Sympathy for the suffragettes came quickly from the public. The government was far from pleased that their little secret was now out. To be seen as humanitarian, they stated that they would not inflict any more punishment on a woman than she could take. Even women who had broken the law, and needed to be punished, would not be given punishment if they seemed to be in a serious physical condition they said. What the government did do was to force feed the women until they were at the point of death. When this happened, they would release them from prison, only to re-arrest them when they had regained their health.

1904 Regardless of what was happening around them, the working classes plodded on. They were oblivious to politics and progress, for their minds were only aware of their own downtrodden world. It was all they could do to survive. In fact the government of 1904 acknowledged the plight of the twentieth century working classes. It set up a committee to investigate physical deterioration. It was thought that there was a 'race degeneration' brought about by poverty. Also noted was the fact that two out of three men were turned down to fight in the Boer War, because they were unfit to do so. Shortly after the investigations were begun, it was announced that free school meals were to be given to children in all state schools. Not only that, medical examinations of all school children would now be made at regular intervals.

1907 The Notification of the Birth Act followed in 1907. This said that all mothers with newly born babies would be called upon by a health visitor. The aim was to ensure both the mother's and child's good health, and to sort out any problems there might be.

Schools, which received grants from local authorities, were also told by the government that they must reserve twenty five to forty per cent of free places for kids from elementary schools.

1908 On top of all the changes that were going to affect the children of the century, the Children's Act came into being in 1908. This stated that it would now be a legal offence to neglect children. And, to promote this law, councils would have to secure the services of officers to enforce it. The Act introduced the juvenile courts system and said also that children under the age of fourteen could no longer be sent to prison. Instead under age offenders would be sent to remand centres called Borstals, which were first developed in 1902.

1909 It was not only working children of the century who had something to celebrate because, in 1909, the Old Age Pensions Act brought joy to the many starving aged. If, by means of a character test, they could prove that their earnings were less than thirty one pounds ten shillings per year, single people over the age of 70 were to receive five shillings (twenty five pence) per week and married couples seven shillings and six pence (thirty seven pence) per week from the government. The government's reason for paying such low rates was to encourage people to make their own provisions instead of beginning to rely on the State to do so. However, regardless of how low the payments were there were tears of joy as old folk went along to post offices to collect their bounties for, after many years of hard toil and suffering, they wouldn't have to worry any more where their next meal was coming from. Now only those who had been to prison or habitually didn't work, and therefore did not qualify for a pension, would have this problem. They would have to continue to make trips to the pawn shops where they would exchange a decent suit or an heirloom trinket for cash. Alternatively they would need to visit the workhouse for charity as folks had always done.

1910 To end the progressive first decade of the century, labour exchanges were opened in 1910. The buildings' doors opened to the public to look out onto queues of people hopeful of finding jobs. Now instead of venturing out on early morning pilgrimages to find work, they could survey the job boards at the labour exchanges to find work.

1911 The National Insurance Act came into being. Under this Act money would be provided for anyone who was unable to work because of sickness. The funding of the scheme was made by way of compulsory contributions from every working person. Each week a set amount of cash was deducted from employees' wage packets. The benefits were that people off work because of ill health would be paid the sum of ten shillings (fifty pence) a week for a total of twenty six weeks. Up until this stage in man's history, his only way of survival had been dependent on his ability to work. Now he was going to receive payment when he was unable to work. Mind, this new privilege was not going to encourage people to feign illness. On the contrary, the working classes were stoic; they had never been accustomed to stopping work just because they didn't feel so good. Therefore, regardless of this newly acquired perk, people would continue to work till they dropped. All that the National Insurance Act represented to the millions of hardworking people, who feared the event of sickness entering their lives, was assurance. Lives of luxury were not expected by the working classes, for it was known that only politicians, bankers, mill owners, mine owners, landowners, etc. warranted these.

1912 Ordinary people living in the slums didn't expect much more than they had. As always they utilised their lives to the best of their ability. However, they were nurturing the idea that their children might know better times. After all, they had witnessed the improvement the past eleven years had brought for children. They had state education, free meals at school, medical examinations and the right not to be neglected. And now, in 1912, school clinics were opening too.

When the news of the sinking of the Titanic came it was with shock and sadness that people received the announcement. The Titanic was a magnificent liner that had been on its maiden voyage from England to America. The boat hit an iceberg in the North Atlantic and sank within hours. Whilst acknowledging the death of fifteen hundred people who were on board the liner, it might serve to observe the survival list. Out of the seven hundred and three people who were saved, sixty one per cent of these were first class passengers; thirty six per cent second-class passengers; twenty three per cent third class passengers, and twenty two per cent crew members. There were also a hundred and eighty Irish people on board and only twenty of them were saved. Three millionaires and a managing director of the company who owned the liner survived by boarding the first lifeboat to leave the sinking ship. Even in a life or death situation, this was surely a reflection of Britain's class-ridden society.

The establishment of unions was beginning to chivvy the working classes into action to obtain their rights and, to prove this, the long-suffering coal miners went on strike. For over a hundred years they had sacrificed their lives to the mine owners' cause but had received nothing more than a pittance for their toils. What their strike action represented was their need to be recognised as human beings struggling for survival. What they asked was a minimum wage to enable them to survive. However, would it bear fruition or would it belly flop for them as it did for the railway workers who staged a strike in 1901? On this particular occasion the long-established railway union had to pay the railway company £23,000 in compensation, in respect of financial loss and damage caused by the strike. Needless to say, the workers did not get a penny piece more in their wage packets.

1913 The suffragettes were still making a name for themselves. Following their rioting in Trafalgar Square in 1908 a more serious incident was recorded in 1913. It was then that one of the suffragettes, Emily Davison, threw herself under the king's horse, whilst it was racing in the Derby. She died in hospital and was given a huge funeral by her comrades. After this incident the militancy of the group increased and their hostility led them to burn buildings, and slash valuable paintings in art galleries.

1914 When Austrian Archduke Franz Ferdinand was assassinated by a Serbian, Austria, backed by Germany, declared war. Then Russia joined in on the side of the Serbians and was followed by France. When Germany attacked neutral Belgium, Britain joined in the rumpus in accordance with the treaty between the two countries which was made in 1839. America took up arms only a year before the war ended in 1918. So, what started as a war between two countries, ended in a world war which merited the title The Great War.

Apart from the conventional vehicles of war – ships, horses, guns and manpower – this one had the additional weapons of motor vehicles and airships. For the first time in war, bombs were being dropped from the sky. These devastating devices were carried by the newly invented flying machines called aeroplanes. There were also hydrogen-filled balloons called Zeppelins. The men of Britain were called upon once more to don khaki and take up arms. It was a bloody war, with ten million dead and twice that number wounded. Out of the six million men and women who served in the British forces, nearly three quarters of a million of them were killed, and one and a half million returned seriously wounded. Apart from the usual injuries of war – loss of limbs, loss of sight or hearing, shell shock – there was another agony to bear this time. Some of the survivors came home suffering the permanent effects of yet another vile weapon – that of poisonous gas, released during the fighting.

It must be noted too that many soldiers' deaths during the First World War, were secured at the hands of their comrades. For, should any man be seen to wander away from the battlefield, he was arrested and executed as a coward. It could not be seen that those men who abandoned their posts were probably unaware of their actions due to the affects of shell shock. However the rules of the British army were that there were to be no excuses for leaving one's post.

Whilst many of the men of Britain were away fighting a war not of their making, the country had to survive as best it could. As well as having to be both mother and father to their families, women were summoned to be the workforce of industry. Millions of ladies were put to work in munitions factories, where they made the weapons of war. Others manned the essential bus and train services, whilst some worked in other industries. Then there was the body of women who, in 1916, formed the Women's Land Army. They worked the farms in order to continue the country's food production.

Since the birth of man his survival had not only depended on a supply of food and shelter, his association with his fellow man had always been an important tool in his survival kit. This fact becomes more visible during times of war, when lending hands are needed more than ever. The war of 1914–1918 was a particular example of comradeship. Untrained working men were thrown together in a live or die situation to fight a horrendous battle, and soldiers risked their own lives to save others. Doctors and nurses courageously patrolled the fighting zones, ready to give medical aid to the injured and dying whilst, back at home, everyone was hoisting the rope in the same direction. Non-working elderly folk were on hand to care for the children of working women, and mothers who did not work did the same for their neighbours' children. When a bomb dropped people did not run away in the opposite direction. Instead they ran to where the bomb had fallen, intent on saving other people's lives. The last thing on their minds was the thought of saving themselves. There was very little that would not be done to help another person.

Money? This was of little consequence – it was only people that mattered. If someone was desperate for food but didn't have a penny in the kitty, there was always someone who did have a penny and would give it to the person who was hungry. Help was on hand at all times for whatever reason. It wasn't just war that made it this way; this is the way it was – in peacetime too.

1918 The end of the First World War however, brought a different outlook to the working classes of Britain. There had been the promise that, when the war was over, the fighting men would return to a country fit for heroes. Throngs of wives, mothers, girlfriends and children waited anxiously to greet their returning men folk. As the crowded trains pulled in, there were tears both of sorrow and excitement. As families united, their feelings were of hope for a better tomorrow. Men either walked, or were carried, accordingly to their fortunes of war, smiling in anticipation of their rewards. Everything was going to be different now for the working masses. The fighting forces had proven themselves worthy of status, and so too had the women who had manned industry for the past four years.

These facts were duly recognised by the government of the day, and, for the first time in history, the working masses were now eligible to vote. Now all men over the age of twenty one, and women over the age of thirty, could elect a member of their choice to serve in parliament (business premises were entitled to two votes at this time).

The year was yet another time of progress for children. The Education Act now stipulated that all children from the age of five receive full-time education that would last until they were fourteen. The Maternity and Child Welfare Act was also brought into being. This Act provided for the building of child welfare and antenatal clinics. Better housing conditions for the poor were also the order of the day. Money was being given by the government to local authorities and private builders with the instruction to 'build, build, build'. Together with the promise of 'no more slums' and the rent registration act, life for the masses had never been so good.

1919 As well as being given the vote, 1919 saw a further recognition for women. A new law was passed in their favour, stating there would be no discrimination against married women who held a job. After all, women had always worked and, only ten years ago, between four and eight million of them had paid jobs. Then, there were the ten million who worked in the home. Of course it shouldn't be forgotten the dangerous work millions of them had performed during the war. This new law started the tongues of liberation wagging and the title of the 'new woman' was born. It was at this time too that women took up the male prerogative of smoking.

Unfortunately the promise of a country fit for heroes did not come to fruition. One year after the war had ended there was much unrest amongst the working people. They had a grudge against the people who had made the promise. They felt that whilst they, the ones who had fought and died in the bloody war, were still poor, the powerful rich had done well out of it. And let's face it – 64,000 of them were travelling at 160 miles per hour in aeroplanes, and nearly 200,000 of them at twenty miles per hour in privately owned motorcars.

The futility of the new anti-discrimination law for married women was more than apparent. Not only was there no work for them, their menfolk found that the only jobs available were either intermittent or underpaid. The final barrier was that there were no jobs at all.

1920 After the war there had been a brief spell of prosperity when industry endeavoured to get back on its feet. However, then profits began to fall because overseas customers had set up their own manufacturing industries whilst the war was in progress, and now they had no need for British goods. Even the railways and coal mines, which the government had supervised through the war years, had been returned to private profiteers. Amidst the great feeling of injustice, the starving heroes threw up their arms in protest. They were shouting for work, they were shouting for food for their families. They were shouting for the railways and the coal mines to be nationalised as they were in the war. Underpaid railway workers' shouts were heard the loudest when they went on strike.

The only people not shouting as they waved goodbye to 1920 were pensioners. They had been given an increase in their allowance and they would now be recipients of ten shillings (fifty pence) per week.

1921 The beginning of a new decade was not a joyous prospect for most. The shaft of light, through which the poorer working classes saw hope, had disappeared into an abyss of gloom. Perhaps life would never get easier for them, despite the promises of those in power that it would. Even the thriving cotton industry, which had been the nation's biggest employer, was in decline. Once again the starving people, with no jobs, were forced to rely on the poor law guardians. Whilst the rich ate sumptuously and grew fatter, the poor dined on charity.

It was pronounced that the country was in a slump. Naturally the government had to cut spending and did so in the zones of housing, health and welfare. These functions had not even been operating long enough for the working classes to have become used to them. When unrest peacked, the coal miners went on strike. Their tolerance had been exhausted beyond the level of reason. They were not prepared to be treated as second-class people anymore. They had recently fought a war, and won a war, and deserved better.

As coal was an essential commodity, both for industry and for living itself, the lack of it brought havoc to the nation. It caused so serious a problem that the government of the day had to declare a state of emergency. This meant that the country's military forces were sent in to man the industries where civil employees were refusing to work. However, as hunger grew amongst the miners and their families, they were forced to return to work after twenty six weeks of the strike.

Ironically they were told that their wages would be reduced instead of being increased. There was not a thing they could do about it.

Pleasure for the working classes was obtained in several ways. For those men fortunate enough to have work and a few spare coppers at the end of a week, a pint with their mates in the pub and a smoke of either a pipe or a cigarette was all the pleasure they asked. The ladies' delights came when the children were in bed, the chores were completed and it was time to sit down. Like their menfolk there was nothing they enjoyed more than a 'chinwag' with their friends, with a cup of tea for support. And, during the day, the streets and backyards were never empty of groups of women, who had taken a few minutes' rest away from their work. They talked together, and laughed together, as if their worries were a hundred miles away. Children amused themselves in many ways. When they were outside with their friends, there were endless games to be played. They would hop, skip or jump to their hearts' content. There were trees to be climbed, places to be hidden in, fights to be fought or races to be won. They constructed carts with wheels from old perambulators, and took turns at sitting in their homemade contraptions whilst their mates pulled them along. The sheer excitement of the movement of the vehicles evolved endless hours of play. In winter months when the snow was thick on the ground, there was so much fun to be had when it came to building snowmen, or skimming atop the slippery white stuff on homemade sledges. And, when the water turned to ice, how exciting it was to skate or slide along the mirrored surface. Of course it was cold, very cold indeed, but the momentum of the fun evaporated the chill of the day. There was always the envisaged thrill of getting warm when they returned home too – so this was also something to look forward to. During the summer months swimming or paddling was the children's agenda. This they did in streams, and the natural pools which formed from their flowing waters. The more adventurous would try their luck in rivers, some of which obviously proved dangerous because of currents and depths.

1922 The ordinary people of the 1900s spent their leisure time no differently from their ancestors. They derived pleasure from the company of each other. However, 1922 brought a new source of entertainment to society. It was then that broadcasting began. The broadcasts were put out by the British Broadcasting Company Ltd. (prior to being converted to the British Broadcasting Corporation on 1 January 1927), and were received in the home through an invention called the wireless. Of course, only those fortunate to have funds to purchase a wireless set were able to listen to the programmes. As well as being caressed by the music that floated through the airwaves, and amused by light comedy pieces, the people of Britain were now able to hear news of world events. Now they would know what was happening in the big world outside their own domain.

One of the first items of news from home, being received via the wireless, was that of a government concern. It related to the presence of tuberculosis in the country. The disease, commonly known as TB, was the nation's largest killer. For this reason the minister of health decreed that all milk must be pasteurised, so that the disease could not be passed from dairy cattle to humans.

1923 Even though the law of divorce had been in operation since the 1600s, very few of them had been granted. For nearly 300 years only 229 people obtained divorces, and just three or four appertained to women. However, the liberalisation of the divorce laws of 1923 now stated that women could break up a marriage if husbands committed adultery. The law also stated that said husbands could have access to children, if they proved to be desirable influences.

1925 Another attempt at ridding yet another killer disease was effected in 1925. This time it was typhoid that was tackled by means of the introduction of chlorine to main water supplies. Together with the filtration system, in use since 1911, it was believed that this new method of sterilisation would help to eliminate typhoid and other waterborne diseases.

1926 More good news again in 1926 when men were told that, instead of having to work until they were 70, they would now retire from work at the age of 65. For women the retiring age would be 60. With this Act came another, which introduced contributory pensions. This involved weekly payments being taken from everyone's pay packet so that on retirement they would receive a liveable pension from the state.

No progressive movements would silence the unrest that the people of Britain felt and over three million people stood to be counted. In a general strike, which lasted for nine days, the country was brought to a standstill. During the strike there were 1,289 incidents of disorder, and 3,146 people were prosecuted. The only workers who did not strike were those employed in essential services such as hospitals, sanitation and sewerage works, fire stations, ambulance depots and food outlets.

Ironically whilst sixty per cent of the British nation was living just above the poverty level at this time, company profits were rising by sixty-two per cent. For the rich it was the time of merriment and good living. They had everything they needed for partying; there was the coming of jazz from America, gramophones and records to play on them, wirelesses and motorcars, aeroplanes and the 'Charleston'. So, why should the rich not know these times as anything other than the roaring twenties? For them things could not have been better.

1927 This was the year that American Charles Lindbergh made the first solo non-stop trans-Atlantic flight from New York to Paris to prove that aeroplanes were making their mark on society.

1928 The country had been blessed with cinema entertainment since the beginning of the century. This was the place where dreams could be dreamed or ambitions fired, as pictures were projected onto large screens. In silence, actors mimed comedy, love, heroism and courage, whilst their delighted audiences watched in awe. Despite poverty levels, nearly everyone had had the experience of 'going to the pictures' (even if it meant sneaking in and then being thrown out). When in 1928 a talking film was released in Britain everyone was so excited to hear an actor's voice emanating from the screen; and music too! No more need for a pianist to sit and manufacture music to accompany the pictures showing above his or her head. A time of revolution in entertainment was noted, but so too was the fact that 'speaking films' were turning people into watchers rather than doers.

But then, there were still the music halls where the public took great delight in joining in. No live theatre escaped the criticism of the working class audiences. If they were enjoying the artiste's rendition of a song, then they would join in, if they weren't, they would either shout out (inviting the performer to leave the stage) or throw rotting vegetables onto it. The theatre was a place of community venture where everybody became an actor in his own right.

Was it further recognition of the female species that induced the government of 1928 to lower the voting age for women from thirty to twenty one? Perhaps so for, in 1920 fifty ladies had obtained degrees from Oxford University; then in 1921 the first woman jury foreman was seen and in 1924 the first woman barrister.

1929 Five years ago Scotsman John Logie Baird who had been experimenting at conveying pictures through the airwaves, had transmitted the first successful television picture. Now in the year of 1929 experimental television to the public began. Once again, few people could afford to buy the instrument, called a television set, that would receive the broadcasts.

During this year too the Local Government Act abolished the Poor Law guardians and transferred their functions to local authorities. This meant that government would now be responsible for providing financial assistance to the poor. This was apart from the aged and infirm who would still rely on the workhouse for monetary help. The new Act must have come as a relief for the two and a half million workers who had lost their jobs after the decline of the cotton industry.

Regardless of the unemployment and poverty that existed in the country, it didn't stop the march of progress for the minority. At this time there were one million cars registered on Britain's roads; driving tests were introduced and the speed limit was abolished.

1930 During 1930 a battle began between the two or three companies who printed newspapers. Their aim to sell more copies promoted them into seducing the better-off public to buy. This they did by giving away gifts to all who chose readership of their particular 'rag'. Another popular media of the day was the one aimed at women. Women's magazines were now on the increase, with articles showing ladies how they could become more physically attractive. On top of these little titbits, there were pieces suggesting how women could better look after their homes and families. It was a sign of the times for those who aimed to leave the dreary past behind, and head towards a world of materialism.

1931 It seemed forgotten that there was still a great depression in existence. So much so that the government was forced to realise that it had a financial crisis on its hands. Unemployment benefits were costing so much that they had to be cut. This was where the means test came into being, when people in receipt of unemployment benefit would have to prove the need for the amount of money they were receiving. Committees of people were employed for the purpose of questioning recipients of unemployment benefit. If the body of people decided that a family could exist on less than a stipulated benefit, then this would be reduced.

With unemployment having risen to nearly three million, the labour exchanges became obsolete and thousands of people reverted to the days of waiting around, from early morning, to get casual docking work. Those lucky enough to have full-time employment were the only ones to benefit from rising living standards. Many of these people were delighted when the Ford Motor Company decided to construct a factory near London, for this would surely bring down the price of motorcars to make them affordable to themselves – the wage earners.

1933 Whilst the fortunate ones were planning their mobility, most families were still living in rat-infested properties, with no water or sanitation. For a lot of families their living accommodation consisted of no more than one room (lots of which were in cellars). In 1933, however the government drew up fresh plans to clear 266,000 slum dwellings. Their aim – to re-house one and a quarter million people by building 285,000 new houses. Because of the influx of buses and motor cars, a lot of properties were now being built in the urban districts far away from city and town centres. This applied to factories too, which meant that, for the first time in history, people were transporting themselves to work by bus or car. The age-old traditional transport – foot and horsepower – was being lost to 'progress'.

The means test was not accepted gladly by the millions of unemployed. They showed their anger against it by holding demonstrations in London's Hyde Park. This was also their venue as people from all over the country, walked in great numbers in a march of hunger.

1934 Was everything going too fast for the government of 1934? Did they think that people were moving so quickly that they couldn't catch their breath? Perhaps so, for they decided to enforce a speed limit of thirty miles per hour for vehicles from that time.

1935 The innovation of hire purchase was the order of 1935. For wage earners, here was the spending power that would bring them much coveted household goods. With a slogan of buy today – pay in instalments, commerce was set to sell more goods than ever before. For the few (other than the wealthy) who had installed electricity, this was the opportunity to buy irons and vacuum cleaners. And, although refrigerators were very rare, manufacturers had high hopes of more sales. Even for the poor, hire purchase was the promise of acquiring the wireless set that still one per cent of the nation was without.

At this point of evolution, people started to take it for granted that the government involved itself in their welfare. However, even though standards of living were beginning to rise for the greater percentage, people remained very much the same. Family life was still as important a factor as it had been throughout mankind's existence. Houses were filled with visiting brothers, sisters, aunties, uncles and cousins. They dined together at least once a week. Usually this was on a Sunday. Normally the meal was taken at tea time – round about 4.00 to 5.00pm. Cold meals were the norm, say cooked meat, or salmon from a tin. After this there would be a variety of cakes from which to choose, followed by one or two cups of tea. When tea was over, the family would sit together and engage in a singsong around the piano (or without a piano if there wasn't such an instrument in the house). Whilst games were favoured, the alternative for them was to just sit and talk. Regardless of financial status there always seemed to be something to laugh about, and roofs would rise with peals of merriment. If there were tears to be shed, then this emotion too would be shared. A problem for one of the family meant a problem for the whole of the family. No one ever carried a burden alone. If one was family-less there was always someone to care, be it a neighbour or friend.

The children's role in the family was to be obedient at all times. When they played outside it was with the understanding that they were back in the house by a certain time. If they weren't they were in trouble with their parents. Their instructions included the unspoken rule of adhering to best behaviour whilst away from the house. If mums and dads discovered that their children had given cheek to anyone, or had damaged anything belonging to someone else, the offender would be scolded or smacked, according to the age-old tradition of discipline. With the threat of punishment hanging over their heads, children knew better than to break the rules. They also had their schoolteachers and headmasters to contend with. If bad behaviour was reported to the child's school authorities, further chastisement would be administered.

Social rules were no different for adults. People possessed the innate instinct of the time; the one that told them that they must respect the society to which they were born. Without having to be told, they recognised that survival depended on law and order, and the function of helping each other. There was no other way of life – this is how it had always been.

If someone was down on their luck, there was always someone there to help. When furniture needed moving to another house, willing hands were at the ready. Should sickness strike, the sufferers were never left to face their load alone. Family and neighbours would share in the nursing of the patient and the running of the household. Support of each other was an abundant source of encouragement to those struggling to survive. The people of the 1930s were following the pattern of human behaviour as it had been since time began. However, on the downside of this pattern came the practice of physical aggression. Despite the lack of family funds, many unemployed men of the time still managed to find their way to the public houses on a Saturday evening. Frequently fighting would occur as the men, having consumed enough beer to render them drunk, left the pubs at closing time. The frustration that unemployment caused them was released in these punch-ups. During these days it was unsafe for police officers to monitor street fighting single-handedly; instead they patrolled in threes.

With the ongoing endeavour to eliminate sickness and premature death, another vaccination was discovered. This one was proven to combat the killer disease of diphtheria. Children were vaccinated in the hope that the death rate from this illness would be reduced.

Mental disorders had always been a source of confusion to those involved in the medical profession. People who displayed unusual behaviour often were classed as 'mad' or 'lunatic' and were locked away in asylums. However, some doctors were still striving to understand the mechanics of the mind. In 1935 steps were taken to develop a cure for those suffering emotional disturbance and the lobotomy was introduced into medicine. This operation involved making a cut in the head so that the part of the brain tissue thought to be the cause of the problem could be removed.

1936 This year saw the end of experimental television. It was clear that the service was now here to stay, so the British Broadcasting Corporation took over the official transmitting rights to begin television broadcasting. Now, all who owned a television set could see what was happening in the big world outside, instead of just being able to listen to it. The little picture boxes caused so much excitement for the working classes. So much so, that they now felt the need to remain in their homes for as long as possible. It was noted at the time that attendances at social centres, clubs, churches and pubs declined when television appeared.

However, not deterred by the thoughts of people spending too much time at home, Billy Butlin opened a holiday camp that was the first of its kind in the country. After all, things were beginning to look up for the working classes, and very soon masses of them would be wanting organised holidays.

1937 The new Factories Act of 1937 stated that, from now on young people under the age of sixteen would not be allowed to work any more than forty four hours per week. Also, with divorce still being reviewed, it was decreed that insanity, and desertion, would now be grounds for divorce. And the national electricity grid was brought into being.

With the Great Depression over, and jobs available in abundance, the working classes were heading further along the road to prosperity. With water supplies, gas, electricity, wireless sets, telephones, hire purchase, motor cars, the vote, unemployment benefit, good housing, a holiday camp and television sets (eighty thousand at the time) what more could be asked? Why not holidays with pay?

At this stage it had not gone unnoticed by government that the working classes were becoming more prosperous. Perhaps, because of this, rent controls were removed under the Rent and Mortgage Interest (Restrictions) Act. This applied to houses worth between £20 and £135 in London. Another encouragement that came from the party of the rich was directed at better paid workers. This was that they buy their own homes and leave the squalor of the masses behind them. Who of them could refuse the desirable properties which were being offered? In roads of tree-lined borders, detached houses with bay windows were appearing. Good quality semi-detached houses, too, were integral to the new urban districts. The people who could afford to do so flocked to buy the houses that would demonstrate their success, and determine their voting status. They regarded themselves now as better off than the working classes, and, therefore eligible to follow the political doctrines of conservatism. The new urban dwellers must also be seen to be correct in their behaviour. To keep oneself to oneself was of paramount importance to their newly acquired status. Any of the 'rough stuff', associated with the working class environment, would not be tolerated. There would be no calls of, "Good morning Ethel, how's Jim, has he got a job yet?" along the tree-lined roads. There would be no peals of laughter with the telling of funny stories. Nor would there be a shoulder to cry on if the going got tough. There would have to be an order of dignity amongst the occupants of better class housing. Gossip! Certainly not, only the poorer working classes did this. However, noted at the time was the fact that many a net curtain was seen to twitch at regular intervals along the 'posh' roads, a sign that the natural instincts of humankind were still alive and kicking, but were being suppressed for effect.

1938 Another breakthrough in psychiatric medicine came about in 1938. This is when electroconvulsive therapy began. It was given the name of shock treatment and involved wiring patients up to machines that administered bursts of electricity to the body.

1939 The Holidays With Pay Act came into force in 1939. For the first time in their lives, working class people were going to be paid for not working. Eleven million people secured this privilege under the Act (for the scheme was not compulsory for employers). For the first time in their lives too, they were going to have the chance of visiting the seaside and countryside. Hordes of bright-eyed children and adults loaded themselves onto charabancs (coaches), eager to enjoy a journey that would bring their dreams to fruition. How their hearts danced with the thoughts of glimpsing the sea, or a mountain. It did not matter that the sum total of their holiday might measure only one day. For the working classes who were proud possessors of some of the two million motor cars on the roads, their one-day holiday provided the opportunity of using these machines. Loaded with picnics, people and power, they trundled along the country roads, tooting horns as they went. The most popular conveyance of one-day holidaymakers however, was the bicycle. As charabancs and motor cars sped past, large groups of cyclists were happy to pedal their way to the rainbow's end. Whatever way people chose to travel, Britain's roads were filled with happiness. After millions of years of strife for the human masses, there was the thought that emancipation was near and struggle would be no more.

Alas, the dream did not last for long as Britain was once again plunged into war. This conflict grew into the Second World War. It was begun by Germany under a national socialist party leadership (which earned the title of the Nazis). The factors preceding the German invasion of neighbouring countries were many. In 1929 the American stock exchange crashed causing depression both in the USA and Europe. By the year 1933, unemployment was rife worldwide as the incidental result of the American financial collapse. Respectively Britain's unemployment figure rose to three million, Americans without jobs numbered twelve million. In Germany between seven and nine million people were out of work. This is when the leader of the national socialist party, Adolf Hitler, aspired for power. He promised to generate work for people, and did so by having them build new roads around Germany. Happy with their newly-found jobs, the people saw this leader as their hero. They rose in salute whenever he appeared in view. They also saluted him because, like the German nation as a whole, he was far from happy about Germany being blamed for causing the Great War. He advocated that any blame for the country's ills should be directed against the communists, but above all – the Jews. So in 1939 Germany's leader began a programme of revenge and began his quest to make Germany great. Firstly his campaign to rid the country of the powerful Jews increased dramatically. Then, his armies marched into countries taken from Germany in the First World War, and regained the territories. The invasions continued into other countries allied with Britain. The Germans' failed attempts to conquer Britain itself began when they attacked the country in 1940. Could it be that some might have likened the situation to that of Britain's acquisition of the empire?

Conscription became the order of the day once again, and every able-bodied man in Britain was forced to don uniform. Women, too, joined the armed forces, but their doing so was not compulsory. Far from it, because they would be needed to man industry and work the land whilst the menfolk were away fighting. There was no lack of enthusiasm when it came to joining the army, the navy or the air force. The pattern of history dictated that people lay down their lives in order to protect their land. In the case of the Second World War, feelings were more ardently inspired this way. 'Jerry' (as the German army was known) was certainly not going to get away with invading Britain and her allies. With a 'kill or be killed' attitude, the British fighting forces determinedly took up arms with the aim to win the war.

As usual, the precise reason for the fight was not known, but it didn't matter. The adamant commitment to protect territory, and drive intruders away from it, was enough. However, there were men who refused to take part in war stating that it was wrong to kill another person. Some went as far as saying that if everyone refused to fight, then there would be no wars. Their views were interpreted as cowardly, and they were tagged with the label of 'conscientious objectors'. The punishment for such cowardice was to be imprisoned at His Majesty's pleasure. Whilst the few brave men who chose to honour their principles were prepared to suffer this way, they were sad that punishment was inflicted on their families also. For some of these were alienated from society, and physically attacked by people who also handed them white feathers (a symbol of cowardice).

As in any war, the strategy was to destroy the weapons and the communication points of the enemy. For this reason London became one of the main targets of German bombing. Raids were many and casualties were high. Ordinary people grew terrified of hearing the loud siren that told them a German aircraft had been seen in the skies. The sound warned they must run for shelter as quickly as possible. Clutching children, or aiding disabled or elderly people, they found somewhere to hide. All over Britain people had constructed underground air raid shelters from sheets of corrugated tin. Groups of neighbours worked together digging large pits from the earth of their gardens. When the hole was big enough, the tin sheets were lowered into place to form an underground room. Some shelters were constructed inside houses from heavy pieces of steel bolted together to form a square. The sides were made of wire mesh and the top, metal sheeting. Those people with nowhere better to go would take refuge in the cellars of their houses, when the sirens sounded. Mother would wake father, and the children, from their sleep and herd them into the cellar. Whatever shelter there was, the idea was to have protection from falling debris. If it meant living under tons of rubble for days, and surviving on the food supplies taken into the shelter, the hope was that eventually, someone would dig them out alive.

For Londoners living close to the underground railway system, this provided them perfect protection. Night after night the station platforms were blanketed with the sleeping bodies of men, women and children who never knew what the morning, and the all-clear siren would bring them. Would their home still be standing, or would it now be a pile of smoking debris? If this were so, what would they do, where would they go?

It was not only falling bombs that Londoners had to fear. In this war there were flying bombs, 'doodlebugs' and rockets flying through the air. These would break through Britain's defences to destroy anything in their paths. Thousands of civilian people in London, and outlying towns and cities, were killed by these weapons.

Apart from having to deal with death and destruction in wartime, it is reasonable to expect that food, and other supplies, will be in short supply. Killing people by taking food from their mouths is a method always used as a wartime tactic. So, in this war, nothing was different, with many civilian merchant ships being bombed as they carried goods to Britain. The death toll and injury to merchant seamen was high.

Despite the shortage of food and other commodities during the war, there was produce available. For those with money to spare, there was always the black market to turn to, offering anything from food to clothing. As well as invading the night to secure animal flesh, the marketeers never passed up the chance of looting bombed shop premises. Their aim – to acquire anything that might sell.

Disregarding the few who made money out of the misery of war, all others shared food, clothing, accommodation, strength, hope and love. As in other wars, the people pooled their resources and their strength. The welfare of oneself always came second to the welfare of others.

The extent of bombing over London and other major cities was so great that the evacuation of children was necessary. Daily busloads of kids left for the safer environments of country areas. As mothers and grandmothers waved goodbye to the tearful children, the look on all their faces was one that portrayed the fear that they would never see each other again.

CHAPTER SEVEN

The Forties and Fifties

1940 The reorganisation of the country was still prominent in government circles in spite of the war that was raging. In 1940, the year that Italy declared war on Britain, a policy of full employment was undertaken. Could this mean that unemployment would be a thing of the past for the working classes in post-war years?

1944 The future of children remained a priority when, in 1944, it was announced that the school leaving age would be raised to fifteen.

Then, though the science of genetics had been long-established, with the patterns of inheritance through genes clarified, the question as to how chromosomes and their genes copied exactly from cell to cell to be directed to living things was yet unsolved. However during this year a Canadian bacteriologist, Oswald Thedore Avery, proved that a bodily substance named Dexyribonucleic Acid (DNA) performed this role.

1945 Europe celebrated the end of the war on 7th May 1945. This was after the German leader's suicide and then Germany's unconditional surrender one week later. However, the war still continued between Japan and America. America, anxious to hasten Japan towards a capitulation, took measures to bring this about. In early August of 1945 they dropped an atomic bomb on Japan's city of Hiroshima. Eighty thousand people were killed in this monstrous action, and seventy thousand more seriously injured. To help the Japanese make a final surrender, three days later a plutonium bomb was launched on Nagasaki. This is how tens of thousands more Japanese people died from radiation poisoning. Disregarding the instant death toll, no one appreciated that, as a result of the radiation from such bombs, the suffering of the Japanese people would continue for many decades to come.

It was not until peace arrived that the true horrors of the Second World Ward emerged. It was then that the title of Holocaust was given to these most dreadful years and the German leader was dubbed a monster. As I was only nine years old at the time this talk of the day was beyond my comprehension. However, when I was taken to the cinema to see the news reels about the war I matured quickly through the images that I saw. These were of groups of emaciated people, barely alive, who cowered behind barbed-wire fences. Their heads were shaven; their eyes sunken and their skeletal bodies scantily clothed. With fear they peered at the soldiers who walked amongst them with white cloths pressed against their noses and mouths, and the men who were frantically photographing them. As the cameras moved away from them, further pictures revealed corpses lying around in contorted positions. With the next clips came gasps of horror from the audience. What we were seeing were massive graves overly filled with thousands of corpses piled one upon the other. It appeared to be that if the pile reached any higher it would topple over. The commentary that accompanied the pictures told that the people we were seeing were those that allied soldiers had found in this place; one of the many concentration camps that the Nazis had built during the war. It went on to explain that the soldiers were wearing masks over their faces to smother the stench of rotting flesh and the odour of imminent death. The masks were also used to quell the smell of burning flesh that permeated the air for, discovered on the campsite were massive ovens used to dispose of the bodies of those poisoned to death in adjacent gas chambers. When I left the cinema I never imagined that the pictures I had seen and the news that I had heard would haunt me for the rest of my life.

During the next couple of years, when eye witness accounts of the atrocities of the Second World War were received from those who had survived them, an accurate story of the extent of these began to emerge and flooded the media.

The Germans built two kinds of concentration camps; those with gas chambers and massive ovens, and those without. The prisoners who were to occupy these camps; military prisoners of war, gypsies, homosexuals, political offenders, conscientious objectors, the disabled and eventual millions of civilian Jews, were transported there by rail. Packed in cattle trucks with no food, water, toilet facilities or air they travelled, sometimes for days on end. When the trains arrived at the camps an order was bellowed out, 'Throw out your dead', for obviously many prisoners died during these horrendous journeys. When the survivors alighted they were made to stand in line whilst Nazis and SS officers (the leaders' henchmen) gave cursory examinations and they were made to move either to the left or to the right, according to their physical condition. The line of those selected for work were led away to camp accommodation. Those deemed unfit for work were marched off to the gas chambers.

Life at the work camps was very hard for in-mates. They were made to work all day long without rest and with only a cup of tea to drink and a morsel of bread to sustain them. At night they slept on pieces of wood, or packs of straw, where lice bit into the little flesh that they had left on their bodies. Daily, workers dropped down dead, if not from shear exhaustion and starvation then from the many diseases that existed there. If they didn't die of their own accord when they reached the point where they could work no more, then they would be sent to the gas chambers. The average time a worker could survive a work camp was three months, but what did this matter? New prisoners, mainly Jewish, were arriving at the camps by the thousands daily.

The mass graves at the camps were long, deep and wide and were constructed by the prisoners themselves. When inmates died of starvation, beatings or disease their bodies were thrown into the open graves to rot. When mass execution was the order of the day the Nazi soldiers would shovel up the carcasses of the dead and tip them into the burial ground. Sometimes, to lessen the work of the soldiers, prisoners doomed for execution were marched to the graves and ordered to stand at the edge, whereupon they were shot. Automatically, their bodies fell into the open pits. Of course the executioners did not care if the bullets they had fired had killed their victims – if they weren't dead now they soon would be. The unfortunate survivors of intended execution were not the only ones to suffer this painful road to eventual death, for prisoners who were dying and littering the campsite, were also thrown onto the rotting mounds of flesh.

With execution and cremation a daily routine, the gutters running from the crematorium were constantly flowing with boiling fat. This liquid was scooped up by the German soldiers and ladled onto bodies to help them burn. When it came to killing babies and young children, sometimes the German soldiers couldn't be bothered to take them into the gas chambers. Instead they threw these innocent little bodies into the burning gutters to meet their eventual death.

At the Polish concentration camp, Auschwitz, a senior medical officer there, Dr Joseph Mengele, had been ordered to discover the secrets of genetic engineering and learn how to remove inferior genes from human beings. This was desired so that Hitler's ambition to create a perfect German race could reach fruition. The doctor, together with a team of others, commenced the experiments required to achieve the aim. These experiments were carried out on Jewish prisoners, mainly children, who were subjected to surgical operations without anaesthetic.

The whole world was so shocked by the occurrences at the concentration camps that when people set about rebuilding their lives, and their countries, they were confident that the Second World War had brought an end to all wars. To support the assumption, in 1945 fifty countries signed a United Nations Charter to prevent any country from being allowed to repeat the atrocities of this war.

1946 In Britain in post-war years there was a desperate shortage of workers. Recruitment schemes were set up to bring stateless persons to the country to work in factories and hospitals. Thousands of Poles, Ukrainians, Hungarians, Latvians, etc. came to assist with the vital task of reconstruction. Many made Britain their permanent home. Recruitment was started in Ireland too.

With war now gone it meant that the television transmitter could be re-opened, and so, in people's homes viewing was resumed.

1947 A farewell to the coal-mining barons was made as the government nationalised the coal industry. No more victimisation of the brave men who tunnelled underground to bring out vital coal supplies. Now the industry belonged to the people of Britain.

Ironically, only ten years after the National Grid had been opened, the government was urging people to save electricity. A warning was given to those people who took a bath on a daily basis. They were told their supply would be cut off if they continued this pursuit. Of course, only the better off people had baths in their homes at this time. The poorer working classes were still bathing as they used to, in the zinc containers that were filled with water from boiled kettles.

But can you imagine the squeals of delight from working class women, who never dreamt that they would be rich enough to own a washing machine, when something called a launderette was opened? This was a place that housed rows of automatic washing machines that the general public could use. After years of scrubbing clothes on washboards, or going to the community wash houses, the lady of the house could now bundle dirty clothes together and pop them into the launderette. Here she would place the garments into a machine, insert a coin, press a button and, lo and behold, the contraption would do the work for her. Idly she could sit and read a book or have a gossip as the clothes swished around before her eyes, happy with the thought that washday's drudgery was over.

Two new Acts came into force. One was the Acquisition of Land Act that was brought into being for the purpose of ridding the country of its slums. As a lot of privately rented houses were unfit for human habitation, councils would now have power to remove these from their owners, offering the minimum of payment in return. The point of the exercise was two-fold. One was that councils could reconstruct the houses to make them fit for re-renting. The other was that houses beyond redemption would be demolished to make room for new buildings. It didn't go unnoticed at the time that many compulsory purchase housing found its way to the ownership of council officials. Many town planners, and building inspectors now took on the role of landlord after having bought rows of houses for a pittance. Needless to say these people continued as other profit-making landlords had done. They had no intention of spending a penny piece to improve their houses, so tenants were still living in properties pronounced unfit. The other Act was the Town and Country Planning Act, created to prevent offence being caused, when 'building on' was intended. For example, if a family were planning to add a bathroom or kitchen extension to their home, or alternatively, a garage, shed or fence, they would have to seek permission from their town council to do so. If a council inspector then visited the property and determined that the intended structure would rob a neighbour's home of light, access or quality, permission would not be granted.

1948 A most triumphant time for all came in 1948 when the welfare state was born. With it came the idea of a 'New Britain'. From now on, the state would provide many things for many people. Care and free services would be provided for the birth of babies and during their early years of schooling. There would be provision for all when sickness and workless days occurred. Benefits would be available too for those experiencing widowhood and retirement. Even costs towards funeral expenses would be granted. Available also was free doctoring, dentistry, medicine and wheelchairs. And, all for just four shillings and eleven pence (almost twenty five pence) out of the worker's weekly pay packet. People not in work could apply for national assistance (this was an upgrade of the now extinct Poor Law).

With medical treatment free for everyone, three thousand hospitals were nationalised. Furthermore, local authorities were made responsible for providing home nurses, midwives, infant carers, immunisation and ambulance services. And, whereas the welfare state, incorporating the National Health Service (NHS), had been created to help poorer people, everybody in the country would benefit.

Another victory came for Britain's population when the railways were nationalised during the year. Nationalisation involved government control of those industries that, because they provided essential services, were deemed to belong to the people by right. Whilst commodities were not supplied freely, the idea was to maintain economical pricing to customers, whilst profiting enough to plough money back into the industries to maintain self-sufficiency. In private ownership, on the other hand, where the dictate was for vast profits to be made, essential services came at a higher price to the public.

Things had never been so good for the working classes. Ten million mill workers were taking two weeks' paid holiday per year, and there was an abundance of jobs. In fact there were more jobs than there were workers, despite the influx of immigrants who had joined Britain's workforce since the war. To encourage Britain's population to swell, the British Nationality Act was passed, and this declared that all British Empire passport holders were entitled to become citizens of the United

Kingdom. The Act provided an open door and enabled much immigration. Thousands of people from the Caribbean, India and Pakistan responded to a persuasive advertising campaign, designed to increase the size of the workforce in Britain. Slogans were put out throughout the countries of the British Empire, saying, 'Come to the Mother Country' and 'Are you looking for employment? Then take a trip to England'. As living conditions were far from good in these countries, it is not surprising that the invitation was taken without hesitation.

1949 Before the first half of the century came to an end, two further improvements were made. The first – the clothes rationing imposed during wartime was removed. This would mean that no more would people be able to profit by selling their issue of clothing coupons to 'spivs', as they had done during the fighting years. Secondly, the gas industry was nationalised.

1950 At the start of the second half of the century, better living conditions were apparent. Most homes in Britain were, by this time, connected to sewers and water mains. A lot of the slums had been demolished and new flats and houses had taken their place. What a thrill it was for some of the working class families to move to a house that had its own lavatory, and a fixed bath with taps to turn. In fact by now sixty two per cent of homes had fixed baths or showers. The only drawback was that people were now being separated from close-knit communities. It had been requested of council housing officials that whole neighbourhoods be re-housed together. However, this was not to be, and families found themselves living in areas away from town centres and apart from friends they had known. The wrench was hard to bear as they adjusted to a new way of life. But this was a new Britain where everything was going to be better, so best make the most of it.

With this in mind it was a shock that, only two short years after the start of the National Health Service, the government was shouting that it was costing the country too much money. For this reason a ceiling was imposed on NHS spending.

Still lacking at this point of the century was an abundance of food. During wartime years food and other commodities were rationed and books of coupons were issued to everyone in the land. This ensured that each member of society be allocated a proportion of whatever stocks were available. Cherished morsels of edibles were shared cautiously within family circles, because, when the week's supplies were exhausted there was no more. When couples were getting married, families would pool their food coupons so that they could offer light refreshments to the wedding guests. As for wedding cakes, well, these were very seldom available. It would have taken too many coupons to acquire the ingredients to concoct such a luxury. Instead cardboard replicas were used, and these could be hired by the hour from their enterprising inventors. Sometimes, the 'cake' would be rushed in just for the purpose of a photograph. The happy couple, knife in hand, would pose whilst the camera clicked on the pretend cake-cutting ceremony.

Although inflation and unemployment were very low these days, there was still the need for newlyweds to move in with their parents for a while. Regardless of the large numbers of houses that had been built over the last years, there were still lists of people waiting to be housed by the public sector, although private renting was also available. Of course preference was towards the newly-built council houses that featured inside WCs and bathrooms, for still there were the notorious racketeer landlords who offered their tenants less-than-adequate accommodation. A lot of their properties were poorly maintained; many of them were damp, dark and dismal and unfit for human habitation. Many houses harboured infestations of rats, mice, lice and cockroaches, as had been the case throughout the years. Landlords were also notorious for evicting people from their properties. If it were seen that there was no good reason to evict a family, other methods would be used to 'persuade' the tenants to leave. Perhaps an outer door would be removed, or a window. In houses that did not accommodate resident rodents, some would be introduced by the landlord. One notorious case told of a landlord who broke into a house and stole the family piano to entice the family to move out. He was flabbergasted when the lady of the house revealed, 'I didn't want the bloody thing anyway, I've been trying to get rid of it for years.'

When it came to house searches on behalf of newlyweds, mother was the one to have her nose to the ground, watching, waiting and listening for news of vacant properties. Of course, if she were looking for a home for her married daughter, then she would scour no further than the immediate neighbourhood. Marriage was not a reason for daughters to move away. The idea was to remain as close as possible to mum, to maintain family connections and, learn from her all there was to be known.

Up until this stage in history only the rich, and higher middle classes, owned property. However, buying one's own home was now becoming the practice of professional people. And there were small numbers of the working classes, who earned higher wages than most, who were taking out loans to become homeowners.

Farming had always been an industry of community effort in man's history. During both planting and reaping it was an all hands on deck situation. Harvesting in particular was a time when there was no time to be lost. The food needed extracting from the ground as quickly as possible, so whole farming communities were required to perform the task. The toil of reaping was hard, but the joining of people made it a happy occasion. Through this method of comradeship, Britain was producing eighty per cent of its own food in 1945. However during the war, when farm workers were called away to fight, the land was worked by the Women's Land Army, and prisoners of war. But now, with the war over and farm workers having taken up other occupations, there was a shortage of farmhands. For this reason farmers turned to modern machinery to perform sowing and reaping work. However, due to the size of the machines, it was necessary for fields to be made bigger, so boundaries surrounding existing fields were removed. This meant that the precious life-giving homes of much of Britain's wildlife had to be sacrificed. The hedgerows of the land were disappearing and little country lanes were to be lost for ever.

1951 Now, just three years after the start of the NHS, where every medical facility was to be given free, the government decided to start making charges for medicine. Charges for dental and optical appliances were also approved. A few Cabinet Ministers resigned from their posts in protest.

During this year another industry was nationalised – this time it was iron and steel.

1952 Last year the government pledged to build three hundred thousand houses per year, and to increase subsidies on council houses, whereby it would now pay £35 towards the cost of building a house; up from £22. Obviously it was recognised that more housing was needed, because of the response to Britain's offer of immigration. During 1952, the first year of the pledge, 216,527 houses were built in the space of eleven months.

At the time of the early fifties, Britain was established in the nuclear power game, as was the rest of the western world. In the race to secure maximum national strength, Britain tested the first of its atomic weapons by exploding a bomb in Australia.

Because of the burning of coal, smog was a feature of Britain's heritage. The smoke from this caused heavy, dark mists to hover over cities and towns. Sometimes this would be so dense, that one could not see one's own hand in front of one's face. Obviously the situation was a health hazard. Although smog had been killing folks along the years, London registered a 'smog disaster' which recorded that four thousand people had died of smoke inhalation. Perhaps Britain's capital would think about introducing 'smokeless zones', as Manchester had done in 1946.

As the headaches grew as to how to solve the smog problems, the year saw the introduction of jet aeroplanes. As the word implies, these are vehicles that shoot rapidly into the air and then travel at great speeds. Of course no one gave a thought to the fumes these aircraft would produce as they roared through the skies, burning up vast amounts of fossil fuel. Not even the aircraft movements from just Manchester Airport, which totalled fourteen thousand, six hundred and twenty five for the year, were considered. It seemed that only the devastating effects of coal burning was important at this moment in time.

1953 Short-lived was the country's ownership of the steel industry, for in 1953 it was sold back to private enterprise. Road transport saw de-nationalisation, too, this year. And in the nationalised gas industry, prices were being raised to the extent that an enquiry was demanded. What was going wrong with the government's running of nationalised industries? Were the country's debts so high that they had to raise money by selling off the nation's assets? And was the general public so affluent now that they could afford to pay more for essential commodities?

It was said of the Second World War that it inspired the construction of many new machines. The confirmation of this might have been seen in a sophisticated piece of machinery born during the year. This was a heart-lung machine that was used during heart surgery.

Schools were in the news too, when television was introduced as a learning device. The kids must have jumped with joy at the thought of watching the little box for a period, instead of having to answer to a teacher's questioning. Already though there was a lot of talk about the effects that television and radio would have on the need for children to acquire reading skills. Another event of the year was that five hundred and fifty car workers were made redundant. It was said that the reason for this was that car sales had reduced since Purchase Tax was added to their cost.

1954 A time of celebration came in 1954 when food rationing came to an end. Abundant were the smiles and great were the sighs, for at last people could go to the shops to buy what they wanted. That is, if they could afford to, for there were still people who earned low wages, or were not in work at all. Then there were families who were rendered fatherless during the war and lived on widow's pensions.

Shopping was the social event it had always been. The local shops were the meeting places of the community. Mainly it was here where current gossip was collected. If you didn't know already who was dead or dying, you soon would. Brides to be, visiting relatives, family squabbles, babies, new acquisitions, were all topics of conversation in the shops. People would joke with one another whilst waiting their turn to be served. And naturally the shop owners, and their assistants, knew all of their customers by name. If life was getting you down, a quick visit to the shops would soon put things right. After the pleasant smile and a 'Good morning Mrs So-and-so' (for it was always the womenfolk who did the shopping), the chance came to have a natter and get things off your chest. The saying that 'a trouble shared is a trouble halved' was still a great belief in these days. After all, if you couldn't help each other through thick and thin, what was the point of life?

Shops were interesting places with items to draw the eye. Packaged products lined the shelves and other items were displayed on large counters. Edibles such as cheese, butter and bacon would be cut to order whilst sugar, flour and salt were kept in drums and weighed out on scales (once again, to order).

Though refrigerators were introduced during these years, the working classes did not possess them. Even the very few people who were lucky enough to be buying their own houses, couldn't afford the luxury of a fridge. Food was stored in larders, which were housed in the coldest parts of the house.
Also the number of shop owners who were proud owners of refrigerators was very few. They relied on cold marble slabs for the preservation of food, and these were generally kept in cold, window-less rooms, sometimes in the basement.

Cold slabs, in cold rooms, were also used by butchers. Mind, it was a well-known fact that most meats tasted better with ageing. Butchers would hang animal flesh for weeks in order to attain a 'high' taste. In other words, the meat was beginning to go off. People had eaten meat of this kind for centuries with no ill effects, so this was not a worry. Nor was there any concern if maggots were seen romping about in the cheese, for they were not a threat to health. All they were was an extension of the food itself. In fact, many older men would insist that eating the little fellows made the food tastier.

Saturday was the day when the shops were at their busiest, this followed payday – Friday, when pay packets were opened and measured out. So much money was put away for the rent, then the gas, or the coal, electricity, clothing clubs and insurance. What was left was allocated to food spending, and the breadwinner's pocket money. The lady of the house would go the shops and purchase the essential items needed for the week. After this she would buy on a daily basis according to the cash left in the kitty. The occasional highlight, associated with cash flow, was Friday night, when a chip shop supper could be had. Mother (or one of the kids) would hurry off to the 'chippie' clutching a basin to carry home the puddings. These treats were for mum and dad's plates whilst the children feasted on chips.

When mum was busy washing, cleaning, ironing or cooking, she would send one of the children to the shop. The child would be given a note wrapped around some money, and be ordered to 'come straight back.' The most common phrase to be uttered by children when they arrived home from school was, 'Do you want anything from the shop?' They used to run errands for neighbours too, and would be given a small reward for their efforts. During wartime years and after, when everything was in short supply, kids often fainted as they queued for hours at local suppliers. They had other ways of earning a little pocket money too. One was to seek out empty glass pop bottles, and return them to the shops. Here the shopkeeper would give them one penny for each bottle. A more hardy labour for them was going around the streets, armed with a bucket and shovel, to collect horse manure. For girls, their favourite money-earner came in the way of babysitting. Many mothers welcomed the chance of having their young ones off their hands for an hour or two. When neighbouring girls knocked on the door and asked 'Would you like me to take your baby out?' they quickly bundled offspring into their prams. Mind, there were instances when some girls were afraid to leave their homes, let alone knock on doors. These were the times when the nit nurse had visited school to find head lice lurking in their hair, whereupon it would be shaven off. Following this their heads would be painted with a purple-coloured substance (to which a name was never given). Obviously, after the event they would avoid going outside if they could.

The gentlemen too had their role to play. When do-it-yourself advice was needed, the local hardware, wood or wallpaper shops were the places to get it, for in these emporiums the shop owners not only sold DIY products, they were experts in their field. And here were the places where the blokes had a natter too. The subject of their discussions was inevitably football, the invention of the British working classes. As well as his pint of beer and cigarette, football was also a great source of pleasure for him. Last Saturday's match would be talked about at length (and no doubt the referee criticised without mercy).

Throughout the century football had drawn great numbers of supporters. Even in 1901 the Football Association Cup Final match drew a crowd of 110,820, all eager to watch twenty-two fellows kick a ball about. And despite the large numbers, their behaviour was orderly. But then, they had gone to watch a football match, not to cause disturbances. For this reason very little policing was required and this was how it had remained until now – the middle of the century.

1955 Something new was happening on the shopping scene. Perhaps following the lead of the Co-operative to bulk buy, to sell cheaper, someone else came up with the idea to 'pile em high and sell em cheap'. Unlike the Co-op, which was designed to share its bounties with customers, this new venture was born simply to make profit for the owners. One very large shop was opened and called a supermarket. The name was derived by acknowledging the wide variety of goods to be sold. Instead of having to go to a butcher's shop for meat; a greengrocery for fruit and vegetables; a fish shop for fish and a general shop for all other edibles, the housewife could now do all her shopping in one place. The one difference was that now she would have to reach up to the shelves for the wares herself. There would be no pleasant assistant to ask what she wanted and pass it to her. No jolly butcher would be asking what size meat she required, and her fish would no longer be presented to her by the smiling man who insisted he'd just caught it himself this morning. Now the goodies would be pre-packed and awaiting purchase. The most impressive feature of the supermarket to the housewife was the refrigerators. How lovely it would be to buy perishable goods that had been kept cool – even in hot weather. But again, it was only the better-off car and refrigerator owners who would benefit from this method of shopping.

1956 Medicine was coming along in leaps and bounds. People were absolutely amazed when they heard that a kidney transplant had been performed. And in this year of 1956 another machine was being introduced. This time it was obstetrics that would benefit from an instrument called Ultrasound. This gadget would enable midwives to hear an unborn baby's heartbeat to signal that all was well.

As was expected, London followed Manchester's lead and became a smokeless zone. Never again would the smog claim over four thousand lives there.

Television was much transformed during this year. A second channel called Independent Television was opened. The funding for this channel would come from companies who would pay for advertising. So now, along with entertainment and news, the residents of the two households in a hundred that owned TV sets, were going to learn about products that might enhance their lives. In sketches called commercials, actors would illustrate how products could improve living standards. The charge to the advertisers for this service was very high. However, this was not a deterrent as it was envisaged that TV advertising would swell the sales of products tremendously. As soon as viewers saw what was on offer, they would go out and buy by the thousands.

Due to the competition that another channel would bring, the existing BBC network decided not to close down for an hour every day. Up until now the screen used to go blank between the hours of 6pm and 7pm.

In the ongoing fight to be rid of diseases, yet another immunisation was introduced to prevent poliomyelitis occurring. This followed a time in 1950 when several cases of polio were identified in Manchester. At that time an emergency clinic was set up to vaccinate fifteen to twenty-five year olds. Because an England footballer had died of polio, the panic of the general public was so great that the vaccine soon ran out.

The same year brought about the Clean Air Act. From now on all fuel burned was to be smokeless. This meant that all harmful gases would have to be removed from coal before it was sold to the public. However, the Act did not apply to the whole of the country. Only some areas of towns and cities were selected as smokeless areas. At the time there were mass installations of gas fires. People were waving goodbye to their versatile friend the coal fire, and replacing it with a cleaner and easier method of heating. Landlords were given grants from local councils to fund the installation of gas fires in their properties. It was a great boon to the gas industry for their profits would be bound to rise sky-high; good for the country's piggy bank too for hadn't Britain just borrowed £201million from the International Monetary Fund? The war had run away with most of the country's pennies, meaning loans had to be sought.

A crisis that required military action arose again, but this time there was no need for recruitment. The regulars of the armed forces were adequate for the job in hand. The conflict was about the Suez Canal in Egypt, which Britain used to bring in oil supplies from the Middle East, and commandeered one third of the canal's use. The Egyptian government decided to nationalise the canal to restrict movement of shipping, hence the conflict. However, the affair fizzled out quickly when the United Nations intervened.

So successful was Britain's first supermarket that another company opened a second store. It looked as if the British housewife had proven that this convenient way of shopping was her 'cup of tea'.

1957 Still in the fight for nuclear prominence, Britain's first hydrogen bomb was exploded in the central Pacific in 1957. Even the most ordinary of people were beginning to get alarmed by these explosions. There were whispers everywhere, and people were voicing their opinions in several ways. They were saying, 'What will these bombs cause?' , 'Bound to effect the weather' , 'They'll shake the world off its axis!' and so on and so forth.

To add to the worry, a major radioactivity leak occurred at Windscale, the country's nuclear weapons processing plant, which was built in the late 1940s. A reactor caught fire sending clouds of radioactive dust up a chimney, and out into the countryside. The dust spread all over Britain and into Europe.

Something that was not causing any concern, at this moment in time, was the nuclear power station which was opened the year before at Calder Hall. It was Britain's first such station and was thought to be of no threat at all to the environment.

There were two further developments this year in the field of television. First, detector vans were introduced to spy out people who had not bought a licence to watch their TV (as with radio, tuning in didn't come free, one had to pay a fee to do so). The vans were equipped to pick up TVs that were receiving transmissions in the area. If a house receiving TV pictures was not listed as having bought a licence, a visit would be made and a fine imposed on the spot.

Perhaps it was noted by the government that there was an increase in general prosperity, because it decided to abolish rent controls. This meant that landlords, whether they be private or public sector, could now charge as much as they liked to rent out their properties. Up until now, restrictions had been in force as to the amount of money any letting could bring.

The Russians were first to explore into space when they instituted a deeper probe of the universe, outside Earth's atmosphere. First, an unmanned rocket was catapulted into the skies, and then a second vehicle carrying a securely-held dog was launched. Of course, when the rocket landed back on Earth, it was falsely reported that 'pooch' was fine. The fact was that she had died during the flight.

1958 At this time in history, there were pockets of people who were more than worried about the use of atomic energy. Their awareness of the great danger of radioactivity propelled them to form an action group. Under the name of the Campaign for Nuclear Disarmament (CND), they joined together by the thousands, and made their first march of protest. No doubt their views were strengthened when the government of 1958 agreed a location for an American missile base in the United Kingdom. The group's views were that there would be possible further atomic disaster.

For those still burning coal, good news came when the rationing of it ended. What a relief it was that there would be no more queuing on those cold winter days for the women and children who trundled their home-made coal carriers behind them.

When it was announced that restrictions on hire purchase were to be removed, again there was rejoicing. For this would be the time of spending today and paying tomorrow, without having need to worry.

Transport too had a part to play during this time in history. Amongst smiles and cheers, government officials paraded high hopes of a faster future. The first eight mile stretch of motorway in the country opened at Preston. Speed was also on the agenda as the six-year tested jet planes took to the air for their first trans-Atlantic journeys.

1959 The removal of hire purchase restrictions showed up greatly in 1959. By now there were nearly 10 million television sets licensed in the country, with ordinary working class people taking to their houses to switch on their picture boxes. If neighbours didn't have the luxury of such an item in their home, they were invited into other houses in order to watch. People sat in groups to goggle together. In wonderment they viewed the action – in awe they welcomed the future. With a no-talking policy applying, people were shushed if they happened to make any noise whatsoever whilst a programme was on the screen. Whilst plots thickened, and excitement grew, rooms were filled with the smoke rising from cigarettes or pipes. But this didn't bother anyone, for smoke was a part of their heritage. The report from the British Medical Association, that smoking was the chief cause of cancer, was therefore taken with a pinch of salt.

It was a wave of good riddance that said goodbye to the mental institutions this year, for a new Mental Health Act was put into force. The aim of the Act was to re-assess patients in these institutions so that they could be rehabilitated into either the community, or other healthcare. Amongst the numbers who had occupied mental institutions were women who had been confined there simply because they had borne illegitimate children. Some of them had spent most of their lives imprisoned this way. Society had had no other way of treating the unmarried mothers of the early twentieth century. The embarrassment that bearing children out of wedlock caused was such that it required the offending women to be locked away from the probing eyes of the public.

At the end of the decade some strange sights were still to be seen. One might have wondered just why walls had been built at the end of some of Britain's roads, and questioned their architectural benefits. However, they had not been built to enhance the locality, but to segregate the occupants of public sector housing from those of privately owned houses. Public sector housing came into being because of the government's recognition that the poor of society fell victim to disease because of the unsanitary conditions in which they lived. Furthermore, that when this happened the whole nation was at risk of contracting these diseases. To eliminate this possibility, therefore, it was considered economically viable for the state to build sanitary homes for the poor rather than fund the medical attention that would be required if epidemics presented. Usually the houses were built en masse on the outskirts of towns, to form estates in their own right. However, occasionally some public sector housing was sited in urban better-class areas, where semi-detached properties were a feature. This is where the walls were born, for the residents of these areas were appalled at having the poor of society 'dumped' on their doorsteps. Hence, they built the high walls that would segregate themselves, the elite, from the riff-raff. There was no way that they would suffer the indignities of the poor in their posh areas.

CHAPTER EIGHT

The Sixties

1960 National service, which required that young men of eighteen join the military forces for a period of two years, ended in 1960. Since its introduction in 1939 this had been regarded as beneficial as, at an age when boyhood was to fade into oblivion, many male teenagers often lost their sense of direction. Lads who were inclined to lounge around all day trying to do nothing, went into the armed forces to come home with a new attitude. This was one that was full of purpose and determination. During the two years of service they received training in many aspects of life. With a regime of strict discipline they had to keep themselves smart at all times. Boots had to be polished to mirror reflection, belts and badges rubbed until they gleamed like the sun. The barracks, where they slept dormitory fashion, had to be kept spick and span. There were to be no shortcuts, the floors had to be scrubbed – on hands and knees – on a daily basis. Every order must be obeyed; there wasn't the option of answering back. When a commanding officer spoke, the only words he expected to hear were "Yes, Sir!" Whole squadrons of soldiers were bound to each other by rules; they were being trained for combat so there was no room for personal speculation. If the order given was to 'fire', then the reaction must be spontaneous. Only teamwork would ensure victory and survival for a group of people forced to move as one. If career plans were unmade, the armed forces provided the perfect opportunity for young men to decide their future. In a community where success depended on every individual effort, there were many tasks to be performed. Young national servicemen had no option but to choose one of the jobs that needed to be done. Therefore, with training and encouragement in abundance, there was no reason for any of them to leave the armed services without the acquisition of a skill. Would the ending of national service prove a sad loss for Britain's young men?

During the year, when spending had reached a high, the government called a temporary halt. Restrictions on hire purchase buying were reintroduced and a credit squeeze began.

The same year brought about yet another agreement between Britain and America. This time it was that the UK would provide bases for US Polaris submarines.

With aeroplane travel now established, it followed that holidays overseas would be sought by many. Whilst the rich were already flying from continent to continent, ordinary people had not yet taken to the skies. So it was now that package holidays by air were introduced. These were spawned by enterprising travel companies who took on the role of tour operators. After buying aeroplane space from airline companies, their task was to fill the seats as quickly as possible. To do this they had to offer holidays which were attractive on all counts. Booked seats on a plane; a good hotel waiting at the other end; transport to that hotel; glorious sunshine; deep blue sea and insurance just in case anything went wrong. People flocked for tickets, whilst the jet planes guzzled up fuel needed for the journeys. Aircraft movements from Manchester Airport during this year had now risen to 34,000.

For those who missed out on package holidays there was another treat in store. This was the year that 'soap opera' (the pet name given to dramas that aimed to represent true life), would be screened once or twice a week on television.

Early twentieth century families were large in number and some women bore as many as fourteen children. However, infant mortality, resulting from diseases of the day, kept population numbers in check. Because of poverty, most pregnancies were unwanted ones, and the birth control used was not always successful. The male would wear a condom (nicknamed 'French Letter') during sexual intercourse, but more than likely the thing would either slither off his penis at the time of ejaculation, or it would develop a hole. In the 1930s some women were fitted with a Dutch cap for birth control. These were soft plastic pouches that were inserted inside the vagina. However, once again, not a great success as the damn things slid about with movement. Great advances had been made in the 1950s, however, because this is when intrauterine devices were improved to produce the coil. Again, a vaginal contraption, but this time, a more secure fit. Then came the breakthrough that would alleviate women of their fear of unwanted pregnancies – the contraceptive pill. The pill, the function of which was to convince the body that it was already pregnant, had been discovered in 1951 and tested on thousands of women since then. Now it was official that this birth control pill was safe to use and could be prescribed by doctors.

Not surprisingly, the Campaign for Nuclear Disarmament was not taking last year's news of Polaris submarines lying down. Instead its members sat down in their thousands, in London, to demonstrate their concerns. The campaign was a popular one and inspired many of the young of the age to join. Some of their numbers believed wholeheartedly in the threat that nuclear activity would bring, others joined the group merely for social reasons.

$714 million was sitting at Britain's portals waiting to be let in, again by courtesy of the International Monetary Fund. Was this the reason why the government relaxed hire purchase controls once more? Could the country now afford to encourage the public to buy now and pay later? Why not indeed? After all, by now 4 million people were jetting off on package holidays, and the aircraft movements at Manchester Airport had risen to 39,400.

1961 Space travel was in the news again when the Russians launched a spaceship carrying a man. The vehicle was in orbit for a hundred and eight minutes and circled around the earth. This historic flight was registered as an extraordinary technological triumph by the USSR.

Not to be outdone, American scientists blasted off a space capsule later in the year – their aim, to overtake the Russians' lead in the 'space race'. However, at this point they were not prepared to put a human into space, as the Russians had done. Instead they strapped a chimpanzee into the cockpit, to discover if it could survive the journey. When the capsule arrived back on planet earth, it was with delight that they found the animal still alive. Unfortunately the poor little chap was not able to convey how he felt about his journey, and whether the experience caused him pain and horror.

1962 In 1962 the Americans did put a man into space and, to prove their supremacy to their competitors, this vehicle travelled three times around the Earth. But, unlike the chimp, the astronaut in the capsule chose to be launched into space.

Back in London, despite the smokeless zones, another sixty people were alleged to have died because of smog. Mind, it must be remembered that the pollution of the air couldn't be cleared in such a short period of time. After all, smoke had filled the Earth's atmosphere since man's beginning.

For hundreds of years past, the medicine to cure illnesses was obtained by way of apothecaries. These were places where the health-giving properties of herbal plants were extracted and processed. The vital parts of the plants were immersed in boiling water then left to steep. After straining, the liquid that was left was the medicine. Of course it wasn't any old plant that was turned into medicine – it was the ones that had been tried and tested. Like wild animals, humans also had the instinct to know which plants were good for them, and which weren't. Throughout his existence man had experimented with, and noted, plants that proved invaluable for treating varying types of sickness. In 1815 the chemists, who operated the apothecaries, were given a licence to practice medicine. It must be said that some of the plants used in medicine were poisonous. However, experimentation showed that, by adding just a small amount of the poison to an otherwise healthy concoction, new medicines could be discovered. This is how antibiotics (the 'wonder drug') were discovered in the 1930s.

Graduation from apothecaries came in the form of drug companies, which had started to appear in the 1920s. These establishments had recognised that the need for new medicines would be great, and that mass production would be called for. They engaged the services of medical scientists who would experiment to discover new healing products.

Unfortunately, a newly-found drug caused a medical disaster in Britain and Europe in the early 1960s. The drug was called thalidomide, and had been used in Germany as a sedative and hypnotic. It was prescribed to alleviate sleeping problems from then on. Sadly, thousands of pregnant women who had taken the drug in the early stages of pregnancy gave birth to babies with missing, or part-missing, limbs. Now the drug was banned because of the recognition that it caused this massive problem.

Still with medicine, another machine was born this year, and this would save the lives of people suffering kidney malfunction. Liverpool was the place of the first kidney dialysis centre. It was here that people would come for treatment when kidney transplant was not possible.

For the first time also this year, a remarkable operation was performed. An arm, completely severed at the shoulder, was successfully rejoined to the body. Surgery of this kind was made possible by microscopes. The surgeons looked through these to see the tiny nerves, and blood vessels, that needed to be re-attached to restore amputated limbs. Less spectacular operations, like rejoining missing fingers or toes, were envisaged. However, this was not surprising, for already man-made body parts such as plastic hip joints and battery-powered prosthetic arms were being surgically inserted into, and attached to, human bodies.

By now things were really swinging in Britain. The general public had never had it so good throughout history. With plenty of work and money in their pockets, there was nothing they could not buy. Happiness oozed throughout the land with the thoughts of acquisitions never dreamed of.

Music had taken on a different role and depicted the mood of the day. Instead of orchestras and bands to dance to, there were pop groups to swing with. Young girls would swoon in hysterical masses as their idols appeared before them. In groups, numbering three, four or five, these young men rocketed to stardom. On the way there they scooped up cash, fortunes and adulation.

The planet itself was swaying with the thud of Britain's dancing feet. When pop groups were out of sight, their music could still be heard. The jukeboxes – which were overlarge record players introduced to the country from America in the 1950s – were piled high with current pop records. Insert a coin, select the music you wanted to hear, then, click, the record would drop into place and play automatically. This was not the only way of having music wherever you went, for there were also transistor radios available. These were small portable radios which could be carried with ease – they crackled like mad as they played, but it was still music, whatever the quality. At this time there were many 'pirate' radio stations cramming the airwaves with rhythm. As they were operating illegally, a few of the networks broadcast from ships.

It was obvious that British teenagers were in the market for further developments. There was money to be made from the trendy sixties kid (who seemed to have it to spend). The 'with it' pop groups called for 'with it' clothes – so why not new gear? The 'rag trade' was quick to take up the gauntlet and trendy clothes began to flood the marketplace. With wages in hands, girls and boys rushed to the shops eager to clad themselves in the latest clothing. Everything in the 'golden age' of the sixties was directed at the young. The new Britain of today required a generation of new people. With pound signs filling their sights, businesses zoomed in on the new age of spenders.

Advertising, too, ran rampant in the race to promote wares. Magazines aimed at the teenage market portrayed images of what they should be buying. And the competition between the written media continued, with free gift offers advertised wildly on front covers.

1963 Children born in the time of the welfare state had nothing to lose and everything to gain – the world was theirs for the taking. So, why not win them over and set a precedent for the future. Unlike their parents, grandparents and great-grandparents, the generation of the sixties had not witnessed poverty and strife. For them life was filled only with fun and hope. Light-heartedness surrounded them in all directions because nearly everyone was happy. They did not know what it was like to be without running water, or not to flick a switch to produce light. Joblessness was no threat to them, nor was starvation, and healthcare was as abundant as everything else.

When the first liver transplant operation happened in 1963, these carefree youngsters didn't raise an eyebrow. They had been born to a world of medical phenomena and technology, so why should this newest venture warrant awe? But for the generations before them, who had witnessed death by disease and poverty, this miraculous operation left them spellbound. These were the people who, during their lifetimes, had witnessed the cure of diphtheria, tuberculosis, typhoid and polio, all said to be by way of immunisation. They had also welcomed the introduction of the rapidly effective antibiotics; kidney and heart transplants, various life-saving machines plus the contraceptive pill, and were of the opinion that medical science was reaching the bounds of genius.

The year saw the beginnings of trouble in the nationalised rail network. The government, looking for a cheaper and better way of running the railways, appointed a committee to investigate the industry. The outcome was that two thousand stations were labelled for closure and a recommendation given that one quarter of the railway track be abandoned. This ironic decision came only 130 years after the toil of many to create the rail network. The outcome would be that many outlying parts of the British Isles would, by losing the rail link, be cut off. But then, there were still the roads. Goods could be carried by way of motor vehicles instead of railways, and people could be conveyed by buses and motor cars. After all, there was only a total of 10,336,000 vehicles on Britain's roads at this time – perhaps the car, motorcycle and commercial vehicle industry needed a boost in their sales.

People earning at least £2,000 a year at the time, were privileged to be given the opportunity of using the newly introduced credit cards. The idea was an extension of hire purchase but, whereas HP warranted proof of the ability to repay, credit cards didn't. The onus of collecting payment fell on the credit card company, and not the shopkeeper. When a purchase was made, the seller would be immediately reimbursed by the credit card company on receipt of the necessary documentation. For the shopkeeper, this was a boon. He was able to sell more goods, and be guaranteed prompt payment for them. For their efforts of boosting his trade, the credit card company imposed a minimal charge on the shopkeeper. As for the customer, he would repay his loan to the credit card company on a monthly basis. For this convenience he would be charged a heavy interest rate. The loan could be added to at any time, and repayments made for as long as necessary. In fact, the agreement could continue throughout the customer's lifetime if required. The more money the customer borrowed, the more the credit card company liked it as long as something was paid back each month. As for the customers using a credit card, they would be paying much more for their goods than they needed to, but this didn't seem to matter.

For some of the people not earning the then enormous sum of £2,000 a year, there were high stakes yet to come. Although multi-storey buildings were nothing new – inasmuch as a twelve-storey block had been built in London in 1873 – it had been decided that it would be a good idea to build tower blocks for people to live in. By 1963, following London's lead, councils all over the country were building skyscraper dwelling places. Having families live one on top of the other would certainly solve the housing problem. And, of course, only small areas of land were required for the purpose of erecting eighteen-storey blocks of flats. Unfortunately, most of the people who took occupancy of the flats were not happy and said that sky dwelling was isolated and lonely. In fact, many people committed suicide because of their sadness. It was said that once inside the flats neighbours were never seen. Alien to the communal prospects envisaged when they were built, these tower blocks caused segregation to a high degree. Making friends with neighbours, living across the corridor of a tower block, would never be the same as standing at the door of a house, to speak to the person living opposite or next door, or chatting to a neighbour over the garden wall.

1964 Up until 1964 there was never any change in the amount of money charged for goods, and mother could manage her cash for the week because she knew how much everything was going to cost. But now that Retail Price Maintenance was being abolished, it seemed inevitable that she would now have to increase her weekly budget.

And how would this affect the newly arrived miniskirt? Could the manufacturers charge as much as they liked for the product? Would teenage girls be running about hither and thither, looking for the cheapest garment in town? Or would they disregard prices and acquire the miniskirt anyway just to be in fashion?

People were pleased that another television channel was opened. With two channels already established, a third would give more choice of programmes to be watched. It was the BBC's Channel 2 that now offered this choice. There was no doubt that all three television channels would want to screen the controversial happenings of the time, which were setting tongues wagging. The newspapers were filled with the antics of the Mods and Rockers, but nothing could beat a visual story. Both these groups of people were hell bent on causing disruption, to prove their desire for freedom from convention. The Rockers' mode of dress was that of all leather, with metal studs fixed on the backs of their jackets. The Mods wore smart suits, ties and high-heeled boots. They said of the Rockers that they were dirty and smelly, and the Rockers said of them that they were poofs who wore eye-shadow. Both groups had motorcycles that they drove recklessly. Southern seaside resorts were their favourite destinations and, when the groups met, violent fighting occurred. Family outings to the seaside were becoming a no-go area as beaches were taken over by groups of Mods and Rockers, who were intent on knocking the living daylights out of each other. Police forces were being called on more and more to enforce law and order in the land and they were seen to be using the truncheons which, up until now, had just been part of police uniform. This never before seen situation was overwhelming as far as the government of the day was concerned, as, too, was the fact that chemist shops were being broken into weekly by these groups, who stole drugs such as 'purple hearts' and 'black bombers'. The folks of Britain in general were saying that these young men should be doing national service or be fighting in a war, instead of going around doing exactly what they wanted and terrorising the public. The government, determined to restore law and order by any means, ordered every police force in the country to use their resources to the full. This they did, and by the end of the year the Mods and Rockers' reign of terror was over.

Tabulating machines had been operational since the early part of the century. These ingenious devices were able to count, and keep a running total. The mid-1940s had seen great advances in the tabulating field when a machine, capable of executing long computations automatically, was launched. This little beauty could add, multiply and divide figures fed into it. However – it was not so little! To cope with the task, the machine measured fifty feet long by eight feet high. The monster, which weighed five tons, was used for government and military purposes at the time. Then, 1952 saw another change in computers when a smaller machine, that could execute payrolls, and prepare and maintain accounts and stock controls, was introduced. Now, in 1964 a machine that could store words came into being, and the first word processor was born. The machine operator would scan the screen of the computer, for the purpose of correcting and editing, before printing out a completed document. A copy of the text would be retained by means of a small disk, and when this was inserted into a computer its details would appear on the screen. Of course, the companies manufacturing computer machines were taking a big gamble. They spent millions of pounds manufacturing a product with unknown potential. They didn't know whether the computer would be accepted into commerce eagerly, or if the idea would fall flat on its face.

1965 brought about several monetary changes. Firstly, prescription charges were abolished again. Secondly, rent control was reintroduced. (Bear in mind here that, as rents had already risen, the controls applied to current figures – meaning they would not be reduced). Thirdly, hire purchase laws were stiffened once more. The government also launched the Redundancy Payments Act. This Act would financially protect employees who lost their jobs because of company reorganisation. Was the reasoning behind this Act based on the assumption that if computers did take off, their capabilities would supersede those of people, to render them redundant?

Even though the country was deeply in debt and had received another loan from the IMF, there were those who envisaged great wealth for themselves. These were the people who had seen the popularity of supermarkets and were increasing their numbers.

The year saw another boom for the British Isles. After a series of drillings in the North Sea, natural gas was discovered. This find would mean that there would be no need to import liquid gas from other countries any more, and that Britain's economy would soar.

For as long as children had attended school, there had always been a dress code. Clothes to be worn in the classroom were required to be of sombre colour, and of standard style. If a school supported a uniform, then this had to be worn during the hours of learning. School gear depicted which establishment a child attended, and was an indication of its standards. Good behaviour was noted by all, as too was the school uniform. But now changes in dress were apparent. The miniskirt was becoming more and more popular and, as the popularity of it rose, so too did the hemline. The skirts were getting shorter and legs were getting longer and, schoolgirls had taken to wearing the scanty garment to attend lessons. This caused a bit of a rumpus because bums were seen as girls bent down, whereas the rule was that skirts should be long enough to touch the ground when this movement was made. Fair enough, one might comment. After all, how could the teachers get the boys' attention if they were constantly on the lookout for glimpses of girls' bottoms? The insistence of school officials that regular length skirts be worn, brought anger to the girls who wanted to be in fashion. The boys too were being brought to heel by school rules. The fashion of the day was for them to grow their hair to shoulder length. However, this did not comply with the regulations that boys should wear their hair above the collar. So the lads were not amused, as they wanted to be in fashion too. A strange observation was noted at the time and this was that, whilst the kids of the day were rebelling against wearing school uniform (which made them look alike), they insisted on donning the fashions of the time (which were all the same), when they were away from school.

Every year the monarch of the country honoured people on her birthday. These honours and titles were earned by individuals who had proven themselves worthy, usually by enhancing the country with their deeds of bravery; their efforts to swell the economy, or their commitment to secure social improvement. However, now an award was given to a pop group. Many thought that this gesture portrayed a lowering of British standards, as it ridiculed the honours system. But then, it was the mid-sixties and attitudes were becoming more relaxed and less pompous. It was the time of letting one's hair down, and 'letting it all hang out'.

Even the death sentence was abolished and, from now on, no one found guilty of murder would be hanged from the neck until dead. The executioners would be out of a job and asked to accept redundancy payments, unless they were to be redirected to the prison services to work as wardens to the increasing number of inmates.

Since the coming of thousands of immigrants, over previous years, hostility had grown towards them, the non-whites in particular. Many Britons believed that housing that should rightfully be theirs, was being occupied by immigrants, and that whilst they, the denizens of the country, were making contributions from their wages to receive the benefits of the welfare state, the newcomers were receiving them without having paid a penny piece. However, now in the 65th year of the twentieth century a Race Relations Act was created to curb that which was called racism. Through this, anyone found guilty of practising the offence would be faced with penalties of fines or imprisonment. The verdict would be decided by newly-elected Race Relation Boards, after evidence pertaining to racial persecution had been heard. Whilst it was assumed by government that this Act would bring about a 'happy ever after' situation between white Britons and their non-white colleagues, did they appreciate what they were asking of the British nation? For practising tolerance towards the beliefs and customs of other cultures, whereby the influence is strong enough to persuade adoption of that culture, is a situation never achieved in the history of mankind. Perhaps this is the reason why the famous saying 'When in Rome do as the Romans do' was penned as long ago as the fourth century by St Ambrose.

During the happy affluent days of the sixties a new discovery was made. Amidst the floods of new-told wealth and joviality, poverty was uncovered. With rapidity, the Child Poverty Action Group was founded to fight for the rights of children living in poor conditions.

With a total of 11,697,000 vehicles on Britain's roads, it followed that accidents were happening frequently. In an endeavour to curb road incidents, a legal blood alcohol limit was introduced for drivers. If people were stopped from drinking and then driving would road deaths and injuries fall?

1966 It was 1966 when government decided that council house rents needed to be raised. After all, these new modern dwellings had brought luxury to the lives of many, so it was time they paid more for that privilege. To this end, they introduced a 'fair rent system' policy that would apply to all council housing. The proviso to this was that those who could not afford to pay increased rents, on account of low earnings, would be entitled to a rebate should they be able to prove their circumstances.

One hundred years or more after inventing the game of Association Football (or soccer), England won the game's highest honour. The World Cup came to Britain amidst the cheers and jubilation of the entire population. Men, women and children alike were proud of their country's sport, and the menfolk who played it.

In the world of medicine, vaccination to stop measles began. Nonetheless, with yet another fight won to conquer childhood illnesses, it was wondered by some if any thought was given to the reason for them. Had the knowledge that they present to children in order to strengthen their immune systems, been forgotten? And was it not recognised that, although measles is one of the most severe of childhood illnesses, it is not usually a life-threatening condition. However, there is a risk of damage being caused to the eyes during bouts of measles and, for this reason, it had always been known that children suffering the illness should be housed in darkened rooms, whilst being nursed back to health.

Perhaps an indication of the growing greed in society was seen when colour television was introduced. Although most of the generation of people who had suffered poverty, strife, and early death, now had food in their bellies, the prospect of good health, and almost certainly a black and white television, their contentment was still not secure. To prove the point, they flocked in their thousands to buy the newly-invented colour television. The manufacturers were delighted to see sales figures rising beyond expectations. A precedent was set here for all manufacturing industry. People were in the market for new inventions and would buy whatever gadgets were offered. Regardless of the plan of Mother Nature that asked that human beings conquer greed within themselves, the sixties folks' appetites for more was growing by the minute.

Disaster struck Britain when an accident happened in a coal mining village in Wales. One hundred and forty four people were killed when a slag heap collapsed onto a school in Aberfan. The tears of horror flowed with deep emotion when it was learned that one hundred and sixteen children had died. Shocked and shaken people raged their anger against 'God' . 'There mustn't be a God if this sort of thing can happen.' 'Why did God let it happen?' No one seemed to acknowledge that this horrific disaster was caused by man. It was he who had built the coal waste mountain; had not envisaged what might happen if the slag heap was piled too high and who had erected the black monster so near to a school. So, why should 'God' take the blame for man's total of errors?

1967 The see-saw of spending was still operational in 1967 and the government again relaxed hire purchase restrictions to encourage people to spend, spend, spend. Perhaps at this stage not everyone possessed colour television, leaving manufacturers with a glut of picture boxes yet unsold.

For hundreds of years past there had been incidences of women wanting to remove unwanted babies from their wombs. Putting their own lives at risk, these women had pushed sharp instruments into their vaginas, in attempts to cause the miscarriage of babies. For a fee, there were other women, and doctors, who would perform this task. Other methods of dislodging babies were used too. These included taking very hot baths or sipping quinine or gin in large quantities. Whereas the first method did sometimes work, the others didn't seem to. Sometimes the outcome of the poking incidents was that the women who had procured the operation were left to bleed to death. It could be said that this was the chance a woman must take, if she had taken the decision to murder her unborn baby. But now the government, acting on pressure from women's liberation groups, introduced the Abortion Act. If two registered doctors believed that pregnancy could cause injury to either a woman's physical or mental health, her pregnancy could be legally terminated. So then, murder had become legal in Britain. Mind, it wasn't recognised as such because the baby in the womb was no longer classed as an unborn human being. Now it bore the title of 'foetus', which means fully developed embryo in womb. Does the explanation of the word suggest that the foetus is not alive but merely an inanimate object? Would modern people rip up a seedling which was just beginning to grow, saying that it was not alive?

Family planning in general was very much on Britain's agenda. During the year an Act was passed allowing health authorities to give a planning service to all who sought it. Whilst the advice itself was given free, charges were to be made for contraceptive items.

It was around this time too that sex education began to appear on the curriculum of some schools. By way of knowledge gleaned from older contemporaries, most children of the sixties were aware of the possible consequence of engaging in sexual activity. Therefore, would the education yet to come be guidance of a moral nature rather than a factual one? Would the kids be told that giving life to another human being is a serious business and that, according to the rules of nature, those who parent children must be prepared to offer them a lifetime commitment? A commitment that is selfless, determined and giving to provide offspring with the security, love and guidance they need as they grow to adulthood. Through this kind of education, therefore, would the youngsters of the day be encouraged to learn how to curb the natural sexual longings that accompany puberty until the day arrived when they were ready to accept such a commitment? In this case, would unwanted teenage pregnancies start to lessen? If, on the other hand, sexual education was such that it offered pupils information beyond their naturally matured comprehension, would it be the encouragement they needed to pursue sexual activity to risk increasing unwanted pregnancies?

During the year the oil tanker, the *Torrey Canyon*, ran aground on the Cornish coastline. The ship was torn open as it hit a reef and a hundred thousand tons of crude oil was spilt out into the sea. Ninety miles of the coastline was polluted by the foul, stinking ooze that was washed ashore. Many, many fish and birds were killed as the poisonous oil engulfed them. This noxious substance meant devastation to plant life too. Was it ever envisaged by the first British oil company formed in the Middle East, that accidents such as this might occur? When the company's maiden cargo of crude oil was ready to be sold in 1902, there was only one way of transporting it to England, and this was by way of the sea. By 1914 the British government saw the potential of oil sales and became the company's principal stockholder. As the oil company's profits swelled, so did the waves in the sea as more and more monstrous oil tankers ploughed the water.

'Flower power' were words often bandied about in the late sixties. Many young people (and some not so young) dressed in brightly coloured clothing, draped themselves with beads and necklaces and decked their bodies with flowers. With the image of peace engulfing their minds, they chanted mystical verses and smoked pot (cannabis). They swayed to the rhythm that the 'rock' bands pumped out and generally had a good time. The older generation scorned the flower power people, calling them hippies. They were disgusted by their lack of convention and, could not come to terms with this new band of people who moved only with notions of simplicity. They were happy and wanted to share their happiness with others – to them the world was a lovely place and their only aim was to spread love. Their favourite greeting was that of 'Peace, man', and with the greeting came the gesture of a flat palm raised in the air. (Had this not been the peace symbol of the ancient native Americans?) A large area of ground was provided to stage a rock concert, which was entitled the Festival of Love. While the sceptics of the age forecasted that violence and rioting would result, not a drop of blood was spilled over the three-day event. The flower power people proved their advocation of love and peace to one and all.

British and French aircraft industries had been busily working to produce the world's first supersonic passenger aircraft. Now, in France, the public had its first glimpse of the long-nosed *Concorde* that was to bolt through the clouds at breathtaking speed.

Britain and the world were amazed at the news emerging from South Africa in the same year. This was that a surgeon there had successfully transplanted a human heart. It was reported that the operation had been straightforward but it was not known yet whether the patient's body would accept the new heart.

Again, regardless of the law relating to the Race Relations Act set up in 1965, the year saw the formation of a group called the National Front. These people were of the extreme right of anti-immigration parties whose aim was to rid the country of the non-white population, and prevent further immigration. The group's tactics proved violently abusive towards non-white people from all walks of life.

Yet another facet of British heritage was to be lost, for since ships had been built there had always been men to load and unload their cargoes, but now machinery was to change the face of the industry. The massive overhead cranes with mechanical loading and unloading facilities were here to stay, whilst the stevedores' jobs were gone.

Despite the fact that history recalls that sex between the same gender had happened throughout the lifetime of man, homosexuality had been illegal since the mid-nineteenth century. The punishment inflicted on men who indulged in sex with each other was severe. They were made to suffer torture and imprisonment if they were discovered, or even suspected of, committing homosexual acts. Now though, as attitudes were becoming more relaxed, the legalisation of private homosexuality between consenting males over twenty one years of age was passed. It had been considered that perhaps homosexuality was not practised as a choice but that nature itself decided one's sexual preferences. It was known by this time that all human beings have both male and female hormones and that prominence of one hormone over the other determines the gender which accompanies birth. However, in some cases hormone levels might be of equal quantity, or just slightly imbalanced. In these instances, it might be that only the development of the spirit could determine the intended gender of the person. Hopefully the new law, just passed, would reduce the pressure on those who had the misfortune of having to live in a body that was alien to their sexual preferences.

1968 brought with it yet another sterling crisis. The government had to make cuts in public expenditure and reintroduce charges on National Health prescriptions. A credit squeeze was imposed once more and hire purchase restrictions tightened. The country as a whole really was spending too much money and it had to be curbed.

Of course the foot and mouth outbreak that started and ended in 1967 would have run away with a lot of Treasury funds, for during the period a total of 429,600 farm animals were destroyed at the government's request and expense. The corpses of the animals were firstly piled together and then either burned or buried. At the time, farmers were sickened by the large numbers of sightseers who came to witness the bizarre funeral ceremonies.

Foot and mouth disease is a highly contagious disease that affects cloven-footed animals. Whilst the illness is reputed to be two thousand years old and exists in most countries of the world, it only arrived at Britain's shores in 1839. The disease is most unpleasant for animals that contract it and causes them to develop blisters on parts of the body where the skin is thin, such as the tongue, lips, mouth, udders, teats and between the toes of the feet. Within twenty-four to forty-eight hours the virus enters the bloodstream, causing fever to occur. During this phase, which lasts from twenty-four to thirty-six hours, the virus is excreted in the saliva, the milk, the urine and the faeces. The mortality rate when a mild outbreak happens is about five per cent, whereas a malignant form of the disease will claim losses of up to fifty per cent. In animals that survive foot and mouth disease, great weight losses occur because they are unable to eat. In dairy cattle that live through their ordeal, the flow of their milk will be greatly diminished. And, during attacks from the disease, it is common for abortion and mastitis to present. Although there was no doubt that foot and mouth disease was contagious and nasty, many people were questioning the mass slaughter that had been effected over the past eight months. After all, foot and mouth disease was to cattle, like influenza was to humans. Whilst mortality might result in some cases, others would live. Of course in both cases, a lot of loving care would have to be administered during the period of sickness. In the case of foot and mouth disease, farmers of the past nursed their animals by gently bathing their blisters with diluted proportions of Epsom salts until the animal regained health.

Concern about the environment was still prominent and the Clean Air Act was tightened in an endeavour to control the amount of pollution released into the air. At this point, pollution did not embrace the effects of smoke from gas fires, aeroplanes and motor vehicles on the atmosphere, because this rose in vapour state to escape the eye.

Despite the efforts of the National Front, politicians and a new Commonwealth Immigrants Act (aimed at excluding South African immigrants), to rid Britain of its non-white population, an ironic fact emerged. This was that doctors from overseas were filling seven out of ten vacancies in British hospitals. With this in mind it was wondered if the National Health Service would cease to function without the services of immigrant doctors.

The new swinging Britain was still swaying with the rhythm of change. 'Way out' was the 'way in' in the minds of the potentially liberated people of the future. Happiness and relaxation were the aims of a nation already boasting a much progressed lifestyle. No room for those fuddy duddy, old-fashioned ideas in this modern new world. It was time to relinquish the ancient standards of life, to make way for new ones. Mr Ordinary had gained so much freedom during the first half of the century – why not more? An 'anything goes' attitude was the one being sought.

There was a cry of, 'Yeah, man' when the power of theatre censorship was abolished during the year. In a musical drama entitled *Hair*, actors pranced about the stage in total nudity for the first time ever. Considering that a body is just a body, and that we've all got one, why did this spectacle warrant yelps of joy? Was the sight of wiggling willies, quivering boobs and shaking bums, so much different from looking through a mirror? But then, it was just another shock attack on the conventional society that thought it wrong to reveal one's body in public. And yes, there was an outcry from the people who thought in this way and who considered *Hair* to be an outrage on society.

Whilst childbirth had been considered a natural function of the female body since man's beginnings, modern medicine was still seeking ways of reducing the pain associated with it. The concept of pain did not fit into the sought after strife free society any more. It was thought more and more that someone should be responsible for stopping suffering on all levels. Unlike their ancestors, the women of today would not be bearing down to give birth, then getting straight back to work again. Instead they would be cosseted with clean beds, hot water and medical attention. On top of all this they would also have a newly-invented epidural anaesthetic, which promised a less painful birth.

Journeying through space was still very much the aim of mankind. At the end of the year an American spacecraft, *Apollo 8,* carrying three men, successfully circled around the moon ten times. When the mission was completed, it was announced that their next target would be to land on the moon itself.

1969 For the up and coming generation 1969 brought with it more goodies. Firstly, the voting age was lowered from twenty-one to eighteen. Whilst the long-dead suffragette movement would have been throwing up its arms in delight at this victory, the eighteen year olds of the day took the decision for granted.

Then, divorce was liberalised. A new Act stated that divorce would now be allowed on any grounds – so perhaps, if a lady didn't like the colour of her husband's underpants (or socks), she could use this as reason for the irretrievable breakdown of their marriage. Her husband too could provoke divorce for the most trite of reasons. So the regarded sanctified state of wedlock was leaving society. No longer would the promise to 'stay together until death' or 'love each other through sickness and health' or 'for richer, for poorer' apply. For these vows would now be hypocritical. Oh yes, the words would still be repeated at times of marriage but would no longer be meant. Throughout history, living as a couple had always had its pitfalls; it was not a new invention created for the modern world of the sixties. Being parents was the paramount responsibility of family life. Married ladies who were fed up with their lot and their husband; those who suffered beatings and rape at the hands of their menfolk, tolerated the situation for the sake of their children. The same applied to married men too. They sometimes grew sick to death of working every hour they could to provide for their families and often became depressed when they had to go home to a nagging wife. But they stuck it out because this was the pattern of life. A child's security of a home with parents, food to eat and clothes to wear, was the recognised priority of life.

But self-sacrifice was something that modern women were not prepared to offer any more. They did not want the grading of second-class citizens or to be thought of as only child-bearers and home-makers; they wanted it to be known that they were people in their own right. Succumbing to their male counterparts, or suffering their bullying, was something they would not tolerate. Therefore the new divorce law (pioneered by liberation groups) would suit their aim admirably. The fact that, throughout the ages, men had borne their own crosses was forgotten in the equation. After all, was it not men (whether they liked it or not) who had to fight in wars; work to provide until they dropped; make important decisions and not cry when the going got tough? Did they never feel that they were banging their heads against brick walls – did they ever tire of being the provider and, occasionally, feel that a woman's role in life was easier? Would the new divorce laws suit them too? Could they now dump the wife when she started nagging, in favour of another wench who didn't nag at all? Could it be that easy divorce would lead to the equilibrium of the sexes?

They said that they would go to the moon, and this is exactly what they did. A million sightseers jammed the roads around an American space centre, from where a 364 foot Apollo II rocket was launched. British television viewers, watching in awe, contributed to the six hundred million people worldwide who watched the lift-off. The world was watching and waiting, not just because the vehicle was to land on the moon, but also because it was carrying three men. Not only did the spacecraft land on the moon, but two of the astronauts walked on the surface. Of course they had to wear very bulky spacesuits and oxygen masks to do so. On their return to Earth's atmosphere, the men had to wear special clothing and live in a sealed container, until tests were carried out on them. It had to be proven positive they had not picked up any deadly infection, whilst the moonwalk was taking place.

Good news for Britain's economy when oil was discovered under the North Sea of the British Isles. It was quite by accident that a large quantity of it was found when a company drilling for oil in the rocks instead struck it in the sea below. The oil lay in deep water in one of the worst storm areas of the North Sea. Bad news for the ocean itself however, for now the seabed here would have to house gigantic steel riggings, equipped with enormous drilling and pumping machinery. Apart from the obvious destruction this type of structure would cause to the sea's environment, much of the sea life around would perish.

Whilst the Earth's substances are benign left in their rightful place, they prove harmful when removed. Wherever drilling for oil takes place, spillages occur as the substance is forced from the earth. On land sites, crude oil escapes at the point of drilling and causes rivulets of the substance to creep slowly away into nearby rivers, streams and pasture land. Death to anything in the rivulet's path is then the order of the day. Animals, insects, plants and grass die. When the water supplies become so polluted, people die. Remembering the sinking of the tanker ship some years before and the destruction it caused, one might ask how much more destruction there would be now that drilling was going to be carried out in the sea itself. Only time would tell.

The sixties could not end without there being another technological achievement. It came in the form of video systems. These were machines that were connected to television sets and were able to record programmes. Now there would be no need for the better offs to miss favourite features if there was reason to leave the house. One could set the video recorder, and hey presto, the programme would be there waiting to be watched on one's return. Bring out the credit cards and hire purchase agreements, there was more spending ahead. Especially so, as it was predicted that. over the next decade, developments in this field would slowly drive down the price to make video systems affordable for everyone.

CHAPTER NINE

The Seventies

1970 With liberation still forcibly apparent, the women of 1970 marched on. To substantiate their belief they held the first national conference of the WLM (Women's Liberation Movement). Another success had come their way in the form of the Equal Pay Act. This Act was intended to prevent discrimination in pay between men and women. However, it was not to become law until 1975. Until that time, women would have to rely on the voluntary generosity of their employers, to pay them the same rate for the same job as their male colleagues.

The aim of the women of the seventies was to not miss out on the privileges men were assumed to have to give them the upper hand. However many of the older generation wondered why women found it necessary to fight for new laws which would broadcast their equality with men, for did they not know that, whilst men and women are different according to Mother Nature's decree, in the equation both are equal? Had it not always been silently accepted that although men are endowed with physical brute strength, it is women who possess endurance and strength of mind? Both bestowed to bring equilibrium to mixed sex living. In fact had women not always laughingly said of men that if they had to give birth human evolution would cease, and had not men always nodded their heads in agreement? What would a legally-bound equality of the sexes mean? By altering the ancient rules of nature would the physical appearances of the genders eventually automatically change to render them on a par? Then, with equality established would the women of the future happily accept their duty to be conscripted if war broke out or, to go out to work full-time to provide for family needs until retirement age?

The momentum of the sixties had a greater influence on women than men. With the media of magazine and television as their inspiration they flocked to buy gadgets that would help them with the housework. These machines released time to them and this they used to pursue other activities. Large numbers of them took up outside work, some part-time, some full and for the first time ever they had money they could call their own. At the time their earnings were known as 'pin money' and were spent on clothes, make-up, jewellery and hairdos. Of course, as always, some women worked to add to the family income. Because many women were out working at the start of the seventies, children were returning from school to empty houses. Many children were given keys to let themselves into their homes. These children became known as 'latchkey kids' and here was born a legacy. The security of childhood past had depended on a parent being close at hand. Having mum waiting at home, when school was finished, was all-important to a child as long as children had been children. Mum would comfort a kid after a bad day at school, bathe a cut if it had fallen, give words of praise when it had done well, spur it on if it had lost faith in itself. Now mum wasn't here to welcome it home, or, offer a drink or a bun; she was out at work, so the child was alone in the house. Instead of talking to mum, the child's alternative was to switch on the television set where it could see other people talking to each other. As sad little faces started to appear, 'latchkey kids' became a phrase that spelt depravity. The role of parent and child was experiencing a revolutionary change.

For the masses of working-class people shopping was still the same as it had always been but, for those who owned motor cars and refrigerators, the supermarkets were favoured over the local corner shops. In these big shops they could buy their groceries more cheaply in bulk. Instead of having to buy perishable goods on a daily basis, they were able to assess their needs for a whole week and store the food in their refrigerators. The success of supermarket shopping was reflected by the opening of yet another store during the year.

When home improvement was on the agenda car owners might also visit the first of a chain of do-it-yourself supermarkets that opened in 1969. Here, wares could be selected from the miles of shelving that housed everything a handyman might require. He could also select self-assemble furniture and house fixtures from the displays featured in the store. The only thing that Mr DIY could not purchase in this great emporium was a chat about last week's football match.

Since the discovery of DNA in the 1940s, scientists had been experimenting with ideals regarding the matter. Now, at the beginning of the seventies, they were developing methods to alter genes. The general public knew little about the subject so it could not be envisaged by them that Frankenstein was anything more than a story of fiction, or that the horrors of the Second World War were gone forever. And still in the world of medicine, a British man created history by having an atomic instrument implanted in his body, a pacemaker, to function as a heart regulator.

Where a heart had lost the capacity to control the slowing down or increased rate of heartbeats, this artificial heart would take over the task.

Britain was still rocking and swinging to the sounds of the music of the day. Pop and rock groups were increasing by the minute and setting a precedent for kids. Fashion houses were in their element reproducing the clothes the stars wore. Whatever they wore, the kids wanted. Hairdos were also copied, so too was behaviour. Disregarding the tradition that involved parents setting examples to kids, it was now the music groups of the day that did this. But then, many parents had little time for their offspring these days. They were busy following their own desires, they had work to do, things to buy and plans to make. Whilst they got on with their lives it was easier to hand out money to their children and instruct them to fend for themselves. It was common practice for the parents of attention-seeking children to offer money to the child instead of their own time.

Pop groups were overcome by the effect they had on the young general public. Everywhere they went swarms of screaming teenagers would accost them, pulling at their clothing, tearing at their souls. Their fame became so intense that it was hard for some of them to bear. Because of this, several of the music fraternity died by way of drug overdoses. Regardless of the vast amount of money the pop stars were earning, it would seem that it was not making them happy. They were trying to buy their happiness in any way they could; they had large cars, large houses, large parties, large groups of friends and large bank balances. But still it evaded them. They sought solace from painting, consulting the spirits, looking for God or moving onto private islands. At the end of the day nearly all of them resorted to alcoholism, drug taking and bad behaviour. Perhaps there should have been a lesson for all that money cannot buy happiness, but there wasn't. The people of the seventies were still courting the idea that happiness could be measured by the amount of money they had in their pockets.

Whereas the security of the human race had depended on the uniformity of society up until now in history, there was a definite defiance of it in the air. As the flower power people had changed the norm in the sixties, other groups were emerging intent on doing the same. Instead of following other teenagers by donning the fashions of the pop stars, some of the kids formed break-away gatherings. They backcombed their hair until it stood six inches in the air, then, sprayed it with lacquer so that it became hard and unmoveable. Some of them shaved their heads to the left and to the right, to leave a Mohican – a centre strip of raised hair. They had holes pierced in their ears and wore several pairs of dangly earrings. Some pushed safety pins through their lips and ears (painful!). The girls wore very heavy eye make-up and lipstick. Clothing was simple, but untidy, with leather coats adorned with numerous badges. The name of these groups? Punks. Then there were other groups of people whose image involved shaven heads and tattoos. Their group name – Skinheads (of course). Like the Mods and Rockers of the sixties, the only goal of many of the members of these two groups of people, was to fight each other and cause as much disruption as possible.

Fighting was happening between rival gangs of kids in school too. But then, schools had rules that all children must obey and if these rules were broken the kids knew that punishment would follow. When fighting in the playground occurred the offending parties would be marched into the classroom where they'd receive a caning from the teacher. It might not end there, for the teacher might want to bestow a further punishment on the child. This would be in the form of 'lines', when the offender would have to write, 'I must not fight in the playground', one or two hundred times. By the end of this exercise it was assumed that the child would have it firmly imprinted in his or her mind what he or she should not do again. One, or both, of these procedures of discipline was enforced in every case of misconduct by pupils. Even sticking old chewing gum under a desk or chair was a punishable offence, so too was being improperly dressed.

If we go back to the very beginnings of education, we will find that school children used to be punished if they had dirty hands. Each morning the teacher would ask the children to stand in a line and raise their arms before them. She would then scrutinise each child's fingernails, and administer a hefty clout to any child found with mucky hands. This would be followed by an instruction to go and scrub the offending dirt away. It didn't take the children long to learn that they must go to school with clean hands. Though the children of the day may have felt that they were treated harshly, the discipline they received here was, it was presumed, for good reason: to rid hands of germs, they must be washed thoroughly to remove all dirt. During the early 1900s, when disease was rife, it was deemed more important to educate children in the art of cleanliness, in an endeavour to curb the spread of disease, than to proffer education itself. What was not known at the time is that disease is not born of dirt, but of exposed matter such as excrement, sputum, stagnant water, fouled air and the like. As far as 'dirt' itself goes, no child should be without it, for it helps to build up the immune system. When children play in soil, or contact particles of it wherever it might be, the micro-organisms contained therein transfer to the body through touch. When these non-disease-causing mites enter the body, the immune system naturally rids it of the invaders. Therefore, bodily immunity grows stronger. (Perhaps in days of old, it would have been better to educate kids into washing their hands after going to the water-closet, than to ask them to remove soil from their fingernails.)

Then, according to the age-old tradition, it was taught that every child must do as they were told at all times, with no answering back under any circumstances. This doctrine was based on the fact that, until a child is old enough to reason for itself, it must accept the reasoning of its elders. The only academic lesson the kids of the day had to learn was their times tables. They would stand for hours on end reciting 'two times two are four, four times two are eight' and so on. The recitations came in sing-song tones to become firmly imprinted in the child's brain. In later years when diseases were on the wane, the lessons of cleanliness took a back seat. In their place came lessons of reading, writing and arithmetic. At the time, it was thought that working-class children needed a minimum of education to prepare them for the workplace. Mind, attentions were directed only at boys, for it was thought that girls wouldn't need education. It was automatically assumed that females, after leaving school, would either marry and remain within the confines of the home, or enter into service. If the latter applied, then the ability to say, "Yes, sir" or, "Yes, madam" would be the only learning they would require. By the time the forties arrived there was a better balance and all students were learning the same lessons. At this time children were not only being taught the basic 3 R's, the school curriculum offered them the chance of becoming acquainted with art, history, geography, games, drama and singing.

Now in the seventies, education embraced subjects such as foreign languages, business studies and current affairs. There were also television sets, typewriters, gymnasiums and film shows in schools. There was so much for school children to learn out of school too. They could look to the skies to see the newly launched jumbo jets flying over their heads, and observe that the appearance of these vehicles could be likened to that of whales. This was because the aeroplanes' main bodies were higher than conventional jets, as they housed both an upper and lower deck, in order to carry twice as many passengers. The kids of 1970 could also learn that, during the past five years, the number of tour operators dominating the market of package holidays had risen to ten.

1971 In 1971 there was a change in the Immigration Act which effectively ended immigration of non-white people into Britain. The exception was in favour of those who held British passports to render them patriots of the Empire. The Act probably came about because East African Asians had been expelled from their own country and had headed towards Britain. The influx of people entering the country since 1967 had risen to about 70,000 at this point in time. Was the change in the Act because the British Isles had its full quota of non-white immigrants, or was it feared that more racial violence would erupt as more of them poured in?

For twenty-three years children had been drinking milk provided free at school. With the knowledge that this contained the essential calcium needed for a child's bone growth, it was considered imperative that all children drink it. However, the news came that free milk (with compliments of the state) was being abolished. Obviously the government felt that parents were now able to provide for their children's needs themselves. Also it was noted that improvements in living standards were proving effective. For example, infant mortality had almost halved since 1950 and, life expectancy for all had risen by approximately four years.

Perhaps the money saved in buying millions of bottles of milk a year could now be better spent. So why not on a Family Income Supplement? This was a system of payment that would boost the family's income. Providing that a parent worked a certain number of hours per week on a part-time level, his or her wage would be increased to meet the liveable income calculated by the government. Instead of this move being a generous redistribution of the milk money, was the aim of the government a different one? Was it their intention to wean non-working citizens away from the social security system, thus reducing the expenditure of this department and the country? Was Family Income Supplement an invitation to employers to reduce their number of full-time workers, in favour of part-time employees who wouldn't cost them as much? Because for every full-time member of their workforce, companies had to pay a contribution to the National Insurance system. Part-time employees were not eligible for inclusion in this system; therefore no contributions were warranted from either employee or employer. And would FIS be the opportunity for employers to pay low wages, knowing that a government handout would be available to their employees? With this notion in mind, one might wonder how many Members of Parliament were also company owners or directors.

To the horror of trade unions, whose beginnings had brought death and punishment to the pioneers of their cause, the government introduced a new Industrial Relations Act to give government broader powers of intervention in industrial disputes. From now on, the people who were prepared to fight for the rights of the workers – the unions – would have a double battle on their hands. Not only would they need to convince the employers of their members' rights to good working conditions, and good wages for their toils, the government too would need to be in agreement with any plans for change. Once again, what number of government members were themselves employers?

Whilst the people of Britain were being reminded by Harold Macmillan that 'you have never had it so good', this was also true of the world of manufacture. Business was booming in every aspect. Products from clothing to motor vehicles were being turned out in their millions, with the sound of cash machines echoing in the land. Even the food for our mouths was piling higher and higher, as supermarket shelves reached overflowing. This method of marketing also offered consumers something they couldn't refuse – variety. Now, instead of bread being bread, and beans being beans, there was an enormous range of products from which to choose. Customers found that their visits to the supermarket were now taking up more of their time for now they had to stand to ponder *which* bread they preferred, and *which* beans would go down well.

The computer industry was expanding to weave its way into everyday life, and now it was introducing the 'floppy disc'. This was an eight-inch circle of flexible plastic which fitted into a computer. Its purpose was for storing information that could be recalled at any given time. The smallness of the disc meant that it could be stored in small places – unlike the vast areas required for keeping paper records.

Like always, whilst there was so much money to be earned by some, others earned very little. In 1968 a survey established that one third of British housing was unfit for human habitation, and it was not different now, three years on. However, low earners had no choice but to live in these properties, to be exploited by the racketeer landlords who unashamedly collected rents from them for the pitiful dwellings. Alas, applying for public sector housing in which to live was not an option for these people, for there were no plans to build any new houses, and there were long waiting lists for those already in place.

The currency of the British Isles had been pounds, shillings and pence for as long as everyone could remember. There were twelve pence to each shilling and twenty shillings to each pound. But now, currency was being decimalised and, in future there would be one hundred pence to the pound. The changeover caused tremendous problems as people plodded their way round the shops, trying to establish the price of goods. Large stores, and supermarkets, displayed posters showing the conversion from shillings to 'new pence'. However, conversion charts soon disappeared as government urged people to stop trying to convert from the old to the new. But then, the urge would be so, wouldn't it, for commerce and government didn't want the public to realise just how much prices had risen during the currency changeover. Blatant cons could be seen by all who wanted to see them. For example, lifting a newly made price tag would reveal the original price of an item. Whereas the old price tag might read – 8d – the new one would read 5p – a profit of four old pence.

There was a cry of despair in the world of space exploration when three Russian cosmonauts lost their lives after successfully docking their spacecraft on a space station orbiting the Earth. It was believed that they were still alive as they started their re-entry into earth's atmosphere, but were dead when the space capsule landed back on earth.

Revolutionary leaps in medicine had happened in 1967 when a human heart was transplanted. Now in 1971 both a heart and a lung were taken from a dead body and placed into a living one.

1972 Regardless of the new Industrial Relations Act, the miners of Britain went on strike in 1972 for increased wages. Because industry was still propelled by the burning of fuel, havoc was caused by the lack it. Large-scale power cuts were unavoidable as electricity plants ceased to function, and industry came to a standstill as lights and machinery failed. At the height of the crisis, a total of 1,500,000 workers were laid off work, and the government declared a state of emergency. In the workplace, gas or oil lamps and candlelight were used and, the government introduced a three day working week. In the home candles (price of which had risen from 1p to 3p) were burnt for lighting. Of course, this didn't bother the older members of society, for they had been used to this form of illumination. For the younger generation, the lighting of candles was something of a novelty that they saw as fun and excitement. Coupled with the state of emergency, the government imposed a ninety day freeze on prices, pay, rent and dividend increases. It was also envisaged that a food shortage was on the way.

For more than three hundred years, the British island of Ireland had seen unrest and bloodshed. The people of southern Ireland were farmers and supported themselves by way of the land. Their main source of diet and income was potatoes. The year of 1845 brought disaster to these farmers when a potato famine struck. Until its end, in 1849, one million people either starved to death or suffered extreme hardship. Furthermore, a million people emigrated. In the midst of their plight, the farmers learned that they were to lose three quarters of their land. The plots of soil they depended on for their living were now to be split into four. Instead of one farmer working a certain acreage of land, there would be three others doing the same. Whilst the starving peoples of Ireland scavenged to reap handfuls of potentially healthy potatoes from their tiny plots of land, their landlords – the English – happily collected their added income. In the eyes of the people, it seemed deplorable that money was being made out of suffering, but the landlords did not see it this way. They said they believed that the sharing of agricultural land was the fair option to enable a struggling community to survive. When the potato famine ended, there was an outcry from the victimised Irish. No more would they suffer at the hands of the English. The land of their birth was their land, hence their fight for independence began. Under the banner of the Irish Republican Army, war on the English was declared. As in any war, many atrocities were committed on both sides and much blood was spilled. After nearly a hundred years of fighting, victory was in sight in 1936. This is when the southern part of Ireland was renamed Eire – which is the Gaelic name for Ireland. Full independence came in 1949 when Eire became a republic. No more would the southern Irish isle be governed by the English. The same was not so for the northern half of Ireland however. Whilst Ulster, (Northern Ireland), won semi-independence by gaining its own government, it was still indirectly under English rule. The Irish Republican Army was not happy with this arrangement. What they wanted was a totally independent Ireland. However, not all of the people of Northern Ireland were in favour of this. Because they were mainly of Protestant religion, they believed their needs would be more fairly heard under English rule, whereas government by Eire would mean that the ruling religion would be Roman Catholic. What resulted was fighting between the two. The violence of the religious war reached a crisis at the beginning of 1972 when fourteen people were killed, on a day that became known as Bloody Sunday. On this day British soldiers, who had been assigned to the Province for intervention purposes, shot civilian bystanders. Now the English government decided to take away the semi-independence of Ulster and, enforced direct rule in its place. This was said to be done to look after the majority of the Ulster population, who were not included in the sectarian violence, and to avoid the threat of Northern Ireland coming to a standstill. Laws were set that anyone suspected of violent crimes would be imprisoned without trial.

Eagerly seeking a free society, the music fraternity had worked itself into a frenzy over the past couple of years. It seemed that pop stars felt that the only way to achieve their goal was to shock people by doing exactly what they wanted. This they had done by wearing outrageous clothing; committing offensive acts in public; promoting free sex (both musically and physically) and blatantly bragging about their drug-taking habits. Their encouragement came from their fans who followed their lead to the letter. However, now the rock and rollers felt that they needed a new direction and, took to the path of 'gender bending'. This involved their wearing make-up, 'girly' clothes, high-heeled shoes and silly smiles. To receive more publicity from the media, some of them also offered the 'shock' news that they were gay or bisexual. As a result of all this, by the end of the year it was becoming increasingly difficult to distinguish the boys from the girls.

Space travel was still in the news and American astronauts made it back to the Moon. They returned to Earth safely after exploring the mountains of the Moon in their Lunar Rover. This vehicle had electric motors and could climb the sides of the moon's craters and hills despite the thick moon dust. The Russians too were happy that their space probe had made a successful soft landing on Venus. Because of the crushing heat here, the probe worked for 53 minutes only.

1973 With supermarkets well established and here to stay, a quicker way of handling the increasing queues of people was needed. In 1973 computerised checkout stations were introduced. These comprised glass prism lenses which held lasers to read product prices. A barcode was already shown on product packaging, a series of black lines, with numbers underneath. The numbers would be fed into the supermarket's main computer and a price allocated. At the checkout, the cashier would scan products over the glass prism and, hey presto, a price would appear in a visual display above her head. The computer would store each price then give out a calculation when scanning was finished. What was left now was for the customer to pay and go merrily on his or her way. Whether customers checked the till roll bill given them was up to them. Before supermarket shopping had become the vogue, ladies would tot up the value of their purchases as they placed them in their shopping bags. Budgeting money had always been essential (because of the lack of it) so everyone made sure they were not overcharged. Would this new system change all that – would it now be considered that the computer would be right at all times?

At banks, too, computerisation was making its mark. A machine called Consumer Transaction Facility (soon to be better known as the holes-in-the-wall) was now operating to enable customers to withdraw money, make cash transfers and make enquiries. No need to stand in bank queues any more waiting to be attended by a cashier.

Then there came the promise that no one need worry about losing a vital body organ any more, because of the achievements of medical science. Firstly, a man received a transplant of a plastic eye that enabled him to see again. Secondly, both a kidney and pancreas were transplanted into one body from another. At this stage of medical phenomena it might have seemed reasonable to ask why the transplantation of organs was becoming so necessary. The demise of people, in the not so long ago past, was attributed mainly to the diseases of the day that were caused through lack of sanitation and nourishment. With this problem eradicated, why were lives now at risk because of defective organs?

In the middle of the century six European countries banded together to instigate the development of a European common market community that would strengthen their position in the world. To bring the plan to fruition, every member country would need to commit itself to the rules of the new community, then apply them to their trading procedures. The first key development in European integration was the set-up of the European coal and steel community following the Treaty of Paris in 1951. The Treaty of Rome followed in 1957 from which a common market was established in the form of the European Economic Community. In 1958 the six member states committed to the creation of a pan-European common market within twelve years. Although the ultimate goal of the EEC was to reach a level of economic integration, whereby there needed to be a single European currency, an intermediate offer was made to countries who wished to bring their economies together with chance to do so without having to integrate or convert them to a single economy. By 1970 however, the twelve year deadline had not been met so 'the six' had to devise another plan to persuade countries to commit to Europe. The British government went to the country with a referendum with the result that in 1973 the British said 'yes' to joining the EEC.

During the year a serious accident happened at the power plant Windscale. This came as a result of a fresh batch of fuel being dissolved on a previous batch to cause a steam explosion. This sent a radioactive gas through the building, with the consequence that thirty-five men suffered serious skin and lung contamination. After the event the building had to be sealed and closed.

1974 With computer power still up and rising, a Police National Computer became operational in 1974. This machine would be capable of providing direct information links to all police stations.

Proving that the anti-discrimination laws in force were still not working, a disturbance occurred at a demonstration in London when the National Front and anti-Fascist groups clashed. During the fighting that ensued one man was killed.

The Anglo-French supersonic passenger aircraft, *Concorde*, took to the air this year. This vehicle would fly at breathtaking speed from continent to continent. Whereas the 3,500 mile journey across the Atlantic by sea had taken five days in 1900, the same journey would now take three and a half hours by *Concorde*. It was in this year too that the worst air crash in aviation history occurred. Two hundred British people were killed when an aeroplane crashed near Paris. All 347 people on board lost their lives.

In line with the speed of happenings in this half of the twentieth century, it followed that there would be a need for fast food too. Hence the first 'fast food' outlet opened where ready to eat meals could be acquired within a matter of minutes.

Whilst burgers were sizzling and French fries were frying, some hospital managers were biting into their fingernails, for they had a recruitment crisis regarding doctors and nurses. Since the late 1960s there had been concern that very few people were entering the medical profession, and it was recognised that, without the 75% of overseas doctors who practised in hospitals these would not function. In an attempt to retain current nursing staff, and attract others into this profession, the government awarded a massive 58% increase to nurses' salaries and improved their working conditions.

And still with the National Health Service there were a couple more advancements. One was a new and better method of seeing inside the human body. This came in the form of a camera, sensitive to gamma radiation, which was developed to locate specific cancers. The other was a laser treatment to save diabetics from blindness when damage to the eyes had been caused.

Since the introduction of video machines, it had become apparent that folk were going out less and cinema attendances fell dramatically. The once cram-packed emporiums were now lifeless with lots of cinemas being forced to close their doors to the public and sell up.

1975 The liberated women of the century had more cheering to do in 1975. It was then that the Equal Pay Act came into force. Also, the Sex Discrimination Act established an Equal Opportunities Commission. From now on, advertisements could not state preference to gender when recruiting. If a lady wanted to apply for a particular job, then the employer had no choice but to offer her an interview (even though the job might have been that of heavy goods driver or scaffolder). The same would apply to blokes too. If they wanted to apply for a job cleaning bedrooms in a hotel, then they could not be refused an interview (of course the job description would have to be changed from chambermaid to chamberperson). No longer would heads of companies be dominated by men – it could be that the women of the future would aspire to these positions. The longstanding title of chairman would then have to give way to the one of chairperson.

Nor did the year see an end to advancements in medical science. Amniocentesis took amniotic fluids from around a foetus (previously known as a baby) – or even foetal blood. These samples enabled doctors to diagnose congenital or inherited problems in an unborn child. Conditions such as hereditary blood diseases, defects of the spine, Down's Syndrome or other congenital diseases. Should any of these faults be found, then parents would be told and given the choice to either maintain the pregnancy, or terminate it by way of abortion. Throughout the ages children born with the condition of Down's Syndrome (previously known as mongolism) were seen to be born to older parents. It was considered, therefore, essential that pregnant women over forty should have the amniocentesis test.

Confirming the wonders of medical science even more, it was announced that the first successful cloning of a mammal had been achieved; a rabbit. One might ask how many unsuccessful clonings there had been and, how much suffering these animals had endured.

Still with medicine, there was concern that surgical operations had a downside. It was said that when bodies are cut open for the purpose of surgery, there is a great chance of infection being caused. For this reason, it was decided that the use of antibiotics would make surgery safer.

By the end of the year people were finding that food was becoming more and more expensive with rising inflation being blamed.

1976 In 1976 the third Race Relations Act established a Commission for Racial Equality. If immigrants thought that they had been victimised because of their race or colour, they could pursue the matter by way of this new commission.

Was the Police Complaints Board, also established this year, to walk hand in hand with this new ruling? After all, many complaints had been made against police officers, alleging racial discrimination. The new board would operate a system whereby an independent civilian would be brought in to supervise cases of complaint, whereas in the past matters of alleged misconduct of police officers were investigated internally. Therefore, it was the police themselves who judged the case and decided whether any disciplinary charges were necessary. Now the complaints procedure would give the civilian supervisor power to question the decisions made by the police and press for these actions if thought appropriate. Though the public felt that this new procedure might alleviate the pressure that complaints brought to the police, it was also seen that it might bring doubt as to the credibility of law enforcement in Britain.

Since 1948, a vast number of immigrants entering the United Kingdom were of Indian, Caribbean or Pakistani origin and with them they had brought their own religions and eating habits. The taste for Indian food soon caught on with British people and by 1976 there were two thousand Indian restaurants in the country. The food processing industry too decided to cash in on the new eating mode and a lot of factories started producing pre-packed Indian foods.

With inflation still soaring, the government was forced to review the policy which promised to maintain full employment. What their new aim favoured was more unemployment as this brings down spending and, therefore, inflation. As to the Treasury's own commitment to cut down on spending, the government introduced cash limits on public expenditure programmes to the tune of £2.5 million. However, regardless of the financial hardship that seemed to be hitting Britain, fifty-three per cent of families owned their own houses by the end of 1976.

1977 Probably one of the most powerful and widely-used inventions of the twentieth century was television. By 1977 ninety-six per cent of British homes owned a little picture box. However, many of the older generation were of the opinion that television had revolutionised children's lives in as much as they did not go out to discover fun for themselves any more, as children of the past had always done. And now at this point in history, a survey revealed that children between the ages of five and fifteen were watching television for approximately twenty-four hours per week. As these children were of school age it meant that most of their free time was spent in front of a television screen.

A good excuse for street parties presented itself during the year; it was the

Queen's Silver Jubilee and not to be missed. The elders of the generation had begun making preparations weeks before the event. They had knocked, door to door, to collect money from residents for food and drink for the parties. Because there were so many motor cars on the streets these days, the venues for the street parties had to be reconsidered and alleyways and garages were commandeered. These were decorated with flags and awnings, then tables were brought in and laid end to end to be table-clothed and decorated in readiness for the coming food. Unlike the street parties that had followed the end of the wars, there was a lack of enthusiasm during the Jubilee celebrations. People appeared distant from each other and spirits seemed subdued. There wasn't so much togetherness any more. Mind, it must be said that during the wars, people were brought together inevitably. They shared food shortages, evacuation, bombings, woundings and losses of loved ones and homes. They worked together, shared air raid shelters and generally helped each other along. When the wars ended, their celebrations were exuberant, with their relationship to each other showing in one voice – one of comradeship and sheer delight. But the children of the Jubilee year had been born to a war-free Britain and knew nothing of hardship; their world was one of plenty with plenty more to come. For many of the teenagers of the day the Jubilee party was just another invitation for them to smoke pot, or indulge in sexual activity, without giving a toss to the tutting that came from their elders.

Another strike this year, this time by the firemen, who were asking for a thirty per cent pay increase. With no one to put out the fires, troops were called in to provide the service.

1978 By 1978 there were over twenty-three million telephones in use in the country. Perhaps as well, for people had the need to communicate quickly to discuss a special event. Something miraculous had happened in the world of medical science – the world's first test tube baby had been born, in Lancashire. This had been achieved by taking eggs from the mother's ovary; placing them in a test tube; fertilising them; then surgically inserting them back into the mother's womb. The world was agog.

Another piece of news was that another oil tanker had come amiss. This time it was the *Amoco Cadiz* which had shed its load of crude oil in the English Channel. This pollution disaster would take its toll on the sea, wildlife and the coastlines yet again.

The government of the day, in its attempt to curb inflation, had stated that wages must not rise above five per cent. Car workers at the time were aware that their employers had made £300 million profit in that year. What the workers wanted was a share of that profit. They went on strike and were awarded a seventeen per cent wage increase (bear in mind that car workers were already amongst the highest paid in the country). When all other workers heard of this increase, they too wanted the same. Tanker drivers refused to work, so fuel became scarce; lorry drivers brought their vehicles to a halt, so no food was getting through. Even doctors and nurses downed stethoscopes and bedpans. As for burials, there was no chance of these as gravediggers had hung up their shovels. Dead bodies were piling up wherever there was space in morgues and hospitals. The final straw of the mass strike came when refuse collectors stopped doing what they were supposed to be doing. Rubbish piled higher and higher in the roads, and rats were multiplying with the swell of their food supply. The reason for the strikes was that prices were rising, so much so that people wanted more money in their pay packet. There was no question as to how much more prices would rise, if large wage increases were recognised. At this point too there might have been the question of – are unions becoming too greedy?

At the end of the upheaval, all the workers who had gone on strike were awarded pay rises well over the five per cent limit, therefore, the government of the day was defeated. This had all happened during a very bad winter when snowdrifts were high and many. For this reason it was recorded as the 'Winter of Discontent' in political history.

1979 And more political history was made in 1979 when a woman, Margaret Thatcher, became the leader of the newly elected government. Her promise was that never again would unions have such power over the country.

The decade could not end without the recognition of another wonder of medical science. This came about when a fallopian tube was transplanted from a dead body, to a living one.

CHAPTER TEN

The Eighties – Part One

1980 Persuading working-class people to become homeowners had been the Conservative Party's policy for the past fifty years. The plot was to spawn the idea that if you owned your own home, your status immediately rose to that of better-off. The government now in power had won the election by giving an incentive to those who were still not homeowners. This was that they would give council housing tenants the right to buy their homes. Now in 1980 new Conservative voters would get their reward by way of a new Housing Act.

Although public sector housing had been built with much government subsidy, these houses were now going to be sold off to tenants at a fraction of their cost. In response to the situation there was uproar from those who had already begun to buy their own homes in their own right. They felt betrayed by the fact that, as well as having paid full market price for their homes, they had also as taxpayers been subsidising council house rents and repairs. What was more, as earnings had risen over the past twenty years it had been observed that motor cars were appearing in front of council houses. Not only cars, some tenants were even able to afford holidays abroad. The general opinion was that if these people could afford these things, they shouldn't be living in council houses. After all, public sector housing was originally destined for families of low earnings. But then, there was no means test to qualify for council housing tenancy. The government were not concerned about injustices, they wanted homeowners and it was homeowners they were going to get. They recognised that people were better off than they'd ever been, so why shouldn't they buy their own homes? They were also aware that owning one's home gave a sense of grandeur to the working classes. A grandeur that raised their feelings of prosperity and superiority to the point of rendering them Conservative.

Yet, buying a house was still beyond the reach of a vast number of Britons. These were the people who numbered the three million who were out of work and receiving benefits. The unemployment figure had not been this great since 1938.

The Treasury, too, was struggling to maintain financial order. Not only was it responsible for footing the bill of National Insurance payments, another five million claims for Supplementary Benefits were also being received. In an endeavour to reduce the number of potential long-term claimants, young unemployed people under the age of twenty-one were being encouraged to study whilst looking for a job. They were promised that if they attended full-time education for up to three days a week, they would not lose any State benefits. Was it the notion of the government that young people were under-educated and therefore unable to get jobs? Was it more economical for the Treasury to fork out even more money on further education, than to indefinitely support youngsters unqualified for the workplace?

Whilst the country's finances were sagging with the weight of the debt of the welfare state, Britain was also experiencing a boom. Millions of tons of oil had been produced from the North Sea fields; but not without consequence. Drilling oil from beneath the seabed not only polluted the sea and its life, but also endangered the lives of the workers who also lived on the oil rigs. When a specially constructed floating hotel collapsed, over a hundred oil riggers were killed. However, damage to the environment and life measured minutely against the enormity of wealth that oil created. Not only was the supply of it from the North Sea ample to fulfil Britain's demand, there was a surplus ready for export too.

What of Britain's demand for fuel at the time? Well, there were more than 19,000,000 vehicles on the road, and aircraft movements from Manchester's international airport numbered 83,300. To support the volume of traffic on Britain's roads there were now thirty motorways in operation. The building of these vast road networks had brought devastation to the countryside. Thousands of acres of green fields and hedgerows had been mercilessly ploughed up and replaced by rivers of grey concrete. Many farming areas became divided by the great expanses of road and the ferrying of cattle and machinery, from one field to another, had to be carried out by way of bridges and underpasses. Houses and other buildings that stood in the path of intended motorways had to be demolished. Of course, as in the case of the farmers who lost land, compensation was paid to the owners of these properties. However whether the farmers or property owners wanted to keep what belonged to them or not was of little consequence. The Compulsory Purchase Act was in force which would override any protest made by people required to relinquish land. The same procedure applied to the building of airports, too. Massive portions of countryside had to give way to the coming of giant excavating machines which would annihilate its existence. It seemed that nothing and nobody would stand in the way of progress.

The motorways of Great Britain were swarming with traffic. More and more goods were being ferried by motor vehicles rather than rail or waterways. In fact it was recognised that lorries had taken over from warehouses, in so much as goods spent more time being loaded on and off vehicles, than they did standing. For instance, after the harvesting of farm produce this would be loaded onto a lorry to be taken hundreds of miles away to be washed and bagged. Then it would be loaded back onto a lorry and returned to its place of origin. From here it would be loaded onto yet another lorry for delivery to supermarkets. This procedure applied to clothing as well. Many big businesses involved in the 'rag trade' were having garments assembled in the third world, or undeveloped countries, to save money. Concern was being shown at the number of heavy lorries that were zooming up and down the motorways. Because of this, an enquiry was set up to establish if weight restrictions should be increased. The current weight limit was thirty-two tons. The question was, should the limit now be increased to thirty-eight, forty or even forty-four tons? It was thought that the number of heavy goods vehicles on the roads would reduce if transporters were allowed to carry larger cargoes.

No one gave mention to the hazardous substances that some vehicles were carrying. Although dangerous chemicals had to be carried in a road tanker bearing the word 'hazard' there was little thought as to what would happen if these vehicles were involved in an accident and shed their load. The word 'hazard' would have been insignificant to the contents of the seventy foot transporter which appeared on one motorway. The vehicle was carrying nuclear waste (in the form of spent fuel) and its journey was to take it from Scotland to Cumbria. Whereas the minimum speed on motorways was twenty-five miles per hour, this vehicle travelled at just twelve miles per hour and would take nine hours to complete the short journey.

On the point of potential danger, the Green Party was at conflict with the government about a British chemical defence establishment. It was here that some of the best equipment for defence against chemical and germ warfare was made. From here, too, anti-nerve gas was exported to the USA every year earning the manufacturers £2.5 million a time. The concern of the Green Party was for the safety of the civilians who lived near the chemical establishment. They asked the government how much money was being spent to protect these people.

Then, for the second time in seven months, it was suspected that dangerous cracks were appearing in power reactors at a Scottish nuclear plant. In an endeavour to prevent the threat of nuclear leaks the reactors were once again shut down to allow examinations to be carried out.

Still with nuclear matters, NATO announced that US cruise missiles were to be based in the United Kingdom. Not surprisingly the year saw the biggest anti-nuclear demonstration since the sixties. A total of 60,000 people, who feared a nuclear holocaust, made their protest heard. An engineering company that had been making 'fall-out' shelters since 1971 was swamped with enquiries from the public. What they wanted was to buy the shelters which, up until now, had been supplied only to the British Army and NATO. The cost of one such shelter was £1,200.

Pollution was becoming a real issue worldwide at this point in time. So much so that an anti-pollution pact was signed by the nations bordering the Mediterranean, and seven major industrial nations agreed a fifty per cent cut in oil consumption by 1990. The world's air quality suffered a nosedive too when bellowing fumes, from a violent fire at Abadan, the world's largest oil refinery, took to the skies. The fire was caused during a war that was raging in the Middle East between Iran and Iraq.

The government had to make National Health Service cuts once again but not before awarding an eighteen per cent pay rise to nurses and midwives. Wages had fallen below the guidelines of the 1974 report and this figure would bring them back into line.

An added increase to the Health Service budget was imminent when a new drug was released onto the market. Interferon was the first of its kind to have been genetically engineered. Genetic engineering is a method of changing the inherited characteristics of an organism in a pre-determined way by altering its genetic material. This is done to cause microorganisms, such as bacteria or viruses to synthesise increased yields of compounds to form entirely new ones, or to adapt to different environments. At this stage no one was questioning the ethics of genetic engineering.

Many other moral issues were, however, beckoning the public's attention. News items had spoken of people being beaten to death, police making swoops on drug-dealing barons, increasing football violence, the increased sale of pornography and the increase of rape (the question here was, was one linked to the other?). But, when news came of a newly released report which told that parents needed help to bring up children, and that this skilled and demanding task should only be undertaken by people who were fully committed to the responsibility, it caused some eyelids to flutter. It was thought that if a specially commissioned government report was needed to remind folk of Mother Nature's rules on parenthood, there must be something wrong with society. Had the innate instincts which accompany parenthood been lost to parents of the eighties? In the adults' march to prosperity had children's rights been trampled? At least the kids of the day had one security they could rely on. They could get together with their friends at lunchtime and tuck into the dinner provided at school. But, oops, no! Not even this was guaranteed any more. The Education Act had removed the obligation of local authorities to provide school meals and milk.

The good news of 1980 was that, according to the World Health Organisation, smallpox had been eliminated from the planet.

1981 With the rapid growth of computer technology a lot of banks, libraries, travel agencies and large commercial organisations were already computerised. Now in 1981, however, the news was that no-one at all need not be. This was because a condensed, portable, and (comparatively) inexpensive machine called a PC (personal computer) was introduced to the marketplace. It was able to store text for users to recall and would therefore come in useful in the home, schools and small businesses.

As unemployment figures reached 2,500,000 a protest was made by thousands of people who walked from Liverpool to London to bring attention to the plight of the unemployed. The large banners that were carried on the route read 'The People's March for Jobs'.

Following these demonstrations of unrest the government took positive action. After the upheaval of the 'Winter of Discontent' they had promised that unions would not be allowed to bring the country to a standstill. So the Employment Act was now to give the power to outlaw secondary picketing at industrial disputes. This meant that it would now be a criminal offence to make protests against employers not directly involved in the dispute. With the announcement that thirty thousand coal miners would lose their jobs when fifty pits closed, what better time for the government to inaugurate these new rules. After all, who knew how much trouble there would be then?

Disregarding the new British Nationality Act, the worst civil unrest of 1981 came when riots broke out in parts of the country. Despite all the Acts that had been put into force to protect the non-white immigrants of Great Britain, there was still much resentment at their infiltrating its shores. There was lots of violence and bloodshed as gangs of Asians and skinheads fought. In one instance rioters burnt cars and looted shops as they fought pitched battles with the police. The incident was described as 'Britain's night of anarchy'.

Unrest was being seen in the establishment of the Church of England also. The source of the disagreement was women and whether they should be allowed to become ministers. There was uproar from the dominantly ruling males of the Church who maintained that, because Christ and his disciples were male, only men ought to be able to minister to the people. Their argument was one that not only indicated that they thought Christ to be God, they thought of him as sexist too. Were they advocating that only men could believe in God and Christ; that women were beyond faith and belief?

As far as we know the human race had embraced the habit of smoking for hundreds (perhaps thousands) of years. We certainly know that the native Americans smoked something called a peace pipe. Then in the sixteenth century, Britons were introduced to the tobacco plant brought into the country by explorers to America. Most of the country's male population took up the habit of smoking and it became a socially acceptable pastime. There were some women who had secretly (or openly) disliked the fumes from their husband's pipes or cigarettes, and who coughed and waved their hands across their faces to show their protest. But then, since the start of the liberation of women, a lot of ladies had taken up the habit themselves. However, the government banned cigarette advertising on TV in 1965 following a report from the British Medical Association that smoking caused cancer. After this some adamant non-smokers got together to promote anti-smoking campaigns on the basis that they, as passive smokers, would also run the risk of developing the illness. By 1979 some supporters of the cause had banned smoking on their premises. However, now smoking was being regarded as the paramount reason for all the ills (from dandruff to ingrowing toenails, it seemed) that befell the population and smokers were being outcast as socially unacceptable. At this point in time, whilst medical scientists were proclaiming that cigarette smoking was known (!) to be the cause of most lung cancer, some bladder cancer and that of mouth, throat and pancreas, they were saying other words that no one seemed to want to hear. These were that, though the process of cancer was not well understood, it was believed that occupational and environmental exposure to chemicals was amongst its causes.[i] So, were even the medical experts of a mind that cigarette fumes measured insignificantly against those that caused devastating pollution of the environment? Could it be that they were conscious of these facts:

1. If one person were locked in a car for one hour and chain-smoked during that time, he or she would emerge smelling and itchy-eyed but alive.
2. If one person were locked in a car with a running engine for several minutes, with one end of a hose attached to the exhaust pipe and the other leading into the car, he or she would die.
3. If three hundred people were locked in an aeroplane under the same conditions none of them would survive.

And, were they aware that even though people had been puffing away on tobacco since the 1500s, the escalation of cancer occurred after the 1950s?

Without doubt, one of the biggest pollutants of the time was the carbon dioxide produced by burning petrol. In this area there was also another danger that came from the substance lead, which was added to crude oil during the refining process. Because large numbers of children who lived near to major motorways were becoming brain-damaged, there came an appeal from the public for lead to be banned from petrol production. After all, hadn't laws been passed to make lead piping in homes illegal when a link was made between this and brain damage in children? Despite the pressure on government to enforce a ban, the only plans that came from it were those to reduce the lead content in petrol.

Ironically, after this, the first electrically-powered commercial lorry made an appearance. One might have wondered why all vehicles could not operate by this method, to annihilate carbon dioxide and lead emissions. Or why there was not an alternative way of propelling our species along.

The year was one when a lot of brave women took it upon themselves to stand up for their rights. They set up a 'Women's Peace Camp' which was sited outside a cruise missile base at Greenham Common. Their intention was to close down the nuclear weapon base by staging a determined protest. They did not envisage staying there for just a night, or two nights, but for as long as it took to get results. Some said that the ladies were irresponsible and should be at home looking after their children, instead of having fun making protests. Those women who could not find alternative childcare whilst they staged their protest took their young children with them. This added fuel to the situation for the tongue-waggers – 'how disgusting to make children live in such appalling conditions' ; 'what kind of mothers are they anyway' ; 'they're just beatniks out for a good time'. A good time was the last thing in the minds of the female campaigners, who had sacrificed the comforts of their homes to be here. Whether they would lose their jobs, or husbands, was of little consequence to them, for they were here to fight for the safety of their children and those of the future. A nuclear holocaust was what they feared from cruise missiles. (These nuclear weapons travelled at low level at a speed of six hundred and twenty-one miles per hour. They appeared as tiny aircraft and were very hard to detect.) As well as the women setting up a peace camp, a massive one hundred and fifty thousand people attended a protest in London. Apart from the fear of a potential disaster, it was being voiced that having cruise missiles in Britain made the country a likelier target for attack.

1982 In 1982 archaeologists dug up something which proved mind boggling: fossils, four million years old, thought to be linked to man. One might have wondered what the people of that time would think of their contemporaries of the 1980s. Would they say their demands on the Earth's resources were so great that there must be growing fears about the planet's future? Of course there was, for the

Earth's temperature had risen to cause a 'greenhouse effect' because of man's increasing need to burn fossil fuels. Throughout the ages of man heat had been acquired by means of burning peat, wood and coal. However the late nineteenth century saw an escalation in fossil fuel demand. This was when machines had started to appear in significant numbers. There were steam trains that needed coal to create their power, and power stations burnt the stuff to generate electricity. Some industrial machines were propelled by steam, whilst others had engines which burnt petrol, derived from oil. And, of course, there was the burning of gas. By the 1980s man's insatiable hunger for power had reached mammoth proportions. On Britain's roads there were close to twenty million vehicles constantly needing refuelling. In the skies hundreds of thousands of aeroplanes burned vast quantities of refined oil to propel them. Gas was piped into homes for heating and cooking, and central heating was being increasingly adopted both by house owners and industry alike. (Needless to say, the larger the area to be heated, the bigger the boiler, and fuel supply, needed to be). Electricity at home was not spent solely on lighting either. There was a list of power-gobbling gadgets waiting to be fed. Televisions, video machines, hair dryers, music centres, refrigerators, irons, vacuum cleaners, washing machines, clothes dryers, musical instruments, power tools, computers and so on and so forth. The commercial world, too, made a heavy demand on electricity, as did the lighting of the thousands of miles of British roads. The most significant waste of power was in the media of advertising, where millions of lights blazed well into the night. It might have seemed reasonable for people to think that, if they were sending so much heat into the atmosphere by burning so much power, no wonder the Earth's temperature was rising.

Then there was another man-made planet destroyer, called chlorofluorocarbon (CFC), to be considered. This product was used in aerosol sprays, refrigerators, air conditioning and foam packaging manufacture. The release of CFCs into the atmosphere was said to be creating a hole in the Earth's ozone layer. The concern about this was such that an international treaty was made to control the release of this chemical from aerosol sprays and fridges. However, considering that the ozone layer surrounds planet Earth to protect it from the damaging rays of the sun, why were not all ozone destroyers to be banned or controlled?

After a United Nations environmental programme reported that there was a six million hectare loss of productive land annually to deserts, it was wondered if it were too late. Had the sun's rays become so strong that they were scorching the Earth's surface and rendering it barren? The programme also stated that eight million hectares of rainforest were being cleared each year. These are dense forests which are usually found near the equator and once covered fourteen per cent of the Earth's land surface. However, at this point of the twentieth century, half of the world's rain forest had disappeared. What has to be considered here is that these forests provide much of the world's oxygen and counteract the air pollution that causes respiratory problems. Added to this, half of medicine originates in these forests, including seventy per cent of cancer drugs like those used to treat childhood leukaemia. Also eighty per cent of food originates there, including grains, fruits, nuts, spices, coffee, chocolate and rice. Destruction of the forests (apart from killing animal and plant life) reduces rainfall which leads to drought and famine in some countries. To become aware of the fact that every minute approximately one hundred acres of jungle is destroyed is to wonder at the damage the human race is effecting upon itself.

Anxiety was also being shown about the effect that acid rain was having on lakes and forests. The trees that were not being murdered for profit were dying from the results of this type of rain, as were the life forms of the lakes. At this point it was recognised that acid rain was man-made, with the main cause attributed to sulphur emissions, especially from power stations.

Television still had a great impact on the general public and sales of advertised goods continued to boom. Inveigling the man in the street to buy, whatever needed to be sold proved so easy and successful that a second commercial channel – Channel Four – was introduced. This followed another event of the previous year when Britain's first cable television came into being. Up till then TV pictures were acquired by means of an aerial attached to the roof, which picked up the airwaves from transmitter stations situated area to area. Making cable television operational involved laying thousands and thousands of miles of underground wiring, then extending these into people's homes. The cable TV company sold their product admirably by promising better reception and more programme choice. Of course there were not many people who did not pick up the gauntlet.

With more channels to choose from, viewing had never been as enthralling, for now, if one programme didn't suit, all one had to do was to press a button on the remote control and another picture would appear (ah yes, televisions were operated remotely these days, so no need to keep jumping up from one's chair to change channels). At this time there was one picture that no one would have wanted to miss. This was the first colour television picture of Venus, taken from a space probe.

In the world of entertainment technology, another first appeared in the form of compact disc (CD) players. When the recording of music first became possible it was by way of a disc made of wax; later a plastic cylinder; then a plastic disc. This item was known as a record and one needed a gramophone (manually operated) to hear the recording. After this, the late 1920s saw the coming of an electrical music player called a radiogram. This combined a radio and a record player in one.

Of course the quality of sound was greatly improved. Then in 1965 a tape cassette recorder was produced and, once again, better sounds were promised. The coming of the CD came with the offer of even better sound quality. So again it was time to throw out the music making machines of inferior status and replace them with the best in technology.

Of course these kinds of advancements had been happening in the zone of televisions and video recorders, too, over the years of their existence. Manufacture of entertainment gadgets boomed as people, who needed to possess the latest in technology, rushed out to acquire the machines which would give them social superiority (and more debt).

The government was faced with a conflict arising from the question of sovereignty of the Falkland Islands. Whilst Britain maintained that the little territory came under its jurisdiction, Argentina claimed that it should be flying its country's flag there. An all-out war resulted and, even though it lasted only three months it was time enough for two hundred and twenty-five British, and seven hundred and fifty Argentinean, soldiers to lose their lives to establish Britain's ownership of the Falkland Isles.

There were a couple of changes as far as motoring was concerned. Firstly, the maximum weight limit of heavy goods vehicles was raised to forty tons. Would this, as envisaged, reduce their numbers on the roads? Secondly, British vehicle owners would now be buying fuel by the litre and not by the gallon. From now on in, who would know how much a gallon of petrol was costing? To establish this, one would have to multiply the litre price by four and a half times. As with decimalisation the British public would soon stop trying to convert prices and would therefore be oblivious to increases over the gallon price.

In the field of genetic engineering the abnormal growth of mice was achieved. It was envisaged that farm animals could also be propelled into fast growth by using the same technique. Another breathtaking vision was that by employing genetic engineering, animals could be made capable of producing pharmaceutically valuable materials. After millions of years of the coexistence of man and beast, whereby the latter's obligation was to provide food for man's table, were animals now to be transformed into money-making machines producing the concoctions of man's technology?

Whilst the victimisation of farm animals and their future was of little concern to the people of the world of 'scientific advancement', there was speculation about a noble sea creature. It had been observed that the number of whales in the oceans was diminishing. For this reason the International Whaling Committee voted to ban commercial whaling. Alas, the ban was not to be enforced now but in 1985, giving whale killers another three years' licence to reduce stocks even more.

As Britain's oil fields continued to produce copious quantities of crude oil, 1982 was the time for the government of the day to release the bounty. Britoil ceased to be state owned and bids poured in to buy this lucrative industry.

1983 The lure of space exploration was still a prominent feature in life when 1983 appeared. It was then that the first sophisticated scientific laboratory took its place in orbit. Aptly it was dubbed Space Lab.

Back on Earth there was growing speculation as to the effects of nuclear usage. It was feared that if a nuclear war occurred it would create a global nuclear winter. In Britain, the government ordered an enquiry into allegations that there were high levels of cancer occurring in people who lived near an English nuclear power station.

Further developments in the health field were realised when British doctors performed their first heart and lung transplant. Also, great progress was being made in developing the techniques of artificial insemination – in-vitro fertilisation. Many hundreds of babies had been born during the years following the arrival of the first test tube baby in 1978. Now the procedure could incorporate the transplantation of fertilised ova from one womb to another.

Whilst scientists were pioneering the art of producing babies, a UK High Court was determining a way of preventing their creation. A judgement was made which upheld the right of doctors to supply contraceptive pills to girls under sixteen without their parents' consent.

With youth in mind still, there had to be a way of getting the thousands of unemployed teenagers off the streets and into employment, and to this end a Youth Training Scheme was established. The idea was to offer cash incentives to employers to find placements in their companies for youngsters new to the labour market, then for them to administer training in the workplace and, after a two year period, issue certificates to the pupils to indicate their level of achievement. The certificate, called a National Vocational Qualification (NVQ), would then be offered to prospective employers by youngsters applying for jobs. The scheme did not guarantee that work would be secured, unlike the days gone by when apprenticeships were the order of the day. Here a youngster leaving school would choose the trade he would like to follow and enter the profession on the bottom rung. By watching, and working with those already skilled in their art, the apprentice would learn the skills for himself and qualify to become a tradesman automatically. The learning process here lasted for several years.

The gamble taken by machine manufacturers, in the earlier years of the century, proved to be paying off as computer sales doubled. Not surprisingly the term 'computer friendly' became well-used and described those who followed the trend of technological advancement.

In contrast to the oil shortages and energy crisis of the seventies, there was now a glut in oil production. For the first time in its history the organisations of oil producing countries were saying that its price would come down. Some economists believed that the cheapness of oil would cause a boom in the industrialised countries of the world.

In the mid eighties the nuclear fuel plant at Sellafield accounted for as much as ninety per cent of the UK's public dose from radioactive waste discharged into the sea. When a quantity of contaminated solvent was discharged by British Nuclear Fuels Limited (BNFL), they were fined £10,000 with £60,000 costs. Further costs were incurred when, under a special compensation scheme introduced in 1982, the company paid out £500,000 to the families of workers who had died of cancer after working at the Sellafield plant. However, BNFL never accepted liability for their deaths. At this time, too, there was much concern about dumping into the Irish Sea, and the parties of the London Dumping Convention called for a moratorium on radioactive waste being disposed of this way. This was a result of Greenpeace's repeated actions against the practice. So, for the first time since the Second World War, it would not be permissible for radioactivity to be channelled through a 2 kilometre long pipeline, then washed out through a daily circulation of about two million gallons of sea water, into the ocean.

With vehicles on Britain's roads numbering well over twenty million, it was not surprising that people were running out of places to park them. Driving on congested roads was bad enough but where to put the vehicle when a journey came to an end was proving a stressful problem. In England's capital, London, people were parking their vehicles in such obscure places that wheel clamping was put into force during the year. The clamp gadgets that were locked onto the wheel of a vehicle made it impossible for it to be driven. A heavy fine had to be paid to the clamping company before the gadget would be removed. Surely the driver's workday was becoming longer, more expensive and stressful by the minute.

1984 The coal miners of Britain staged an all-out strike when they realised the National Coal Board was determined to close twenty uneconomical pits. They too were determined, but their aim was to keep the mines open and retain twenty thousand jobs. At the same time their plea was for better pay and conditions. The strike began on an aggressive note but, as it reached the twelfth week, it became more and more violent. Police had to wear full riot gear during clashes with mobs of picketing miners, and only charges by police on horseback managed to break up the groups and restore order. Many people were injured during the rioting and atrocities were committed miner to miner. For example, a block of concrete was dropped from a bridge onto a taxi ferrying a non-striking miner to work – this man was killed. Other 'scabs' had their houses burnt by their striking comrades. Over twelve thousand miners were arrested during the strike which had warranted the largest ever peacetime mobilisation of police.

When their local council agreed to pay them £351 each as compensation for sexual discrimination in the classroom, three British schoolgirls achieved legal history.

Although unemployment had reached a figure of over three million, it did not deter teachers from running the risk of losing their jobs. They went on strike for better pay, as did ambulance personnel, dockers, firemen, car and shipyard workers. However, to illustrate that new government polices were working, a group of shipyard workers were told by a High Court judge that they would be jailed for a month if they didn't end their sit-in at a shipyard.

The government of the day, with the Treasury in mind, was still looking for ways of either making, or saving money. Firstly, it began a major privatisation programme to sell off half of the lucrative British Telecom industry to the public. Now, instead of profits from this industry being ploughed back into it to maintain low charges for users, prices would automatically rise to accommodate the extra profits required to pay the new generation of shareholders.

Secondly, in order to save Treasury money, the National Health Service was being surveyed. Instructions were given that hospital support services be put out to private tender. This would mean that the tasks of cleaning, portering, maintenance, laundry, security and laboratory work would be undertaken by private companies under contract to the hospitals. This method would ensure that, whilst the essential routine of hospital support was being maintained, the National Health Service would be free of individual administration costs. Was this a sign that the thirty-five year old NHS was proving a financial liability to the country?

The vows of marriage were undermined further when a new Act stated that a divorce could now be obtained after only one year of wedlock. This replaced the three year period a man and wife had to wait to renounce their union with each other. There were many thoughts as to why people entered into marriage in the first place. Did couples get married now just to experience the pomp of a wedding ceremony? Were the words of the marriage vows incomprehensible to the couples who said them – or could it be that the people who made the vows did not understand the words they were saying at the time? The big question was, did the people of the mid-eighties really know what the word 'love' meant any more? In an age when everyone was used to getting what they wanted, and when they wanted it, there was little room in minds for thoughts of others and compromise. The government of the day had actually spawned the idea of looking after number one first. People were being encouraged by them to get on with their lives, grab everything they could from it, and forget the ones who were too weak to make the grade. In this 'dog eat dog' environment selfishness seemed to thrive on a diet of shredded love.

After a three year display of unselfishness, the women who had manned the peace camp at Greenham Common were defeated. Authoritatively and forcefully, police and bailiffs went into the camp and evicted the occupants. When this was done they sealed off the site completely, ensuring that it was impossible for the women to return.

The space race between two mighty powers was still apparent. Russian cosmonauts spent two hundred and thirty-eight days in orbit and created a new record, whilst American space travellers performed the first untethered space walk from a space shuttle.

On Earth there was more speculation as to how the greenhouse effect was affecting the planet. With the years of 1981 and 1983 being the warmest on record, it was wondered if the human race was quickly escalating towards a sizzling end. But then, with space exploration proving so successful, did it really matter; could not the species move to another planet if Earth became unbearably overheated and polluted?

And, oh dear, the Commons Environmental Committee reported that Britain's power stations were responsible for a 'plague of acid rain' across Europe.

By now there were a total of 3.6 million computers in the United Kingdom with yet another invention at hand. This was proffered by the launch of the first properly portable machine which had a full-sized screen. Now no one need be without a computer, wherever they might be.

Since the birth of computerisation it had been the practice of many big companies to transfer employees' salaries into their bank accounts by way of this technology. Before this, people performed a week's work, and at the end of that week, received a wage packet. Pay day, which usually fell on Friday, was the day that everybody loved, for it was then when it was felt that the efforts of the week had not been in vain. After getting up early every morning, performing a day's work, then arriving home tired after the day's toil, this day was the one that spurred people on, for it was so nice to open the pay packet and count the cash. After setting aside the monies needed to maintain the home for the week, what was left was spending money for the family. However now most people were paid on a monthly basis, by the direct banking method, and counting out cash was a thing of the past. But then, the country had reached the point where robbery was not very far away from anyone, therefore carrying cash was seen to be unsafe; especially for companies conveying large amounts to fulfil their payrolls.

Cash transactions were also being discouraged by some large retail outlets, for they, too, were launching schemes whereby customer payments would be made by way of the bank transfer system. Instead of leaving a deposit on an expensive purchase, then paying off the balance in cash on a weekly or monthly basis, payment would now be made via electronic transfer. Something else which would please the retail industry was the government committee's enquiry into shopping laws. This recommended that all legal restrictions on shop opening hours and Sunday trading should end.

According to a government report, childhood leukaemia was ten times the national average amongst those who lived near the Sellafield nuclear processing plant.

Bad news arrived also through the discovery of a virus named AIDS, which stands for Acquired Immune Deficiency Syndrome. This attacks the immune system of the body, rendering it unable to combat illness and disease. The condition is preceded by HIV, which stands for Human Immunodeficiency Virus, and this often causes the development of AIDS. People with the virus suffer unbearably before inevitable death occurs.

As 1984 neared its end it was evident that the plan of Mother Nature's for human beings to care for family members who became ill, or were near to dying, had been abandoned by many. This was because the majority of families at the time were too busy to offer this service and, therefore, allocated the task to others. In particular, when aged kinfolk grew too feeble to look after themselves, they were quickly shipped off to the profitable nursing and care homes that had sprung up over the last decade. Then, although the UK hospice movement, founded by Dame Cicely Saunders, began in 1967 with the opening of just one voluntary hospice in London, there were now many such charitable organisations operating throughout the country that cared for the terminally ill. Some may have wondered how much the people of the time were missing out by not nursing their relatives themselves, for it had always been recognised that to nurse someone one loves is to capture their heart to become one with them.

---

i Medicine – Microsoft ® Encarta

CHAPTER ELEVEN

The Eighties – Part Two

1985 In 1985 Greenpeace and British nuclear test victims called for a Commonwealth Enquiry into the effects of British nuclear tests held in Australia, and Christmas Island, in the Pacific, in the 1950s. Information, which had been suppressed as a military secret, had now come to light and revealed the terrible crime which had been committed against innocent people. There were a total of sixty-six atomic and hydrogen bomb explosions between 1946 and 1958, carried out during Britain's nuclear testing. None of the residents were told of, or protected from, the fallout of radiation and its effects on plants, animals and man. It was not mentioned that even the smallest dose of radiation produces adverse genetic effects. People in the Marshall Islands in the Pacific were left for three days, unprotected, in the path of fallout from the first major hydrogen bomb before servicemen came to evacuate them. By that time the fallout was three inches deep and the children thought that it was snow. The radiation burns, and subsequent diseases, suffered by the people had been used as a blueprint by US scientists to study the effects of nuclear war!

And still fighting nuclear atrocities, 200 people made their protest known at a cruise missile base in Cheshire. As usual the protesters were quickly and forcibly evicted from the site, to silence the voice of public opinion.

During the year it was announced by the World Health Organisation that there was now a worldwide epidemic of AIDS. There was also a discovery made that a certain species of monkey may have had a similar disease for thousands of years. What was thought to have happened is that this seemed to have somehow jumped the species barrier from monkey to man. How? Well, although no one knew for certain there were several ideas buzzing about. One was that it could have been transferred whilst monkey kidney cells were being extracted in order to produce oral polio vaccines. Another, that as handlers were regularly bitten or scratched by the large numbers of animals kept for this purpose, HIV could have transmitted from monkey to man. Then it was rumoured that AIDS could have been the result of a laboratory accident. In a newspaper article it was even suggested that 'the virus responsible for acquired immune deficiency (AIDS) may have been man-made as a biological warfare weapon.'[i] Britain's Health Minister announced that AIDS was not to be made a notifiable disease, but that health authorities would be given powers to detain victims in exceptional circumstances (one man was actually kept in hospital by order of a Manchester Magistrates Court). And at a cost of £4 million, 2 million blood donors would now be tested for AIDS before blood was taken from them.

Other health matters were also causing concern. Another new ailment named Legionnaires' disease claimed the lives of thirty-six people in Staffordshire, whilst a further sixty-eight patients with symptoms were being treated. The Medical Research Council announced a system to licence the work carried out in test tube baby clinics, and to check all laboratories carrying out experiments on human embryos. And – shivvery shivvery – the Department of Health ordered a review into the sale of human kidneys for transplant operations.

There was also much concern about the number of cot deaths which were occurring. A report was published refuting claims that many cot deaths were due to parents deliberately, or accidentally, smothering their children. The report, the result of three years' work covering 988 baby deaths, proved that only nine cases of death were due to infanticide and that, in fifteen more cases there was unproven suspicion of this crime. The solution was said to be that three hundred baby deaths a year could be prevented by better training of parents and doctors to recognise when a child was seriously ill.

Then a health warning was given after five people died and seventy-seven others developed liver damage after taking a drug called Nizoral. The drug was not going to be withdrawn, but doctors were being urged to think carefully before prescribing it! And, a woman who gave birth to a thalidomide baby was seeking a legal injunction to ban further use of the drug in Britain. Strange that the drug was still being prescribed after its supposed banning in 1962. How could this be? However, on the packaging of the product was a warning to women who were prescribed thalidomide – this was, not to get pregnant!

To round off the health worries of the day, the British Medical Association and Health Education Council set sail with the launching of an anti-smoking campaign. Perhaps many of the over three million people who were unemployed at this time would be inveigled into stopping smoking for financial reasons, rather than health warnings.

Unemployment was far from the minds of British Airways and British Airport Authorities as they totted up their takings from people anxious to secure air travel. British Airways announced a record operating surplus for 1984/85 of £315 million, whilst the British Airport Authority's record annual profit measured a mere £72 million. With 95,600 air movements in the year from just Manchester International Airport, it would be easy to figure out how these vast profits were made if the movements from all the airports in the United Kingdom were taken into consideration. Mind, perhaps the profits would not be so high if airline companies were liable for paying tax on the vast volume of fuel their aeroplanes consumed.

Following an incident earlier in the year, when thirty-nine people were killed and 240 injured when rioting broke out between English and Italian supporters at Belgium's Heysel stadium, the British Football Association had to take action. Their decision was to order the withdrawal of all English clubs from European competitions for the coming season. The Belgian government, in turn, banned all British football clubs from playing in Belgium, and UEFA banned a British team from all European club competitions for three seasons, and later banned all English clubs from competing in Europe for an indefinite period. To round off the punishment FIFA banned English professional soccer clubs from playing anywhere outside England.

The matter of soccer hooliganism was now becoming so serious that the government arranged for a meeting to be held with the Football Association, and League, to discuss the situation. Some weeks later a Bill was rushed through the House of Commons to ban the sale of alcohol at football grounds. Then British Rail announced it was to stop running football specials for soccer fans, and end cheap excursion fares to those travelling on scheduled services. What was happening to the traditional sport that had been enjoyed for hundreds of years? Had the game of football become a substitute for war?

Still in the world of sport, the British Amateur Athletic Board announced it was to introduce an open register for athletes willing to have random drug tests, with the proviso that only those who signed would be eligible for major competitions. Again, was nothing sacred anymore? Taking part in sporting competitions had been enjoyed by athletes and spectators for unnumbered years. Showing off one's athletic prowess had always been acknowledged as a fun thing. A sporting event was a place where the worries of the day could be put aside for a short time whilst people indulged in some light-heartedness. However, this legacy of fun-seeking seemed to have been abandoned by the human race. The competition that had developed in the field of athletics had grown so fierce that competitors, intent on winning and breaking world records, felt the need to take drugs to improve their physical body power to promote super-human performance.

Although narcotics had been used by people throughout the ages of man, some being medically supplied up until the early twentieth century, the need for drugs generally had increased dramatically. Illegal substances such as cocaine, marijuana and heroin were being sold on the streets for large sums of money. This resulted in there being many police and customs swoops in England on drug smuggling syndicates, and many of the operators were jailed for long periods of time. Although the consequences of smuggling illegal drugs were widely known, it served as no deterrent to those whose only thoughts were to make millions of pounds from their transactions. Sadly, too, at this point in time there were thousands of youngsters who had become addicted to using other mind-destroying substances, to find an escape from life. Easier to get things such as glue, lighter fuel and gas were being sniffed by kids eager to lose sight of living for a while. Unfortunately, many of them lost sight of life forever. In one incident of solvent abuse a seventeen-year-old boy killed his mother and grandmother in a few moments of frenzied madness, then jumped to his own death from a window. Drug abuse in general was so great at this time that the government gave an extra £5 million for the expansion of services to help drug addicts.

Race riots were still raging and these appeared to be more violent than ever. In an area of Birmingham, which housed a large black population, firefighters tackling a blaze were attacked by a mob of youths who hurled petrol bombs, bricks and bottles at them. Police wearing riot gear cordoned off streets during the rioting, which lasted into the next day. Many shops were destroyed, factories set on fire and cars overturned and set alight to make barricades as mobs looted businesses and demanded money from their owners. A number of police officers and firefighters were injured, whilst two Asian brothers died when their shop was set alight. In another incident, a mob of mainly black youths rampaged through Brixton after a black woman was shot, and seriously wounded, during a police raid on her home. Petrol bombs were hurled at police; shop windows were smashed; goods looted; fires started in the streets and motorists dragged from their cars to be beaten up. Then in London a further riot followed when a policeman was hacked to death and others shot. The attack was made by hundreds of black youths following the death of a West Indian lady, who had collapsed when police searched her house. The injury list on this occasion was two hundred and twenty three police and twenty civilians.

A historic agreement was signed during the year between the British and Irish governments. This stated that the government of the Irish Republic would be allowed a say in British policy towards the province of Northern Ireland. It said too that there would be closer co-operation between British and Irish security forces. Would this stop the bloodshed that had been happening up till now, both in Northern Ireland and Britain? Would innocent people cease to be the victims of

IRA bomb attacks? Would both Catholic and Protestant communities stop firing guns at each other? Perhaps not, because Protestant politicians in Northern Ireland were already strongly against the agreement.

And still in Ireland, contraception was legalised. As Ireland is strongly influenced by the Catholic Church, the use of artificial contraception had never been condoned. However, the people of Ireland would now be able to buy contraceptives in shops, the same as every other European country.

Contraception was far from the minds of an American couple who paid a British woman to be artificially inseminated to bear a child for them. The lady was paid £6,500 for her trouble and so too was the surrogate mother agency, who introduced the parties to each other. However, when the child was born there was something of an uproar in political circles. The government stated that it intended to ban commercial surrogate mother agencies. In the meantime, the baby was made a ward of court and taken to a place of safety, where she awaited applications for her custody. Strangely enough, custody was granted to the American couple who had bought her birth.

1986 Following the rioting which had taken place in the previous year, the government announced new measures in 1986. The first was that approval had been given for all police forces to be issued with plastic bullets and CS gas to counteract any serious rioting. Also that police manpower was to be increased by three thousand, two hundred. The second step involved the purchase of twenty-four bullet-proof vehicles and eighty personnel carriers for police use in dealing with future riots in London. Another area of policing was in the mind of government when it announced that sub-machine guns would be issued to police patrolling London's Heathrow Airport.

Prime Minister Margaret Thatcher replied to a Russian call for a nuclear-free world by the end of the century by saying, "Nuclear weapons will continue to make an essential contribution to peace and security for the foreseeable future". Still promoting the ideal of keeping Britain safe, the Prime Minister also set up a special committee to consider ways of cracking down on hippy communities!

Perhaps an area of violence the government might have wanted to consider was that of rape, for a survey they had commissioned showed that rapes and attempted rapes reported to police had increased in England and Wales by twenty-nine per cent, and in London the number had risen by more than half. Then a report, published by the NSPCC (National Society for the Prevention of Cruelty to Children) stated that the number of children known to have been sexually abused in England and Wales had risen by ninety per cent in 1985 and that there were considerable increases in reported cases of mistreatment.

Although crime, murder, rape, kidnapping and child abuse had existed throughout the history of mankind, why now was it so much on the increase? Why was violence so prevalent? Were the laws of living being forsaken for a 'do as you want' attitude to life?

Perhaps this attitude might be spawned in the classroom of the future for the government proclaimed that corporal punishment in schools would be banned. This followed a European outlawing in 1982, and a Lord's decision in 1985. Would the banning of such punishment lead to self-discipline in pupils, or would it result in anarchy in education? Wise or not wise – only time would tell. Whilst a lot of parents supported the ban, there were lots more who believed that punishment was necessary in order to enforce discipline in schools. Perhaps these were the people who acknowledged the fact that children needed to be disciplined, until they learned to discipline themselves.

As to sex education in schools, the government decided to add a clause to the existing curriculum. Whereas pupils were encouraged to engage in sexual pursuits, inasmuch as contraception was made readily available to them, now they were to be advised to have due regard to moral considerations and the value of family life. Had someone perhaps remembered the important rule Mother Nature had laid, that human beings joined together as one before embarking on procreation programmes? Surely the kids of the 80s were perplexed by the messages being given, and wondered what it was that was expected of them.

Early in the year the world's worst nuclear reactor accident occurred. It was at Chernobyl in the Soviet Union, at a plant where a serious fire followed explosions, to cause radioactivity to be released. Days after the accident, increased levels of radioactivity were recorded throughout most of Europe. The Soviet Union was condemned for the delay in admitting to the disaster and criticised for its slow response in dealing with it. The Soviet Union at this stage appealed for Western help. There were varying estimates received as to the number of people killed, or seriously affected, in the immediate area and in neighbouring countries. It was not known either what the long-term impact would be on the incidence of cancer. The Soviets (as would any other country) continued to deny reports of the extent of the disaster. A couple of months after the incident, the British government banned the movement and slaughter of sheep and lambs in areas of Cumbria and Wales because of radiation caused by the disaster. This ban was to last for twenty-one days. A similar ban in certain areas of Scotland was applied. Later in the year Soviet scientists presented a report on the cause of the accident to the International Atomic Energy Authority. Then a Soviet press conference was held and this blamed human errors and disregard of safety rules by workmen, for the disaster. The report stated that thirty-one people had died and over two hundred were suffering from acute radiation sickness. These casualties were in the immediate area of the accident – but what about the rest of the world? How many other people might have been suffering radiation sickness, and what of the long-term effects that cause cancer? Should not the whole world at this point be questioning the great danger of tampering with nuclear matter? Was there no one with sense enough to realise the danger that inevitable accidents could cause both mankind and the planet?

Perhaps Britain should be taking a serious look at its own nuclear plants, for at Sellafield nuclear fuel processing plant there had been two radioactive leaks in a matter of twelve days. However, two new clean-up plants opened there in 1985 were said to be proving effective, for lower levels of radiation in the area had now been recorded. However, keen fish eaters along the Cumbrian coast were still receiving over half their official allowable radiation dose – just from consuming seafood!

When the human race first decided to dabble with nuclear fission and fusion to create power and weapons, did it ever give a thought to what would happen to the waste products? Radioactive means radioactive – it does not stop being so for such a long time. For instance, uranium ceases to be radioactive in a little over one and a half billion years. So, dumping it into water or burying it underground will not cease its activity; it will continue its momentum into the future of mankind. Yet, when the general public deem it their human right to complain about the situation, they are taken to task. This is how it was when a High Court Judge granted an injunction against nuclear protesters. What these people were doing was trying to prevent contractors from carrying out tests at three possible nuclear waste dumping sites. Who would like to think that future generations of families would have the threat of radiation sickness in their lives? All there need be, to uncover the deadly monsters hidden in the earth, would be earthquakes, excavations or landslides.

Who also could envisage the effects of biological warfare? Say anthrax for instance, for the Scottish island of Gruinard had to be decontaminated with hundreds and thousands of litres of formaldehyde to kill anthrax spores there. What happened was that forty years ago the British government dropped test anthrax bombs onto the island. Needless to say every living animal on this little part of Britain was annihilated because of this chilling biological warfare experiment. Though anthrax mainly kills herbivorous animals like cattle and sheep, humans can be affected too. With humans, infection occurs when spores get into the skin or lungs. Skin anthrax appears as a large pus-filled blister which can cause infection of the bloodstream. Lung infection is more dangerous – this can lead to pneumonia and internal bleeding. Who could imagine that a British government would ever contemplate using such a cruel weapon of war?

With the emphasis on the environment there were some goodies on offer from the government. An Anti-pollution Inspectorate was set up for England and Wales, as was a £600 million ten year programme to clean up Britain's coal-fired power stations to reduce acid rain. Then £280 million was given for a programme to clean up the sea at more than 350 bathing beaches around Britain.

It seemed good news too that never before had there been so much money floating around the country. Left, right and centre there were companies anxious to rid themselves of copious amounts of cash. The general public were being seduced into acquiring the easy loans which were available to them; the main purpose being to buy houses. Another encouragement for couples to buy their houses *now* was that there was going to be a change in the taxation system. When the transformation had taken effect it would mean that tax relief on house purchases would be greatly affected. With this, and loans sitting waiting to be collected, people stampeded the housing market, eager to buy. Investors too could not wait to scoop up as many properties as they could to ensure a great chunk of this potentially lucrative market. This caused there to be even more money flooding in from the financial capitals of Britain. The result of this activity produced an astounding (it seemed) overnight fifty per cent increase in house prices. Property investors were delighted with the outcome and were rubbing their hands at the thought of them rising even further. It was not only investors who sought to gain from the property boom, for working class people, too, seized on the opportunity to invest. Some, who could afford to, bought run-down properties which they cheaply modernised to rent out. All these new self-made landlords had to do was to sit back and wait for house prices to escalate into profit.

At this point in history it was obvious to see that being house owners had changed the general attitude of the working classes. Whereas life throughout history had encompassed 'being in the same boat and pulling together' for working people, owning one's home had set people apart from each other. The main topic of conversation in the late 1980s was about whether your home belonged to you, or to someone else. Those still in rented accommodation were looked down upon by those with mortgages to pay. Folk who paid rent were somehow regarded to be in the low pecking order of society. Aye! In 1986 you were nowt unless you owned your own home. Owning one's own home also raised the status of the working classes by moving them into a category of 'will makers'. In the past only the rich and upper middle classes nominated the people who would inherit their worldly goods, when their moment of demise arrived. And in this circle of the 'haves' there had always been friction in mourning family units as to who would receive what and when. Inheritances seemed to cause nothing but strife and greed for them. Whereas in working class quarters of the past, when death arrived people had nothing to leave behind but the memory of themselves. However, would the situation take on a different face now for the working classes as their children and siblings became inheritors?

Something else had changed dramatically too, and this was the way that people spoke to each other. In the past there had always been an air of friendliness as folk addressed each other, proudly using the dialect of their district. The speech of the middle and higher class people was always regarded as 'posh' by the working classes. Of course the 'poshes' were better-educated and had a well-founded knowledge of the English language. The consequence of this was they all sounded the same as they spoke. When they greeted, and bade farewell to acquaintances, they didn't say, 'How you doing pal?' and 'ta-ra'; they didn't say, 'Wotcha cock' and 'toodle-pip'; not even did they say, 'Hiya'' and 'cheerio'; their welcoming greeting was 'hello' and their departing one 'goodbye'. Now, despite the fact that the education of the working classes was the same as it always had been, it was felt that one should watch how one spoke. After all, affluent house-owning people shouldn't be thought of in the same way as the riff-raff who rented their homes. Hence they adopted the language of the 'posh' (which they had gleaned through radio and television) and introduced 'hellos' and 'goodbyes' to their vocabulary (mind, the goodbye was generally modified to that of 'bye bye', or 'cheery bye' or simply 'bye'). The consequence was that the ancient dialects of communities were rapidly dying, leaving only local accents to distinguish the individuality of one's 'roots'.

Having said this, individuality in general was gradually seeping away from society these days. The character of people appeared to be merging into a oneness. The way people lived, conducted themselves and spoke all seemed to be the same. There appeared little possibility of bumping into someone who possessed a character of note, who would impress your memory with their personality. There even came the introduction of grouped nicknames such as yuppies, dinkys and Nimbys, which mean; young urban professionals, dual income no kids yet and not in my back yard. Towns too had been affected by the individuality drain. Visiting other counties in the country had always meant that you would see features native to the area. Shops, for instance, would be of the traditional type where country fayre was made and sold. The names over the doors of these shops would also indicate the birthplace of the proprietors telling that they were locals. But these small family local character businesses had been forced to give way to monopoly. Now supermarkets, superstores and chain stores were the shops of the day with their names advertised boldly on large hoardings for all to see as they journeyed along.

Travelling the roads of Britain had become dull too because of their sameness. There were now ring roads, roundabouts, flyovers or one-way streets where there used to be quaint buildings, old signposts, town antiquities or cobbled streets. Of course, these changes had been effected because of the sheer volume of traffic ploughing the roads.

Something that had stayed the same in Britain were the waiting lists at hospitals. Despite governments having invested millions of pounds each year into the National Health Service, there was still an ever-increasing queue of people waiting for operations. However the government was now to attempt to 'make things better' once again. The Health Minister announced a plan to reduce waiting lists by appointing several thousand more senior doctors. Also, the intention was to create a new grade of hospital doctor, and to increase the number of consultants to a total of 23,000 over the next fourteen years. But would waiting lists ever diminish when it was considered how many life saving procedures had been developed over the past thirty years, and how many people now needed these operations? Even now there were still many firsts happening in the world of medicine, such as the world's first triple transplant of heart, lungs and liver and Britain's first artificial heart transplant. Then, when a two-and-a-half year old child received a new heart and lungs it became the youngest person in the world to undergo this operation. Furthermore, the world's first test tube quintuplets were born.

Then, with AIDS still on the increase, it was decided that a special Health Authority would be set up to direct a public information campaign about the disease. The cost of this project would be £20million, but it was thought that money would eventually be saved by the Treasury if the public were made aware of the dangers of contracting AIDS. An extra million pounds was also to be given for research into its cause. The government also announced that it had made plans to provide clean needles for drug addicts, to reduce the risk of AIDS being passed between those who shared them. Though little was known about HIV and its treatment, it had been established that the vast majority of new transmissions occurred amongst gay or bisexual men. As up to one thousand cases per year were developing in predominantly male population groups, there was the suggestion that unprotected sex between men was increasing. As far as heterosexuals suffering with AIDS was concerned, it was discovered that most of them were long-term, needle-injecting drug users. Another health worry during the year was that there were fourteen times the national average of meningitis cases in the Midlands area. The outcome was that health officials had to begin a project to screen the whole population of the district.

The baby market was also a matter of concern to the DHSS (Department of Health and Social Services) and plans were announced for comprehensive legalisation to control test tube baby fertilisation. The same rules were also to apply to experiments on human embryos and non-commercial surrogacy.

Space exploration saw a setback as an American shuttle exploded shortly after lift-off, killing the five men and two women who were aboard the vehicle.

In the world of entertainment there was yet another 'goody' awaiting the general public. This would come in the way of a new television system called satellite. Contracts were given to several companies who would transmit TV pictures by means of satellite receivers or dishes. These were large concave metal plates with built-in aerials which, when attached to outside walls of properties, transmitted pictures to television sets. Once again, time to dig deep into one's pocket (or credit facilities) to purchase the 'best ever' system of receiving a multitude of programmes.

Television was transforming football at this time, too. TV companies started to pay top division football clubs extortionate amounts of money for the rights to televise their matches. This led to top footballers demanding larger salaries from their employers for their expertise, and newly acquired stardom. It also followed that increased transfer fees were demanded club to club when footballers were to be bought. The top footballers themselves were becoming so famous and admired they now needed agents to manage their affairs. These people would negotiate contracts for their clientele with club management; arrange media interviews; transfer fees and, of course, ensure that their salaries were as high as possible. Britain's national sport of football, which had been enjoyed by so many for so long, changed dramatically overnight. The game had become big business.

In other events, signs of the downfall of sport were being indicated. In fact when one read the newspapers of the day, it would seem that friendly competitions were being replaced by aggressive ones. These told of two prison sentences imposed on rugby players; one was a policeman who bit off an opponent's ear and got six months; then another player was jailed for one month for assaulting an opponent.

Determined to rid itself of nationalisation, the government put British Gas up for sale. Dealings opened on the stock market and people rushed to buy their shares. It was alleged on this occasion that civil servants were involved in insider share dealing, and an enquiry was opened. Perhaps another enquiry should have been set up to question why the government had it in their power to sell yet another commodity that belonged to the people of the country. As to the greedy better-off working classes who participated in share buying, did they not appreciate that gas already belonged to them? Did they not know that the profit that they would receive from their shares would be obliterated by higher fuel costs? Did they not give a damn for those obliged to pay more for their gas without the benefit of a share payout?

Contrary to Race Discrimination Acts, and the fact that passport holders could enter Britain freely, the Home Office announced that in future people from India, Pakistan and Nigeria would have to obtain a visa before entering the country. Could this news have been in the minds of the hundred black youths who bombarded police with stones and bottles as they were making a raid, and were race relations getting worse?

So that it would be known that government policies on striking were still very much in force, a county court judge ended 1986 by saying words that would leave no one in doubt. What he said was that railway unions could be sued by ticket holders for losses and inconvenience caused by any industrial action – if that action was called without the endorsement of a secret ballot.

1987 After the visa rule, brought into being in the previous year, there followed a new development in 1987. This was that airlines would face fines of up to £1,000 for transporting people into the country who did not hold a valid passport and visa. Then, contrary to the rules, the government announced that nearly 500 Vietnamese boat people would be admitted to Britain over the next two years.

Once again it was being seen that the Race Discrimination Acts in force weren't really effective. An illustration of this was when parents living in Yorkshire refused to send their children to an allocated school where eighty-five per cent of the pupils were Asian. The parents sought their rights at the High Court and were awarded £700 costs, and the outcome of the hearing was that their children were offered places in schools of their choice. So much for the government's attempt at making laws intended to bring about racial integration. There was even a lot of violence at the Notting Hill Carnival this year, where running fights broke out between police and mobs, and one man was stabbed to death.

Violence was still prominent in the sporting arena also. But dear, oh dear, it had now arrived at the doors of Britain's gentlest game – cricket. During the test match between England and Pakistan, trouble started in the ground and a fan had his jugular vein and windpipe severed. The incident caused quite a stir amongst Board officials, who made preventative measures for the future. These were that flags, banners and musical instruments would be banned from test matches, and fans would be prevented from taking excessive amounts of alcohol into the ground. Also it was agreed that there would have to be more stewards at matches.

In football, punishments for violence were handed out. Firstly, the two ringleaders of hooliganism at a football match were jailed for ten years. Secondly, the government signed extradition warrants for twenty-six fans who were to face manslaughter charges in Brussels for their part in the match rioting there. And then, forty-four football hooligans were arrested following a police undercover operation. Would the person who fired a canister of tear gas into the crowd at a Scottish football match this year also be identified and punished? Tear gas! Wasn't this something to do with chemical warfare?

Regardless of the wars of football there were people begging to become involved with the sport. For example, some rich pop stars and millionaires of the time were eagerly bidding against each other to buy football teams. Was their intention to gain publicity from owning a football team or did they wish to profit from the venture? After all, the game of football was attracting mega bucks and the players were becoming colossal entertainment stars.

Environmentally the government was making noises in the right direction. It was to spend £170million in a ten year programme to combat acid rain pollution. During a conference on North Sea pollution it agreed to reduce the level of pollution coming from Britain. But hang on a minute – didn't the government, earlier in the year, order a search for a deep underground site which would be suitable for housing nuclear waste? One might ask just where the government stood on nuclear matters, when five women were arrested as they protested (along with 595 other people) at the Greenham Common base. Their protest was to mark the eighth anniversary of the deployment of cruise missiles in Britain.

The Central Electricity Board was busy, too, with thoughts of environmental matters. It decided to introduce plans to reduce the amount of sulphur emitted from power stations. Probably spurred by the Soviet nuclear disaster of the previous year, British Nuclear Fuels (BNFL) too, had to put on its thinking cap. Obviously the management had been shocked out of its complacency by the Soviet accident and its effects. Particularly so as three former managers of the plant there had been sentenced to ten years each in labour camps for blatant violation of security regulations, with other officials having received jail sentences of two to five years. The result was that BNFL announced a £50million programme of improvements to the Sellafield nuclear complex. It might have been a wise decision for nuclear processing plants to give some thought to the conveyancing of their nuclear waste, for although it was announced that there was no contamination involved, part of a railway station in Kent had to be sealed off after liquid was seen dripping from a rail wagon which contained nuclear waste.

In the world of health the demand for more money was still a headache for the government. They announced a further plan to reduce hospital waiting lists by ploughing another £25million into the NHS to enable more operations to be performed. Next came the offer of £6.5million for the London Health Authority to help them cope with the ever-increasing AIDS problem. Later in the year came another promise that a further £100million would be given as emergency funding. At the time it might have seemed that a lot of this money would be needed in the accident and emergency (A&E) departments of hospitals, for more accidents and disasters seemed to be happening these days. One such event happened in Berkshire, when a man ran amok waving a gun in his hand. He shot fifteen people dead and wounded sixteen others (two of whom subsequently died) and then he shot himself. After this there came another man in Bristol who killed four people – two by bludgeoning and two by shooting. Then with over twenty-two million motor vehicles on Britain's roads, it was inevitable that accidents would occur, especially so on the fast moving motorways, where speed preceded sense. And of course there were the victims of aeroplane crashes, drug abuse, train accidents, and alcohol abuse, who sought attention. To add to the catalogue of speed travelling accidents, there were those involving another source of speed – the wind. In 1987 a storm of hurricane force hit southern England to cause damage to hundreds of thousands of buildings and blow down 15,000,000 trees. During this storm many people were injured and thirteen were killed. And of course A&E departments were called upon to administer aid to the victims of violent attacks from bombs, shootings, stabbings, fires, flooding and so on.

Early in the year the official crime figures for the previous year indicated that a record had been reached. These showed that three point eight million crimes had been committed during the twelve month period. Prisons were becoming so overcrowded that officers at several of them were refusing to accept any more remand prisoners. They said they couldn't cope any more, and that prison numbers had to return to manageable proportions. Of course, these days prisons were being filled with a variety of offenders, like sporting violators, terrorists, child molesters, drug addicts and drink drivers. And a new kind of crime was recognised as ten animal rights extremists trundled through the prison gates. They had received nine months to ten years for petrol bomb attacks on premises where animal experimentation took place.

In the days of yesteryear those who found themselves behind prison bars were mainly murderers or thieves, who served their time in conditions of hardship. Nowadays, because people had campaigned for criminals' rights prisons had changed out of all recognition. Cells were now equipped with television sets, music centres, and proper lavatories. Mess halls housed table tennis, snooker, darts and other games. Some prisons even proudly boasted gymnasiums. Then, for prisoners who wished to participate, there was the opportunity to gain a university degree. On top of this every inmate could be sure of three good meals a day, a place to bathe and a warm bed in which to sleep. One might have wondered if the hardship of prison life was any different from that of the outside, where most people were honourably ploughing their way through the days. But then, prisoners did not think that what they had was so good. An illustration of this came when inmates at a Scottish prison took an officer hostage to protest about conditions. Then, would one particular prisoner feel happy with his lot when he thought of how he had got nicked, for he had become the very first person to receive a conviction where the evidence of his crime (rape), was proven by the DNA genetic fingerprinting technique. Perhaps the general public might have thought that there should be a throw-away-the-key prison system for the people who carried out sexual offences on children, for the NSPCC announced that more than 2,300 such abusers had been reported to them in the year. During the year two sets of arrests were made of child molesters. In one case, eighteen adults were taken into custody as police and social workers attempted to break up an alleged child pornography ring. In the other, the same fate was bestowed on sixty men after a sex ring involving young boys was uncovered.

Following the previous year's housing boom, the dilemma of where to build more houses was arising. With demand for homes increasing due to the surge of people anxious to become owners, builders couldn't build fast enough. The government realised that land would be required quickly and, for this reason, announced a major relaxation of planning controls in the countryside. This would mean that the system of retaining a green belt area around towns would be no more. From now on, it would be allowed for towns to spill out further into the countryside.

1988 In the politics of 1988 the National Health Service was still a matter of great concern. After all the infusions of cash governments had prescribed over the years, it was not improving. Now yet another large sum, £90million, was to be given to the failing system. However, it appeared that the government had had enough of forking out willy nilly, and announced that a major review of the NHS would be necessary. This was after their statement that no additional funding for the NHS would be made available through taxation. But how was there to be a solution when the health of the country was failing rapidly, and the demands on hospitals and other medical outlets were increasing daily? Were hospitals to close their doors on the victims of the day's medical emergencies, for there were lots of them in 1988. Outbreaks of meningitis were occurring in various parts of the country, either claiming people's lives or making them seriously ill. The newly-discovered Legionnaires' disease was doing the same. To make matters worse, the fight against infectious diseases had become more complicated because antibiotics were not working any more. It had been found that microorganisms were growing resistant to them. Then there were epidemics of food poisoning caused by salmonella. Two major accidents had occurred in the North Sea – first the explosion of the Piper Alpha oil production platform, where one hundred and seventy men were killed. The second was an explosion at the oil rig Ocean Odyssey, where sixty-six men were rescued from the sea and one man was lost. And in a serious train accident thirty-four people were killed and 111 injured. The death toll was nearly three hundred when a horrific crime on mankind was committed. A bomb placed on a jumbo jet exploded over the town of Lockerbie causing the plane to crash to the ground. On top of all this, the number of deaths from AIDS this year was over one thousand. It seemed likely that an extra workload would be on its way too after a study had been carried out. This revealed that women who had used the oral contraceptive pill for ten years or more were four times more likely to contract cervical cancer. And how could the world of medicine shut its doors to the new discoveries that were being made. For instance, during the year a brain cell transplant operation was performed for the first time.

With the enormous responsibility that faced medical personnel, could it not be wondered how easy it would be for them to make mistakes. Might this have been the case when a Devon hospital revealed that more than 150 cancer patients might have accidentally been given excessive doses of radiation treatment. The patients were, of course, recalled to be checked for this event and the NHS would be hoping for good results to avoid the onslaught of litigation, for already during the year it had suffered great financial strain by having to pay out large sums of money in compensation claims. For instance, a boy who suffered irreversible brain damage was awarded £491,000 and a girl, who also suffered brain damage after a simple operation, was awarded £800,000.

Concern was also being shown about air travel and its safety. It was true that over the past couple of years there had been more aeroplane crashes than usual. The Civil Aviation Authority announced that the near misses and other safety concerns that were currently reported by air traffic controllers, would in future be investigated independently. One particular incident under investigation by safety officers was that of an aeroplane that successfully landed at a major airport, despite a fault which should have caused it to crash. The aircraft was an older vehicle and, when its wheels touched the ground, a wing flap failed to close. With air movements from just Manchester International Airport numbering 144,820, and with passenger lists reaching the millions, how many of these airborne travellers ever thought of the possible dangers of flying?

What of Britain's violence and drug abuse status of the time? Well, it was alarming to realise that three children, under the age of sixteen, had killed four people during the year. Sadly too, two children had lost their lives at the hands of adults. In football and rugby there had been three incidents of violence from fans (in an endeavour to curb such incidents, the government announced that identity cards would be compulsory for football spectators in England and Wales). In other areas of sport, drugs seemed to be the problem. Four British Olympic competitors were found guilty of using illegal substances to enhance their performances, and lost their qualification status. Two snooker players were banned from tournaments for the same reason. In the equine arena, as if horses did not already suffer enough at the cruel hands of man, a trainer was found guilty of administering steroids to one of his noble animals.

With the increasing demand for illegal drugs came the ever-bigger opening for opportunists to make lots of money. Drug smuggling and dealing was rife these days, and much police time was spent tracking down gangs trafficking the deadly substances. Three convictions of such organisations were made by police during the year, one of them being one of the largest drug rings in the world. Apart from seeking out and convicting drug smugglers, police had to deal with the incidental occurrences relating to the drug trade, for instance, the nationally unreported violence and killing that took place between drug dealers who fought amongst themselves to retain their patches.

Lots of other blood-letting crimes, related to drug abuse, were being committed too. Robbery and rape were top of the list here, with not only the young and agile falling victim to drug addicts, for old people were being attacked and beaten in the streets for their cash or valuables. Homes, too, were invaded in order to secure the cash required to procure addicts' fixes. It was sickening to realise that the elderly and infirm no longer had the privilege of respect in society to protect them from the evils of life. So when stories were heard of old ladies in their seventies, eighties or even nineties being raped by young men, overwhelming nausea was felt by most. It was being asked – what young man in his right mind would want to have sex with an old woman? The answer would be that only a mind overtaken by drugs would commit such a noxious crime.

Many felt that occurrences of violent crime had reached a point where something needed to be done. Opinion was that the law ought to take tougher measures, suggesting that the death penalty be brought back. Whilst capital punishment had been administered to criminals since the early beginnings of man, this changed when the death sentence was abolished in Britain for every crime other than treason. So it was a difficult debate the government of the time was asked to undertake to establish if capital punishment should be restored as the maximum sentence for murder. The outcome was that the House of Commons rejected the motion.

The saying, 'People are getting away with murder' was a popular one at this stage in history. When the news came that more than a hundred inmates at a prison rioted because they were ordered to remove pin-ups from their cells, and at another jail eighty prisoners climbed onto a roof and hurled missiles at prison staff and police, the public opinion was one of fury as to the rights criminals expected.

Mind, not all people imprisoned for breaking the law were criminals. Prison sentences were being imposed on those who failed to pay council tax, income tax, motoring fines or those who might have demonstrated, or picketed in an employment dispute, or protested for a cause. Take the thousand Greenham Common peace campaigners who received convictions for merely trying to rid the country of nuclear missiles. Triumphantly, here a Crown Court ruled that the Ministry of Defence regulations, which were used to secure police convictions, were illegal.

During the year a new vaccine was introduced called MMR. This was to be administered to small children to combat the illnesses of measles, mumps and rubella (German measles). Vaccination involves inoculating a modified virus of a disease into the body in order to produce it in a mild form so that a serious attack of it may be prevented. However, small as the inoculated dose might be, most times it is enough to cause patients to feel unwell. So, how were little children to fare when three doses of different diseases were to be injected into their bodies at the same time? And how would this inoculation affect the immune systems of children, for these three particular illnesses presented naturally in childhood to strengthen the immunity required to combat any serious illnesses they might contract in future life. However, the government were happy to know that a treble inoculation had been developed, for this would eliminate the need to inoculate children with three separate vaccines and, therefore, prove cost-effective to NHS coffers. As the MMR inoculation programme began, however, there was chaos. Part of this came about because many Health Authorities did not have enough money to become involved in the scheme, but those who did could not acquire the vaccine because it was in short supply.

Environmentally, matters were not improving. There was much concern about a mystery virus that had killed thousands of common seals in the North Sea. Scientists announced that the infection killing the seals was canine distemper, rather than environmental pollution – although the latter may have affected the seals' immune systems! A wild fowl association in Germany warned too that the virus which had caused the deaths of the seals was also killing seagulls. Then came approval from the Minister of Agriculture for the testing of a vaccine that would improve the resistance of seals to canine distemper. It was also announced by the government that £500,000 a year would be spent on research into North Sea pollution. Perhaps the researchers would do well – and save the country a lot of money – if they looked towards the oil rigs for their answers.

Still with matters of water, the government warned that measures to give Great Britain safer water, cleaner rivers and pollution-free beaches would lead to higher water charges. One could ask here, was it not down to the sheer inefficiency, and greed, of the water authorities that pollution had become a major problem in the first place? Had the public not been paying enough to safeguard the standard of water available to them?

The government also had a little confession to make. After years of denying the allegation, their experts confirmed fears that children living near nuclear plants ran an increased risk of developing cancer.

Britain was one of the sixty-five countries that signed the London Dumping Convention, with the intention of introducing a global ban on burning chemicals at sea by 1994 (perhaps by 1989 would have been better!).

And the Natural Environment Research Council's Marine Science Committee agreed to spend £1.7million on research into the effect that ozone depletion had on the climate. Who of us could forget the greenhouse effect? Comforting to know though that there would be no further damage, because it looked as if the answer was known. Earlier in the year a leading manufacturer of toiletries undertook to phase out chemicals in aerosol products blamed for causing damage to the Earth's ozone layer (in the past it had been said that it was thought that cows' farts could be a contributory factor!).

There was no answer, however, to the risks involved in the transportation of oil. This was proven yet again when a thirty eight ton oil tanker overturned on a British road, spilling six thousand gallons of petrol and one thousand gallons of diesel.

In the wealthy years of the eighties and the housing boom of 1986, it was hard to envisage that there were still people who did not have a home. The problem was such that the government of the day announced that local authorities would be given an extra £24.1million to tackle homelessness. Ironically, at this time a district council in the West Country decided to proceed with the sale of its entire housing stock. This decision was taken despite an overwhelming vote against the sales by its tenants.

'Big business' were still the main words in the world of football, and cash was flowing freely. Another record fee was recorded when a mammoth £2.8million was paid for one player. Then twelve soccer clubs threatened to form a breakaway 'super league' and accept a £32million television deal from a commercial station. In response to this the British Broadcasting Corporation, and British Satellite Broadcasting, made an offer of £42million to all ninety-two British football clubs.

We cannot leave 1988 without mention of the crazy antics of a group of gay protestors who abseiled into the chamber of the House of Lords to protest Clause 28. Clause 28 is a section of the Local Government Act 1988 that states, 'Local authorities shall not intentionally promote homosexuality, nor teach in schools that homosexuality is acceptable as a pretended family relationship.' The law was stating here that even though it had been recognised by society that homosexuality was not the crime it had been made out to be, heterosexual relationships, where procreation was achieved, was the foundation of family life – the one that Mother

Nature had intended. However, since the decriminalisation of homosexuality, gay groups had campaigned vigorously for the rights believed to be theirs. They moved about in groups shouting that the law should protect them from discrimination of any kind, allow them to marry, and permit them to have children by means of adoption or surrogacy. Whilst society had acquiesced to homosexuality being accepted in these liberated days, gay groups did not appear to favour integration into community life. They had their own clubs, pubs, carnivals and marches, where they would blatantly display their sexual preferences. The consequence of their actions was that they produced the very thing that they had been fighting against – the alienation of homosexuality from society.

1989 In 1989 several more incidents proved that Britain's environment was at risk of worsening. A Commons Select Committee on the environment published a report saying the government 'had endangered public health by failing to maintain adequate controls on toxic and radioactive waste.' Then a twenty nation survey, carried out for the United Nations, found that twenty-five per cent of forests in the United Kingdom were being killed, partly by pollution. A government-sponsored report by the Inter-governmental Panel on Climate Change, said that Britain's energy consumption could be reduced by up to sixty per cent over the next fifteen years, if the government gave higher priorities to conservation methods.

But then, the government was thinking of conservation, for hadn't it promised a £50million scheme to plant trees in central Scotland over the next twenty years? What was it thinking of, though, when it announced that our precious water industry was to be offered up for privatisation, saying that cut-price shares would be offered to people investing in the water companies serving their areas? Looking after the interest of Britons however, a European Commission publicised correspondence with the British government over the legality of certain clauses in the Water Privatisation Bill. The Commission said that the Environmental Secretary did not have powers to exempt temporarily English and Welsh water authorities from meeting European criteria on the cleanliness of water. Thank goodness that someone was trying to ensure that Brits would be saved from water poisoning because of cut-cost management of the utility. But, tut tut, the Environment Secretary didn't raise our hopes of it remaining safe when he said that it would cost £300million to meet European water standards, indicating that the word he was searching for was 'tough'. Meanwhile though, people living in a Berkshire village were taking their own steps to ensure the quality of water. They won a private prosecution against the water authority serving their area over excessive levels of pollution in the river which ran through their village.

Fighting, too, to safeguard the planet were the environmental organisations that had sprung up over the past eighteen years. Friends of the Earth, for example, launched a campaign for the reduction of carbon emissions from diesel vehicles. But still nothing was happening in the field of oil transportation, and another three accidents occurred during the year. The first was when more than two thousand gallons of crude oil leaked into a Cheshire river from an underground pipeline linking refineries in the area. The leak caused a ten mile slick in the estuary, threatening wildlife and holiday beaches. The second incident was when two oil tankers collided off the east coast of Britain to cause a twenty-mile oil slick, and inevitable death and suffering to many, many sea animals and birds. A third accident happened on the Cormorant Alpha oil platform in the North Sea, when an explosion caused the Brent Oil Field pipeline system to be shut down completely. Obviously another disaster for the sea and its occupants. After hearing of these events could we not ask at what price 'Black Gold'?

Despite the Civil Aviation Authority's measures to improve safety matters in air travel the previous year, it hadn't stopped accidents happening. In one incident a 737 aircraft suffered engine malfunction and crashed onto the M1 in the Midlands, killing forty-four of the eighty-two on board. Then the forward cargo door of a 747 plane blew off during a flight over the Pacific Ocean causing eleven people to be sucked out, and seventeen others to be injured.

On the train network, too, serious accidents were still occurring and three of them caused the deaths of seven people and injury to 138 during the year.

The weather was again claiming its fair share of fatalities and injuries. With thunderstorms and flash floods battering the South of England and Wales, at least twenty-one people were killed.

The news about football was that identity cards would have to be carried; the Legalisation of Professional Sport on Sundays was published; football managers and clubs were still bringing the game into disrepute and, businessmen were still buying large shares in football clubs. But there was one piece of news which no one would have wanted to hear. This was a tragedy, recorded as being the worse in the history of British football, that occurred at the Hillsborough stadium in Sheffield. When police opened a gate to ease the pressure of people waiting outside to see the FA Cup semi-final match between Liverpool and Nottingham Forrest, thousands of fans swarmed into the ground to cause a crush in one of the stands. Those fans already in their places were pushed forward by the volume and weight of the newcomers. The horrific consequence was that ninety-six people were killed and hundreds more injured.

In the days of the late eighties, news of bomb attacks; armed robberies; kidnapping; murder of children; murder in general; rape; and child abuse was accepted as the norm. With regard to guns, no one seemed to ponder their being, to ask, 'How do people acquire guns?' or 'Who makes them?' and 'Aren't guns illegal?' Take, for instance, the case of a man in Yorkshire who took to the streets with a gun in his hand and shot dead one man, and injured thirteen other people. Why was the law allowing incidents like these to happen? Racial agitation too was commonplace, so the news that the Notting Hill Carnival had ended with violent confrontation between police and youths did not come as any surprise.

As far as child abuse was concerned, courts had had to listen to three horrific tales of this. In one case a judge passed jail sentences on nine adult members of the same family, for abuse against their own children. Another case resulted in four men being convicted of manslaughter of a fourteen-year-old boy during a homosexual orgy. The third was one that sickened the judge so much, that he had to delay sentencing so that his own anger could subside. Had he not taken this action, the sentence for the man who had sexually abused a four-year-old boy would have been life imprisonment and not a mere ten years.

Again Britons seemed to have much to fear with regard to health. Food safety was at the top of the government's agenda and it announced that a campaign was to be launched to advise the public of the dangers here. Ironically there followed three instances of food poisoning – one of botulism, another a discovery of listeria, the third an outbreak of salmonella. In all cases either death or hospitalisation occurred. The Department of Health had also to deliver messages to twenty-two health managers with regard to waiting times and treatment. They were told that if they did not cut down their lists, they would lose the performance-related part of their pay. Hmm – that should help solve the problem. Another way of cutting down waiting lists in any hospital would be to close down the establishment completely. In an attempt to save £1.4million, a seventy-five bed hospital in London did just that. At the time it wasn't surprising to hear the Department of Health making the statement that National Health waiting lists were higher than they had been for six years.

This was the year that Britain was in danger of losing a lot of its general practitioners as well as everything else. The British Medical Association was warning that many GPs would resign rather than accept new contracts being imposed on them by the government.

Claims against the NHS were still in the headlines with the news that a ten-year-old boy was awarded £1,002,799 for brain damage incurred because of mistakes of hospital doctors. And would further litigation arise in the case of an eleven-year-old boy who died of inflammation of the brain after being vaccinated against MMR? It was said that the batch of vaccine used on this occasion was withdrawn from circulation so that analysis could be undertaken.

As to the ever-increasing AIDS epidemic, because protection schemes against the disease were not working, the Health Education Authority decided to close down its AIDS division. Then the government announced that an extra £19million would be made available to help haemophiliacs, who had contracted the HIV virus after receiving infected blood. Of course, this would never happen again because in 1988 doctors had started to use genetically engineered blood clotting agents to treat haemophiliacs. Therefore the risks of contracting AIDS through blood transfusions would be eliminated. Along with this came the announcement that the mass anonymous testing of blood for HIV would come into force in 1990.

The year also brought chilling stories of an alleged 'kidneys for cash' trade, which involved a British private hospital. When the outcome of an enquiry into the matter (ordered by the British and Turkish governments) revealed that people had been paid to donate kidneys for transplant operations, a renal surgeon and a physician were referred to the General Medical Council.

Donations too were being accepted gladly at a Manchester hospital that had become the first to open a human egg centre.

And to close the medical diary of 1989, it was announced that the hepatitis C virus had been discovered.

---

i Thomson Prentice, Science Correspondent, The Times, 20 Dec 1985

CHAPTER TWELVE

The Nineties – A–D

Animals

Though twentieth century man proclaimed his superiority by stating that he was 'civilised', his victimisation of more vulnerable creatures of the planet continued. Cruel animal experimentation in this century was taken as man's right in his endeavour to pursue his own well-being. Agonising tests were performed on animals, from mice to chimpanzees, to determine the safety to humans of a range of man-made products. From the hundreds of millions of experiments carried out yearly, here are a few:

- In sleep deprivation experiments cats were kept awake by placing them on a narrow piece of wood and sealing them in fifty-gallon drums of water for twenty-four hours. If the cats attempted to lie down to sleep they fell into the water and drowned. If they survived, their skulls were sliced and their brains poked out to be analysed.

- Experiments to test man-made joints were made by way of mice. Whilst their little innocent bodies were fully conscious, their tiny bones were broken and then examined to discover how they functioned.

- Rats, rabbits, dogs, guinea pigs and monkeys had substances dripped into their eyes; poured onto their shaven skin, or forced down their throats to test how cosmetic, toiletry and household products affected them. Alternatively the animals' cages were filled with just the fumes of such products. These unsedated creatures wore restraining devices so they could not escape the pain, and some animals broke either their necks or backs trying to retreat from their torture. What resulted from these tests for the animals was blindness, burns, mutilation and bleeding from the nose and mouth.

- One hormone replacement therapy (HRT) drug was made from the urine of pregnant horses (a substance that is particularly high in oestrogen). Pregnant mares, selected for the programme, were housed in barns in individual stalls where harnesses were suspended from the roof. Into these went the animal's hindquarters, so that their urine would cascade into waiting receptacles. Some horses might develop chafing and sores caused by the urine collection devices. Others might suffer the same injury by rubbing against the sides of their stalls when they were too small to allow the animals to lie down comfortably. When the mare's foals were born they were sold off cheaply because they were of little use to the urine farmers. From here they were fattened up quickly and then slaughtered – usually for dog food.

In food production, too, animals were forced to endure whatever man handed out to them. On factory farms cows, pigs and chickens were nothing more than machines. They were born in the cramped quarters of dark sheds, where they were raised unable to move their limbs or stretch a wing. Their living conditions caused them to suffer injuries and disease, and their diet included cement dust, shredded newspaper, recycled animal waste laced with antibiotics, pesticides and hormones (all of which were passed on to consumers). These animals were deprived of the chance to play, to enjoy the air, or develop a loving natural relationship with others of their own kind. They would never hear a warm word or feel a sensitive hand. The 850 million a year British animals raised and slaughtered this way would never realise their right to happiness.

When it came to making money in a big way, there was no need to look further than the canine arena. With pedigree puppies selling at a premium of hundreds of pounds, unscrupulous dealers mated the dogs in their care until they died. Until then, when their puppy-producing days were over, many of the dogs lived in appallingly cruel conditions.

In the twentieth century there was really no end to the torturous exploitation of animals which, in some cases, put species at risk of extinction. For example, gorillas were hunted to capacity with their flesh being sold for bush meats; their hands for ashtrays and their heads for ornaments. The prehistoric turtle too was meeting the same fate. The murderers of tigers reaped large profits from the sale of their skins and heads for rugs, their bones for aphrodisiacs and food recipes. Elephants were slain solely to acquire their ivory tusks which were turned into trinkets, or piano keys.

Even the creatures of the sea had no refuge from the greedy hand of man.

During the latter half of the twentieth century fishing the seas was performed by way of drift nets measuring two and a half miles long. Whilst the aim of the fishing exercise was to procure sea flesh palatable to man, as the fishing boats trawled the nets behind them, all manner of sea life was engulfed in the traps which scooped them up. The use of these nets in high seas also meant inescapable death to the dolphins which were ensnared by them. As well as pointlessly killing the sea creatures which were of little use to man, drift net fishing meant that whole communities of edible fish were being annihilated. This fact seemed to have escaped clever twentieth century man until it was discovered that there were not many fish left for him to catch. However a Sea Fish Conservation Act came into being and fishing limits were imposed. This didn't go down well in the industry and in 1993 both British and French fishermen took it upon themselves to protest their objections to the ruling. The environmental group Greenpeace recognised success after a fifteen year fight when, in 1998, the European Union banned the use of drift nets by European fishing fleets. This followed their success in 1992 when a world-wide ban on the use of high seas large drift nets was imposed. River fish were much at risk too, and in the nineties thousands of tons of them were killed. The deaths here resulted from poisons such as cyanide, hydrochloric acid, sewage, caustic soda, slurry and other unknown chemicals being leaked into the waters.

With so much cruelty being imposed on animals it was not surprising that small minorities of people found the courage to come to their aid. After all, animals couldn't speak for themselves and say, "Please don't hurt me," could they? In one instance, in 1995, a group of supporters of animal rights protested against the export of live calves. The police were called in to sort out the problem and found themselves clashing with demonstrators. The port organising the export had listened to the animal rights protesters' views, and decided that the export of live animals would cease. However the law came into play as High Court judges ruled that bans by ports and airports on the export of live animals for slaughter, was illegal! During the protest, which continued after this ruling, a lady animal rights demonstrator, who was trying to stop a lorry carrying veal calves for export, died. She fell underneath the vehicle.

Another human activity of this century involving cruelty to animals was that of blood sports. With the purpose of killing deer or foxes, men and women on horseback would chase them for many miles until they were cornered. Then the hounds that had preceded the hunt, to make them run with fright, would be sent in to kill the victims. Needless to say it did not take much of an attack to kill a fox or a deer that was still alive at the end of the chase, because these animals would already be near to death from fear and exhaustion. It had been known for deer to meet their death by falling into ravines as they tried to jump them in an endeavour to escape their persecutors. In 1995 Somerset County Council imposed a ban on deer hunting – realising the cruelty of the 'sport'. However a Court of Appeal ruled that this ban was unlawful. The law intervened again in 1997 after the National Trust for Scotland had decided to ban fox hunting on its land two years earlier. However, in this case, a ruling could not be imposed as the land did not belong to the State. All the High Court could do was to advise the Trust to reconsider its ban on hunting. At the time, the same court granted West Country deer hunters the right to seek a further hearing, to challenge the legality of the ban imposed by Somerset County Council. Because of the public's demand on the government to stop hunting, 1995 saw a Private Member's Bill in the House of Commons where the vote was in favour of banning all forms of hunting, including fishing and shooting. Fruition was realised in 1997 when Members of Parliament voted to ban hunting with dogs, and the National Trust decided to uphold its ban on fox hunting. However, none of this went down well with country dwellers who screamed that this would diminish the revenue received from hunters. In 1997 tens of thousand of them held a countryside rally in London, to protest against the proposed legislation to ban fox hunting. The contention was that the killing of deer and foxes was essential to the well-being of the countryside, as the animals themselves were predators. It was maintained that hunting the animals down, killing them, then wiping their blood on one's face, was a humane method of reducing their numbers.

But then twentieth century man showed so little respect for animals and claimed to imagine them to be immune from suffering. This point was proven when, in 1997, the National Trust felt the need to commission a survey which might reveal how deer react to being hunted. The findings of this seemed to come as a surprise to many and caused a talking point. It said that there was strong scientific evidence that deer suffer high levels of stress when hunted. Would it take yet another survey to discover how much pain was endured, before reaching death, for the two hundred and seventy-seven creatures which were the failed attempts of sheep cloning. Or would the news in 1997, stating that the first mammal clone named Dolly the sheep had been created, eliminate all else but the superiority of man's science?

Birds

It had been noticed by many that there were not a lot of birds to be heard in the days of the nineties. Regardless, it came as a shock to learn just how much bird life had been lost. In 1997 a report, commissioned by the Environment Department, showed a sharp decline in at least twelve varieties of farmland birds in the last twenty-five years. Then more revelations came from the Royal Society for the Protection of Birds who, after undertaking a huge survey, pronounced that half of the seventy species monitored by them had declined since 1970. Little wonder that the voices of the common house sparrow and the tree sparrow had become a rare sound, for their numbers had declined by forty-three per cent and a massive ninety-five per cent respectively. As for the other twenty-seven species of birds monitored, the percentages registered showed declines from twenty-seven per cent to seventy-eight per cent.

There were several reasons for the sad loss of Britain's bird life. First there had been the farming community's decision to rip up the hedgerows that surrounded their fields, to make way for the giant machines that would plant and reap their harvests. These hedgerows provided homes and nesting places for birds – the sparrow in particular. Farming, too, was responsible for taking away the source of food for birds. The reason for this was, because the British public had developed the desire to be provided with unblemished fruit and vegetables, farmers had to constantly spray crops with chemicals to kill invading insects. This meant that there were no live insects for birds to eat. There were plenty of dead ones lying about but, unlike human consumers, birds would not eat anything contaminated with poison.

The vast road and airport building that had taken place since 1970 had also robbed the birds of the trees and bushes that were their homes and source of food. Other factors related to maintaining a strong economy were also to blame for the decrease in Britain's wildlife. For example, in 1996 a European Court of Justice ruled that in 1993 Britain had acted illegally by excluding a special protection area on a river reserve listed under the European Union's Bird Directive. It suggested that Britain favoured economic interests over interests of the environment. In the same year leading environmental groups published a report saying that three hundred wildlife sites were under threat from policies pursued by water companies, industry and agriculture. In response the government published a strategy for protecting the rarest and most threatened life forms in Britain (did this include the human species?).

In areas that housed airports there was a policy stating that there should be no trees or bushes planted in the vicinity where birds could nest. It was well known that if flocks of birds were sucked into the engines of low flying aeroplanes, the vehicles would plummet to the ground because of engine failure.

Perhaps the meanest method of discouraging bird life was the one adopted by some town councils. In an endeavour to save money, many of the parkland bushes, homes to hundreds and hundreds of birds, were mercilessly cut down to the ground. This ritual was performed to save the need to pay gardeners. Then the public in general was partly responsible for the decline of the country's wildlife, for using chemicals in gardens to kill unwanted insects, which meant that the birds' natural food chain was gone.

Late twentieth century environmentalists were saying that, probably, the only wildlife that could survive the future would be crows and bluebottles.

Children

Whereas the natural method all animals have of deterring their young from committing wrong is to cuff them when they do, late twentieth century society frowned upon this moderate physical chastisement of young human animals as it was considered to be bullying. Instead it was believed that children should be coaxed into good behaviour with kind words such as, 'Please don't do that,' or 'Put that down please.' Alternatively, to explain to children the nasty consequences that might arise from their misdemeanours. However, what these reasoning methods caused the children of the day was confusion, for they had not yet developed the ability to reason as adults do.

Because there were no hard and fast rules being taught to children as to what they were allowed to do, and what they were not, the young of the nineties took this to mean that they could do as they pleased. They also knew about their rights as children not to receive punishment, which meant that they could commit naughtiness or vandalism, and use abusive language or violence against adults, without fear of censure. For adults, however, a fear was born and this was that children might bring accusations of assault against them if they attempted to challenge their bad behaviour. Then, there were so many child protection laws in force that even the police were not allowed to reprimand kids who were either breaking laws or causing a nuisance. There were many incidents where children as young as five were saying to policemen, 'Fuck off, there's nothing you can do to me'. Neither were the police allowed to lay hands on young people in case they should be accused of sexual motivation. As far as the latter was concerned, no one escaped the nagging finger of those who whispered 'child abuse'. Even parents of young children had to be very careful how they physically touched their offspring, for, with large dolls as models, there were times when kiddies would be asked, 'Show us where Daddy touches you when you are playing'. Old folks too were at risk of suspicion of child molestation and had to abandon the age-old tradition of watching children play, chatting to them, or inviting them into their homes for a visit. The same suspicion applied to dear old Father Christmas too, for now it was not allowed for him to lift children into his arms to deposit them on his lap when they visited his festive grottos. In future, children would have to stand aloft of him to voice their Christmas wishes, instead of whispering them into his ear as they had always done. And of course, this was to prevent allegations of child abuse being brought against him by parents or guardians.

These child policies also meant that schooling was a tough assignment, both for teachers and children. With potential child abuse deeply ingrained in minds, education authorities had to make rules to protect their staff from any allegations of the offence. The directive for staff was that there should be no physical contact with children under any circumstance. This meant that if a child became upset teachers, or school helpers, were not allowed to comfort them with an embrace. If a small child had difficulty pulling up knickers, or fastening trousers after going to the toilet there would be no one to help because adults were not permitted to touch their clothing. Even the application of sun protection cream to a youngster's skin was forbidden to these guardians of children. And, when schools staged open activities such as plays or sports days, teachers were responsible for ensuring that parents and other attending family members did not take photographs or video recordings of the events. This policy was enforced to deter any possible family paedophile from taking pictures of children for reasons other than to store them for posterity.

As for education itself, well there was the National Curriculum and school league tables. These had come along under the Education Reform Act of 1988, in a barrage of long, meaningless words. It was said that this new Act would bring about substantial changes in education – and indeed it did. The bottom line for children was that they were all expected to reach the same academic achievement at the same time. Measuring the children's capabilities meant that testing them at frequent intervals was necessary. Even children as young as seven bore the responsibility of trying to attain the 'cloning' requirements. When the National Curriculum was well established the league tables followed. These started in 1993 with the aim of highlighting the examination results of every state school. The ideal was to make schools accountable to pupils (who needed good results to meet university offers), to parents and governors, and to successive governments. With reference to this last, schools would be reviewed by way of an inspection system. Included in the Education Reform Act was the option for individual schools to remove themselves from local authority control by taking charge of their own management and finance. Instead of schooling embracing Mother Nature's plans for children to be taught how to find their own capabilities, learn the difference between right and wrong and develop in their own right, the exercise now had a new vista. This was one that seemed to disregard the child totally in favour of a regime designed to take education into the competitiveness of big business.

Government-determined policies, however, did not function without problems. Surprisingly in 1996 it was reported that half of all eleven-year-olds had failed to reach the expected standards when they sat National Curriculum school tests in English and Maths the previous year. In the same year teachers in a junior school took strike action. They refused to work because of a ten-year-old boy they judged to be out of control. The school closed for nearly two weeks. In another school teachers threatened to strike unless sixty pupils, deemed by them to be unteachable, were excluded. After being closed for a week the school re-opened with a new head teacher in command. He made the decision to exclude twelve of the nuisance pupils, and suspend twenty-three others. In response to the situation the Education Secretary said that corporal punishment was a useful deterrent. However, the Prime Minister's reply was it would 'not be brought back into schools.'

Perhaps the alternative to restoring discipline in schools would be to give cash prizes for behaving oneself. For indeed, teams of American pioneers were currently working on a system whereby rewards of £200 a year were being received by star pupils. If it were seen that the project worked well – long-term – then it was thought that Britain, too, would start to buy good behaviour from children. Would this cash incentive be used to bribe school kids away from taking drugs too, for this underage pursuit was rife at this point.

As many late twentieth century mothers, either out of necessity or desire, had to go to work. they demanded that places be provided where care would be given to their young children. Private nurseries sprang up quickly and enormous fees were charged for their services. However, only high earners could afford to pay the price for these facilities, leaving low paid workers relying on the government to provide childcare centres. The perfect solution for the ladies of the day would be that all employers provide crèches for their young offspring. It did not seem amiss for them to campaign for these facilities to be created in large stores also, leaving them free of infant demands whilst they shopped. In the meantime they had to make do with the limited nurseries and playschools provided by local councils. Alas, even in these out of school centres, children were not free of the testing ethos and were monitored frequently to assess their ability to play. Then there were council-run after school clubs which catered for children who had nowhere else to go until mum finished work. Here again children were subjected to the watchful eyes of those engaged in measuring their successes, or failures, as people.

Throughout the history of man, in accordance with nature's intent, children born to the world had looked for security from the two people who had given them life. With mother and father as protectors, they lived together in a place called home. However, in the nineties this procedure was considered old hat. In these days parents' needs came before children's, and with the sanctity of marriage gone it was so convenient to move on to the next partner if all was not going well. Modern couples did not believe in staying together for the sake of the children; in fact, they scorned the idea, saying that it was much better for kids to grow up independent of parents. Hence the responsibilities associated with parenthood diminished tremendously, with late twentieth century Britain seeing an increase in one-parent families. The young of the day did not have to worry any more about engaging in sexual intercourse that might result in pregnancy. Both male and female parties knew that, if a baby was produced from their intimacy, the State would look after it. A rent-free house, together with a weekly income, and a host of benefits, would be provided for mother and child without either parent having to provide one penny towards the child's upkeep. Many of these babies were parented by youngsters who had not yet taken up employment since leaving school (statistics of the day revealed that Britain had the highest rate of teenage pregnancy in Europe). One-parent families were also created when couples living together as partners or in wedlock, decided to end their relationship. Once again it was a generally assumed notion that the state would be on hand to pick up the pieces by providing housing, and financial aid, to the parent left in charge of the child or children.

Children of broken relationships had to cope with many complexities. With their parents having arranged visiting rights between themselves, kids found that they were to be shuffled around between Mum and Dad. Weekdays might be spent with their mother, and weekends with their father – or vice versa. Or either Dad or Mum might see their children for only one night a week, or once every two or three weeks. Some children, however, spent the same number of days at Mum's house as they did Dad's. In the cases of re-marriage, or re-partnership, children might be asked to address a new spouse as 'Dad' or 'Mum', leaving kids asking, 'Why have I got two dads or mums?' and 'Who's my real dad or mum?' (sadly, too, this was a question they might soon be asking of same sex parents, for homosexual couples were calling for the laws of nature to be changed so that those of the land could be revised to favour their adoption of children). Sacrificing one's own life in favour of offspring did not come into the equation of modern parenthood. Many mums and dads of the day were not prepared to put their lives on hold, just because they had borne children. They felt it their right to carry on living life as they had always done, without being hampered by parental responsibilities. This meant that babysitters were recruited to take charge of children, whilst Mum or Dad pursued their own pleasures (which could range from a night out with the girls or the lads, to holidays abroad). Of course it was a convenient arrangement, in cases of partnership or marriage breakdown, that the stay-at-home parent be allocated care of his or her children, whilst the other went off to do her or his own thing.

Whereas children of the past had filled their thoughts with imaginary places and people which took them on journeys into the unknown, the excitement for late twentieth century kids came ready made. Because of the fear of allowing children to play outside together, in case they were approached by ill-meaning strangers, fun was mainly confined to the home. Here kids would sit alone in front of a television set and watch children's programmes or videos. Alternatively, they might choose to use a computer where they could acquire information or, play computer games (most of which were of the violent variety). If there was more than one child in the family, then playing with one's brother or sister in the back garden was permitted. But on the whole the children of the day had lost the capacity to create their own fun. Their imaginations had been sapped by the ready-made entertainment always on hand. Even family outings were generally of the organised variety, with trips taking them to expensive theme parks, water parks, bowling alleys, activity centres, etc. It was thought that, unless money was being spent profusely, children would very quickly utter the dreaded words, 'I'm bored' (which would send their guardians into panic).

Because of the litigation culture of the day, physical activities thought to be dangerous for children were denied them. It was the prime objective of schools, and other organised institutions, to prevent accidents happening to children (to avoid being sued by parents). Therefore ball games, climbing, conker competitions and all other boisterous adventures were being banned from sponsored premises.

Another area where schoolchildren might experience hurt was that of bullying. Several victims had been driven to suicide during the nineties because of the abuse they had received from contemporaries. Head teachers were bound to investigate all allegations of bullying, brought about by parents, and administer severe action to offenders found guilty of physical abuse – for example, expulsion from school. However, the word 'bully' was now applied to kids who indulged in pranks, and mischievousness, once associated with normal childhood behaviour. Things such as pulling another's hair; sticking out one's tongue at someone; snatching a school satchel; breaking another's pencil; pushing someone over and so on and so forth.

Crime and the Law

Britain's murder convictions for the last decade of the twentieth century numbered 248 and were split as follows:-

By shooting	-	54
By stabbing	-	54

By decapitation	-	3
By other methods	-	58
Murder by children	-	14
Murder of children	-	65

Fifty convictions were made for sexual abuse on children, where a small proportion of victims suffered death at the hands of their torturers. Arsonists too caused death and injury and convictions here numbered nineteen. Many people were killed or injured when 147 IRA bombs exploded over the ten year period. Four people were arrested for kidnapping, and there were a couple of convictions for crimes of rape and sexual assaults on the old[i]. These figures would have risen enormously if all murderers and abusers had been caught and brought to justice, for in the nineties vicious crime was rife. Week in, week out, bodies of murdered people were found, old people beaten up, women raped, but many assailants escaped undiscovered. Robberies came on a daily basis, with hundreds of houses being burgled, cars stolen, goods taken from warehouses, shops or container lorries. Cash was inveigled from banks, either by armed robbery or ram-raiding (this involved driving a heavy vehicle through the wall of a bank to release the wall safes). According to statistics seventy per cent of robberies were drug related. Once again the conviction rate was low in comparison to the numbers of robberies committed.

One might have possibly shuddered to look at the number of children convicted of murder. In 1961 two eight-year-old boys killed a little boy, and in 1968 a ten-year-old girl killed two children, hence murder by children was nothing new. However in the space of the ten years of the nineties fourteen children took the lives of others. In one particular case two boys admitted in court that they had killed a man 'for fun'.

It could not be forgotten that Britain's police force was armed with guns and CS gas and had, not surprisingly, shot dead half a dozen people and gassed one man. Neither was there anything new with regard to violent rioting, and here sixteen cases made headline news. And, following the pattern of the eighties, drug smuggling and dealing offences were thriving. Another lucrative crime that had arrived in Britain was that of people smuggling. Daily, organised gangs would ferry illegal immigrants into the country. Although these people had paid their couriers enormous fees for their passage, they were conveyed in ship cargo holds or unventilated lorries. In a couple of incidents during the decade many immigrants died before they reached Britain. There were also organised gangs who would ferry illegal immigrants into the country *without* asking for a fee to be paid. However these passengers were children, from the age of three upwards, who were brought to Britain by the gangs to be utilised for profit. After having been kidnapped from their countries of origin, or bought from their parents, these children would be sited on British streets to beg for money, pick pockets or become prostitutes.

What was Britain doing to combat the ever-increasing crimes of the day? Well, people were being encouraged, via government agencies, to secure their homes and cars more fervently. The line was 'put locks on your windows; bolts, chains and mortise locks on your doors; security lights on the outside of your house, and burglar alarms on your walls'. In respect of cars, they were urged not to leave anything on seats for burglars to see, and never to leave doors unlocked. Steering wheel clamps were favoured as, too, were immobilisers and alarms. With regard to the personal safety of people, they were encouraged not to go out alone at night, or to carry a panic alarm if they did. For shops and warehouses, security in the form of heavy metal shutters and closed-circuit television was advised.

There had been three violent attacks on school premises during the decade. The first was when a man, using a fire extinguisher as a flame thrower, attacked a class sitting exams and three pupils were seriously hurt. The second attack came when a man shot dead sixteen children and their teacher, injured twelve other children and two teachers, and then shot himself. The third incident was when a man with a machete attacked infants in a playground and injured three children and four adults. Because of these attacks, fears for children's safety were growing. School security had to be tightened, making it essential that all doors be locked as soon as the children were inside the premises. Again closed-circuit television was encouraged, as was the erection of metal fencing. Some schools went as far as installing metal bars around the doors. With locked doors and metal bars, schools were beginning to resemble prisons.

Other mass attacks on folks had happened and in one of these cases a man stabbed fifteen people in a department store. Another incident happened when a man entered a church whilst a service was being conducted, and injured eleven people with a samurai sword. Then there were a couple of incidents of people being held hostage by men brandishing guns. Apart from installing more closed-circuit television in stores and public places, what else could be done to safeguard the public from attack?

What other action was being taken by the government of the day to reduce criminal activity? Well – in 1996 a firearms amnesty was arranged to take place (this is where the general public can hand over to the police any guns they might have without fear of prosecution for having the things in the first place). There followed a House of Commons motion to impose a total ban on handguns, but this was defeated. However, in the following year another vote was taken whereupon it was agreed to ban .22 pistols, making ownership of all handguns illegal. Another measure announced by the government was that they intended to cut down on youth crime by forcing parents to take responsibility for the behaviour of their children. However, parents might have asked how they could achieve this when the right to discipline their children into good behaviour had been taken from them by government decree.

Meanwhile, police forces were endeavouring to bring criminals to justice to illustrate that crime doesn't pay. However, their efforts were being thwarted constantly by the fear that they might not have enough evidence to bring about convictions. This was because during the decade there had been several incidents where people imprisoned for criminal offences had made appeals to the courts, and had had their sentences quashed. In these cases the judge's summing up generally said there was lack of substantial evidence. In one case a judge halted the trial of a man accused of murdering a woman, as he strongly criticised the undercover police operations which had led to his arrest. The consequences of court intervention was that the police were made liable to pay compensation to people claiming wrongful arrest. During the nineties there were half a dozen such cases which resulted in the police paying out approximately £500,000 in claims. So they had to tread very carefully to ensure that their evidence could satisfy the protocol of the law courts – and avoid the possibility of their becoming the accused themselves.

Perhaps this news item of the day might portray the absurdity of the law of the nineties:

> *A young man was on a bus with three pals returning from a night out when the vehicle was boarded by three men who proceeded to rob them. Other people on the bus alerted the driver to the situation and he bravely took action. After securing the door of his vehicle he switched off all internal and external lights and drove on. He knew that by doing this he would draw attention to people on the outside – hopefully, the police. Sure enough, it worked and two unmarked police cars were observed to be accompanying the bus – one in front and one behind. The officers concerned cottoned on to the fact that the bus driver's intention was not to bring the vehicle to a halt until it reached the terminus, and they were bright enough to alert police controllers to have more police officers waiting there. When the bus came to a standstill the criminals were arrested by several police officers who also took statements from all the passengers aboard the bus. With the criminals having been caught red-handed and there being witnesses galore – what more could be wanted by the law to send these three lads to prison? However – it wasn't enough. The lads appeared next day at the magistrates court and pleaded not guilty – whereby they were granted a hearing in the Crown Court!*

Perhaps in police arrests of the future there might be convincing evidence to offer the courts as to the guilt of the accused. This would be from the world's first national computerised DNA database set up in 1995 by the Forensic Science Service. The aim of this device was to assist the police in criminal investigations.

It was not only the law enforcers who had to answer to the law courts, for the government, too, had to come to heel sometimes. When the Home Secretary announced plans to end the early automatic release of prisoners, and ensure longer prison sentences for habitual criminals, it didn't go down well with one Lord Chief Justice. He said that longer sentences would not deter criminals, and that mandatory minimum sentences would be inconsistent with the interests of justice. Comments from other sources described the government plans as 'short-sighted and irresponsible'.

Perhaps the government's plans for the long-term reform of prison conditions would be more palatable to all, especially to the inmates who instigated seventeen prison riots in the years of the nineties, causing death and injury to themselves and custodial officers; and concern for the private companies who currently managed eleven out of Britain's one hundred and thirty-nine overcrowded prisons.

Compensation

From 1990 to 1999 billions of pounds were paid out in compensation. Whereas famous people, and notoriously rich business folk, had always regarded it as their right to take out libel suits against anyone uttering words they didn't like, the fashion was growing. Now football personnel were joining the suing fraternity and a newspaper found itself liable to pay a very large sum of money to a football manager who had cried 'libel'. Also, sportsmen were taking libel actions against each other for one thing or another. Then, a television broadcasting company had to make a £1.5million apology to a drug company because of the offence that bad publicity had caused it. In the area of damages the National Health Service paid out nearly £20million to three children who suffered brain damage whilst undergoing hospital attention. An award was given to a man who suffered post-traumatic stress disorder, after seeing people crushed to death at the Hillsborough football disaster. Forty police officers also received considerable compensation for the same reason. A rugby player, who was paralysed after a scrum collapsed was awarded damages against the referee of the game. It was said that the ref had failed to exercise reasonable skill in preventing scrum collapses! Then a former footballer received a lot of money from a football team and its captain for the negligence which had ended his career. An actor's family was paid compensation in respect of his death, which happened during a filming accident. Relatives of eleven people killed in the air bomb disaster accepted an out of court settlement from the airline company. A man received an enormous sum of money after being involved in a car crash. A nuclear power station parted with lots of cash to a former employee's wife after her husband died of leukaemia. There were three cases where the police had to pay large sums to people who claimed wrongful imprisonment. And, in a landmark judgement, a High Court ruled that a former owner of an asbestos factory was liable to compensate people who lived near the site, and had developed cancer caused by asbestos dust.

There were a couple of compensation claims yet to be heard as the chimes to herald the coming of the new millennium rang out. These were:

- the case of a hundred thousand miners who had developed lung diseases and were claiming compensation from their employers who, they say, failed to take responsible steps to minimise the harmful effects of coal dust;
- a boxer who had been given permission by the High Court to sue the British Boxing Board of Control for the brain damage he suffered in a fight.

(But then, neither of these claims could be as wacky as the one in 1988, which gained the sympathy of the judge hearing the case. He awarded damages of £23,632 to a family who stated that a group of Hells Angels had moved in next door to them, and had driven them from their home).

There had been many compensation payments which did not hit the headlines in the nineties – only the big ones made this grading. Other claims for damages had varied from people alleging that they had fallen on badly repaired roads, to those claiming discrimination in the workplace, etc.

It was true to say, that by the end of the twentieth century, Britain had developed a compensation culture. So much so that companies, intent on gaining money by way of other peoples' misfortunes, were materialising out of thin air. They invested in television advertising, encouraging folk to contact them if they had had a recent accident. With their slogans 'no claim – no gain' they soon had people clamouring on their phones, eager to relate their mishaps and grievances, especially so as the companies were promising that if they did not win their compensation claims there would be no fee to pay. It was not only television which sold these companies' images. The newspapers, too, carried advertisements aimed at the people who might want to use these law firms to cash in. It didn't stop there, for in hospital and doctors' waiting rooms, pamphlets were ready to be picked up and notices waiting to be read. The messaging here was, 'Had an accident? – make a claim'. When the 'ambulance chasers' reached people's front doorsteps many people slammed doors in disgust as the man or lady standing there asked, 'Have you had an accident recently?' Even in the streets, folk were being accosted by those who sprang out from nowhere to ask the same question.

Illustrating the grotesque lunacy of the 1990s' compensation culture there were reports of the following incidents:

- a mother who requested to give birth to twins was suing the fertility centre she had attended, because she had given birth to triplets;
- the parents of a brain-damaged child were suing the driver who had knocked him down. The insurers of the driver counteracted the claim by saying, that they would sue the parents of the child, and the child-minder, for allowing the child to go out alone on his bike in the first place; and
- families were attempting to sue airline companies after the death of kinfolk who had travelled by air, and developed deep vein thrombosis.

As the country was beginning to sag under the weight of litigation claims, many folk wondered what silly demands would come next. Whilst insurance companies were paying out millions of pounds in respect of damage to people's property and vehicles caused by the hurricane winds and floods of recent years, compensation for personal suffering was not catered for. So! Why not find someone, other than themselves, to blame for the weather conditions that created havoc in their lives – and sue accordingly.

Computers

By the time the nineties arrived the nickname 'computer friendly' had become obsolete, for now, because systems worldwide operated by means of this technology, it was essential for all in the workplace to be 'computer proficient'. Necessary was it, too, for children to be schooled to use these machines, for the computer would be their teacher of the future. The technology, which was deemed infallible, had the capacity to store no end of text, so it was with confidence that man entrusted the extent of his knowledge to its keeping. For record purposes alone, computerisation was the ideal engine for storing and updating information.

With security at a premium in the nineties it was considered essential for details of every UK resident to be held in computerised databases, for identification purposes. To this end, when making an enquiry of any kind, from any source, one would need to relate one's name, address, birth date and telephone number. If these details did not align to those held in the database the enquiry would be terminated. The basic information on UK citizens stored in databases came from various sources.

This could be gleaned from electoral registers, censuses, and the facts related by oneself in answer to official questioning. However the database technique did not end in the security department, for it had proven a great asset to those who wished to sell their wares, or information. To gain the latter, companies would commission surveys to be carried out on their behalf. These involved interviewers stopping people in shopping venues to ask their views, preferences, financial status, desires, etc, etc. The alternative was that these details be secured by means of telephone contact. Of course, as no one would willingly offer their time to answer questions, the companies enticed them to do so by offering a variety of rewards. From here people would be plagued with junk mail dropping through their letterboxes daily and wonder how the senders could know that they liked continental holidays, boats, shoes, river cruises, fast cars, nice clothes and so on and so forth. Surveys were not the only way of squeezing personal information from people, for they happily 'revealed all' when applying for store cards operated by credit companies. Then there was identity theft, when crooks would steal information on people by any means. Surprisingly, too, there were many GP practices that gladly sold on details of their patients' ailments to companies marketing various health aids.

Computers were proving to be the superior power that was envisaged, for there were many miraculous tasks that they were capable of performing. For example, in 1997 a machine called Deep Blue beat the world chess champion in a game ('twixt man and beast) in America. Then, computers could compose symphonies; create pictures; design buildings; write stories; predict the future; work out problems; diagnose illnesses, etc. etc. At this point it might appear that all man's talents and aspirations would soon wane into insignificance, for computers seemed ready to supersede him. This would render his reason for living to function only as an extended piece of technology.

Like every other life form, computers needed a mother to bring them into being and maintain their progress. In this case, mother was a very hot and buxom wench, named a server, who might occupy vast amounts of space. Mum's size would depend on the number of offspring she needed to feed, with the heat produced signifying how hard she had to work to do this. In very large organisations, where computers numbered hundreds, many mummies were housed together in large areas – say a whole floor of a building, or even two or three levels. As for single computers at home, these functioned via a hard drive when connected to a brainy motherboard.

Computerisation was the mainstream of life, so much so that the government was pouring funding into a scheme aimed at creating more specialist computer teachers. Also, as there had been a prominent additional advancement to the system, it was envisaged that everyone in the land would need to be 'computerised'. The little darling that no one would want to live without was called the internet. This system was initiated in 1973 by an American agency intent on developing computers to communicate across multiple linked networks. The internet grew throughout the eighties, permitting email, but it was not until the beginning of the nineties and the invention of the World Wide Web that the system really took off. By the end of 1991 the Internet had grown to include some five thousand networks in over thirty-six countries. These served over 700,000 host computers that were used by over four million people, and rapid growth was predicted. It was thought by some that servers would either have to get bigger, or multiply, to cope with the hundreds of thousands more computers that were anticipated. And of course this would mean that even more electricity would be needed to feed them. But, as the internet system operated by way of the telecommunication network, when it grew would existing power lines be sufficient to cope with the onslaught, or would the seabed be forced to undergo the trauma of having more crushing cables laid on its surface?

Gaining access to internet facilities would mean that one would first have to buy a computer, and all the accessories that were needed (which would burden the credit card somewhat, but delight machine manufacturers no end). Then, one would need to connect computers to telephone sockets (use of which would increase telephone bills enormously but create tumultuous joy for communication companies). Then, after paying a monthly subscription fee (to a telephone company of one's choosing) for the privilege of going online, and armed with the standard equipment of a browser and a mouse, the magic of internet could begin. There was nothing that could not be learned, or bought, via this fascinating network. Researching writers, students, marketers, etc., could save themselves laborious hours of reading by choosing to access information by way of the internet. However, seldom was it questioned as to why, on many occasions, information received differed from website to website. Therefore the bigger question, 'Which version can we take to be valid?' was never asked. Holidays, air/rail/bus/show tickets could be booked on the spot; entertainment venues rapidly bought online or, if the desire was to listen to current pop music, then downloading was the method of achieving this. Not only could one listen to the music of the day, the computer was capable of recording it too – that was, if the necessary equipment for the purpose had been bought and fitted. (This procedure was not welcomed by music producing companies, as it meant that their sales of CDs plummeted.) Then, for those with a more serious shopping objective, the Net could open up a world where babies and children, brides and grooms, human organs, surrogate mothers, etc., could be bought. Sometimes one might stumble on a World Wide Web site which showed tantalising titbits of bestiality, child or general pornography; bomb making practices; assassination procedures; body enhancing programmes and so on and so forth, and be asked to pay a fee on the spot (by credit card) if one wanted to see more. (Of course, those who were regular visitors to these obscene sites didn't have to stumble because they knew their exact location.) The internet had become the shop window of the world and there was nothing that could not be bought if one had a credit card to hand. Busy people found it a boon to surf the Net, instead of legging it around the shops, to search for goodies to buy. Weekly food shopping could be done without moving from one's chair, as too could buying promiscuous underwear; wheelbarrows; clothes; sex toys; books; underground piping; the services of a prostitute, etc., etc.

Internet chat rooms were a favourite when it came to searching for companionship, love, friendship or sexual interludes. People would spend hours on end 'chatting' to people they had never met, by way of computer messaging. Then, often the two might quickly decide to meet because of the attraction they had developed towards each other (even if they lived continents apart). Sadly the chat rooms encouraged lies to be told and legs to be pulled, especially so amongst the young where teenagers might add years to their age whilst endeavouring to attract an internet suitor. In the late nineties there were several incidents when young teenagers left their homes to join with people many years their senior after meeting them on the Net.

Whilst the internet in the main presented itself as a marketing tool to promote spending, there were web sites available for the sole purpose of providing information. For example, all public sector servicing advice was given freely. In particular here the National Health Service was on the ball when in 1999 it introduced a World Wide Web site called NHS Direct. Here online patients could reveal the symptoms of their illnesses, then wait for their screens to advise on treatments or actions which might alleviate their problems. As in all other informational internet requests, the only costs to be incurred would be those of the charge of telephone time. As Internet fever increased it was recognised that addiction was becoming a problem for many. However – help was on hand, for a psychiatrist in America had the answer. For $55 a time he offered a cure for addicts – all they had to do was to join his programme on his website, pay their money and get online.

Another facility created through the internet was email. This was a computer-to-computer messaging conveyance, which might have been seen as a replacement of the telephone. If one did not want verbal contact with another, or could not waste time travelling the phone channels, email was the ideal alternative. All one needed to do was to tap an email address into a computer, enter the message and then wait until an answer was mailed back. However, instead of this system bearing the fruit of time saving, the opposite seemed to apply, for folks were inundated with emails to plough through to facilitate replies (a quick phone call might have proved a more expedient way of dealing with an enquiry). Then there were the junk emails to negotiate. Having accessed email addresses, companies would convey their advertising material to screens in an endeavour to promote the sales of their goods. As in mobile texting, emailers made full use of abbreviated language to save time and effort. The habit of shortening words, and using acronyms, came so naturally to late-twentieth century folk that regularly one would hear uncompleted sentences being spoken. As examples: 'The CE expects us to work 24/7 to get the FR ready for the AGM' (The chief executive expects us to work every hour of every day to get the financial report ready for the annual general meeting), 'I need an amp to make my mike work (I need an amplifier to make my microphone work.) A sign that the art of speaking was becoming obsolete was the fact that emailing was preferred when inter-office communication was necessary. Now, instead of walking to another's office to ask a question, make a comment or give a directive, a message would be sent via computer.

Computers were so human that they developed illnesses akin to man, like viruses, worms and bugs that rendered their systems unworkable. When this happened computers were said to have crashed or have gone down, with announcements saying that business would be resumed when the system came back online. Then, there were various ways of the mothering servers catching the ailments that could lay them up for a while. For example, installing new software or hardware could cause her to temporarily malfunction. Then she would certainly not work if she became overheated. Very occasionally touching a computer's keyboard or screen would cause the static that could bring about collapse. But most of the bugs, worms and viruses that affected a computer's well-being were those deliberately inflicted by people, for those with knowledge would introduce material into computers with the intention of scrambling programming functions to cause mass malfunction. Finally, as mummy server dined on electricity, obviously she would come to a complete standstill if this were denied her. However, she had been cleverly designed to cope with this eventuality and was capable of retaining all the information contained in her memory, until her food source was returned. When computers did go down everything came to a halt. With all records temporarily lost, companies could not continue trading; no one could find out what time the next train would arrive; banks did not have a clue as to whose cash was whose; doctors were at a loss to establish patients' medical histories; stock exchanges could not flaunt their monetary wares; passengers could neither board planes nor leave the ground on them, etc., etc. It was at times like these that one could not fail to wonder what would happen if electricity ran out completely (as it was likely to do in the first decade of the twenty-first century), or earthquakes ate up all the mother servers in one foul gulp. However, without these eventualities the 'civilised' world was more than concerned about the computer's future, for the system had reached saturation point. It was feared that present modules could not accommodate further data using the silicon chip facility already in use. Therefore if computers were to survive the intake of more and more information and requests for miraculous happenings, they would need to undergo major changes. It was envisaged that the newly discovered science of nano-technology, where atoms and molecules would replace the silicon chip function, could be the answer to the continuation of computerisation and therefore – the world! However, although it was a widely-held opinion that the world would come to a halt without the miracles of computerisation, it seemed that some of its downsides were overlooked. The two most important being that it was computers that had robbed the workplace of millions of jobs, and that crime, corruption, greed and the like had heightened in the world since the birth of the internet. Had these issues been observed it might have been recognised that, whilst the boast was that computerisation had brought much good, this could have been said of the Second World War also, for what is widely known is that many medical advancements in current use were made possible through the horrific experiments that were carried out on the Jewish prisoners of that war. This being so, could it be claimed that the Second World War was then justifiable because of the benefits it brought, as was being said of computerisation?

---

i Compiled from Whittaker's Almanacks for the years 1990–2000, A and C Black Publishers Ltd.

CHAPTER THIRTEEN

The Nineties – E–L

Environment

There were many reports in the 1990s to indicate that the people of the time were destroying the environment and the air that they breathed. However, the majority of late twentieth century people paid little heed to the situation, as their thoughts were filled with immediate hedonistic ideals that did not embrace the future, or ponder the past. If the plight of the planet was of little concern to the people of Britain, did they feel threatened by the environmental happenings around their own shores? For instance:

- it was reported that up to one thousand mile stretches of rivers were more polluted than they were in 1985;
- the environmental group Friends of the Earth's survey showed that hundreds of Special Scientific Interest sites were under threat from pollution;
- a government-leaked report stated that more than half of the wetland nature reserves had been damaged, or seriously threatened over the past five years;
- 'light pollution' was causing concern and a conference was held in London calling for action;
- at an oil platform in the North Sea, Greenpeace protestors were fighting to stop an oil company from polluting the ocean more by sinking a disused oilrig;
- nearly one million tons of crude oil had been spewed into the sea and over coastlines, in four oil tanker accidents;
- canisters of potassium cyanide were washed up on the southern coast;

- thousands of folk were forced to stay indoors when a cloud of poisonous gas leaked from a chemical plant;
- another chemical leak found its way to, and polluted, the water supply of a quarter of a million people;
- a countryside survey revealed a widespread loss of hedges and wild flowers in Britain since 1984 (ironically in 1997 a county court ruled that hawthorn hedges were protected under an Act that had been in force since 1765!);
- on a southern coast a sea wall was breached in order to relieve pressure on other coastal defences in the area, and twenty hectares of marshland was flooded by the action; and by way of a government decision, it was decided that some parts of the mid-English coastline was to be sacrificed to the sea as part of a 'peaceful accommodation' with nature.

If none of these events had any impact on late twentieth century Brits, there was one piece of news that might have caused folk to consider their environment. In a report made by the International Agency for Research on Cancer it was said that dioxin is a known human carcinogen – (cancer causing substance). The environmental group Friends of the Earth revealed that, according to government figures more than thirteen thousand tons of carcinogens were spewed into the air in 1996. On a list published by them, it was seen that the worst hit areas of Britain were Cheshire and the North East, where pharmaceutical and chemical works, together with oil refineries, were the purveyors of poison. These poisons, such as lead, chloromethane and vinyl bromide, had been identified as recognised carcinogens. Others were suspected of triggering the disease. Greenpeace was already campaigning against the production processes involved in the manufacture of PVC which causes the release of dioxins. Electricity manufacture, by means of nuclear processing, was also proving to be a cancer promoter and, despite government denials over the years that the workers at Britain's largest nuclear fuel plant were safe from exposure to radiation, in 1993 a health and safety report confirmed otherwise. It said that children whose fathers worked at the plant ran a risk fourteen times the national average of developing leukaemia and non-Hodgkin's Lymphoma.

The question 'how much radiation is directly seeping into the atmosphere?' should have been the question that everyone was asking in the nineties. At one nuclear processing plant, the safety level of nuclear reactors was criticised. After an accident at another, a fine was imposed on the company because of serious lapses in safety procedures. At a third it was stated that the complex suffered from many chronic safety problems. However, safety seemed of little concern in the area of dumping nuclear waste. Since the start of nuclear processing it had seemed appropriate to dump both this, and industrial waste, into a world separate from the human one – the sea. However, because Greenpeace had fought against this practice over the years, it was agreed worldwide that it would cease by 1995. The question was, would it, or would this promise follow the empty ones relating to greenhouse gases? As far as Britain was concerned, the government had opted out of the international ban on dumping radioactive waste at sea. However, before the century ended there was a change of mind. Then it was said that it supported proposals that discharges of hazardous and radioactive substances into the sea should be reduced to as close to zero as possible by 2020. Hence, Britain had no intention of operating a ban, not then or ever. The government was not ashamed to admit also that radioactive waste had been dumped in Beaufort's Dyke, off the coast of Scotland, in the fifties and sixties. Nor did heads bow when it was rumoured that governments past had withheld a matter of public concern. This related to a supposed fire that occurred in 1958 at a Ministry of Defence establishment in Berkshire and contaminated the county with radioactive fall-out. During the late eighties the government had made the promise that no longer would nuclear waste be dumped on British land sites. However, surprise surprise, before the century ended they made plans to create a nuclear waste dump near the site of Britain's largest nuclear processing plant. Fortunately Greenpeace, and other parties, were on hand to challenge this move and the plans were supposedly cancelled. Because Britain had withdrawn nuclear bombs from service it might have appeared that nuclear activity, at the processing and re-processing plants, would be lessened somewhat. Unfortunately not so, as it was opted to retain Trident missiles as the country's only nuclear weapon; meaning that dabbling with radiation would continue into the next century.

The demands for electricity had reached a high point by the end of the twentieth century, and there was a dilemma as to its future production. Power stations had been ordered not to burn a bitumen-based fuel called Orimulsion because it caused acid rain, and nuclear fuel plant reactors were operating beyond their envisaged lifespans. Could it be then that electricity produced by wind might be the answer? Thinking that it might, the government of 1992 gave permission for fifteen eighty-foot wind generators to be built on a Site of Special Scientific Interest in Cumbria. Then in 1996 the largest wind farm in Europe opened in Wales.

According to a report published by the World Wide Fund for Nature, one eighth of the earth's natural resources had been lost since 1973. Environmental decay was also noted in a United Nations report, which predicted there would be serious environmental disasters in the twenty-first century as a result of global warming. Researchers at the Institute of Terrestial Ecology envisaged too that billions of acres of tropical forest would turn into desert because of this situation.

Meantime, scientists reported an event that had already been caused by the greenhouse effect. This was that a twenty-five-mile long section of an ice shelf had broken away from Antarctica. Though scientists had established that sea levels had risen continuously over the last 19,000 years, one might have wondered about the consequences if the entirety of the ice in the Polar regions were to melt into the waters simultaneously. Imagine dropping a couple of blobs of ice into a glass already filled to the brim with water!

Environmental groups worked hard to persuade the governments of the world that they needed to effect the changes that would protect the Earth from further damage. However, despite the protocols that were adopted by world leaders, supposedly to cut levels of the greenhouse gases which had burned a hole in the Earth's ozone layer, nothing changed. In fact, as the twenty-first century approached the need to burn fossil fuels was increasing. To add to this, the leaders of developed countries were saying that their economies would decline should the fires of 'progress' be dampened, and that mass employment would be the outcome. Perhaps one could liken this attitude to that of an unemployed man who decided to create work, and wealth, for himself by knocking down his house. First he would remove the roof and sell it. To raise more money he would then sell the top bricks, then the middle, then the bottom until there was nothing left. The man would then find himself, not only jobless, but homeless too – what then?

Food

In the late eighties many British cattle herds developed an illness never seen before. The symptoms that cows showed were tremors of the head, poor co-ordination and weight loss. The convulsions that accompanied the sickness affected the animals to such a degree that their bodies shook uncontrollably, earning the malady the name of Mad Cow Disease. However, it wasn't long before a medically designed name came into being: Bovine Spongiform Encephalopathy – or BSE for short. Despite £12 million being given by the government in 1990 for the purpose of research, by 1996 the disease had claimed the lives of a 158,000 cattle. But then, had not the cause already been identified when it was acknowledged that herbivore cows should not be eating the brains, heads, kidneys, tongues, bowels, intestines and livers of other dead animals (despite assurances from government scientists that these diets were safe to feed to cattle)?

When, in 1996, the deaths of ten young people were investigated it came to light that they could well have died from another illness, born around about 1995, called Creutzfeldt-Jakob disease. CJD was to humans as BSE was to cows, and the link was formed by food consumption. Cows were dying because of the food fed to them by humans, whilst human deaths were happening because they had eaten the carcasses of infected bovines. However, Britain's Health Minister proclaimed that because some types of offal were banned in 1989, these recent deaths were most likely caused by a new strain of CJD identified to eating beef from cows having BSE before the time of the ban! In 1996 there was much ado with regard to British beef. Firstly, beef prices fell sharply because of the link between BSE and CJD (even though it was said there was no scientific evidence of a link). Then, European countries imposed bans on the meat (which the government said it would challenge through the European Courts of Justice). However, to be fair, whilst European Union ministers were adamant that the worldwide ban on British beef would stay, they did volunteer to provide financial assistance for the government to take measures to eradicate BSE in cattle. The actions that followed were:

- a ban on the sale of meat from newly slaughtered animals over thirty months old;
- an announcement stating that up to forty thousand cattle over thirty months old would be killed to prevent them entering the food chain; and
- a package of measures to help cattle farmers, and the beef industry, cope with their losses (which included £55 million for the slaughter and destruction of cows).

However, in the midst of all this activity, there came an agreement from the European Committee to examine new scientific evidence that BSE would die out naturally by 2001 – hence slaughter plans were abandoned. However, they were reinstated by the government when it was thought that about one hundred thousand cattle could have been exposed to the disease. Even though it had been said that there was no scientific evidence of the connection between BSE and CJD, new scientific evidence was still being published. For example, during the year a governmental advisory committee on BSE declared that children were no more susceptible to infection from it than adults! To top it all, in 1999 the results of experiments suggested that a higher proportion of the population may have been at risk of the BSE variant – Creutzfeldt-Jakob disease than was previously thought! But had not BSE been eradicated by the slaughter of thousands of animals, and the cause annihilated by the ban on offal feed?

Furthermore, had not potential cycles of infection, which could be caused by eating pig meat, been eliminated by the ban imposed on feeding MBM to swine herds (MBM is a protein feed made up of pig meat and pig bones and is produced at very low cost)? But then, whilst it was not permitted to feed British pigs on this diet, pig farmers were still producing the stuff and exporting it to Denmark and Holland. This meant that the bacon proudly sitting on Britain's supermarket shelves could, after having been imported from these countries, have come from pigs that had eaten British pig remains.

Considering the totality of stupid errors regarding food safety during the years of the nineties, it might have been presumed that lessons would have been truly learned, and that the public's health would not again be put at risk for money's sake. But – not so, for in the last two years of the decade came a plan that would not only endanger human life, but life itself. This was one that proposed to develop food by genetically modified (GM) means and posed the question, 'From mad cows to mad crops?' The ideal of genetically modified farming was to cultivate crops which promised high yields and low disease. The agro-chemical companies, who were eager to promote the scheme as quickly as possible, insisted that the potential benefits of producing food this way were immense to the Third World. There was much jubilation from all quarters when this news was heard, for it was believed that this method of farming would feed the world's populations (what the general public did not take into consideration at this point was that there would already be enough food in the world to feed the starving if the surplus food produced by countries within the EEC was not destroyed in order to maintain pricing levels and the people of these communities stopped throwing tons of it away as waste). In particular, it was quoted that the poor farmers of Africa and Asia regularly lost half their crops to pests and disease, so it was they above all who needed protected crops. However, one might ask, how would the poorest people in the world be able to pay for the highest technological scheme ever to be devised? What about rich countries, how would they benefit from GM crops? – well, spring onions and tomatoes for example would be more uniform and would not go off as quickly as conventionally grown produce.

Genetic engineering entails messing about with genes, and transferring them from one place to another in order to alter the natural function of a particular species. When this science is applied to crops, its purpose is to produce growth which will be resistant to the pests that would otherwise nibble away at them. This would mean that farmers need not constantly douse their crops with pesticides to destroy the little demons. All that they would need to do would be to spray unwanted weeds with the stuff. However, research in 1998 revealed that GM crops had spawned a new generation of prolific, aggressive superweeds with inherited resistance to herbicides. Some went along the laboratory line that these hybrid monsters had been born through intermingling gene frolics. The thing is, Superweed looked no different from his brother Normal Weed, meaning that farmers would have to spray every weed in sight to observe which ones died. If genes from GM crops had accidentally produced an indestructible weed, what other possibilities were lurking? Apparently even Neolithic farmers had known that crops and wild plants exchanged genes, and that related plants do this by sex. More up-to-date sciences proclaim that unrelated plants can also exchange genes via viruses. Hence there was the fear that the resistance genes put into GM crops may well get into wild plants and cause incalculable ecological consequences.

An even more frightening aspect of this potential gene swapping problem would be if pharmaceutical products were incorporated in a GM food, for it was the vision of the agro-chemical companies to make this a reality. Their initial ideal told them that vaccines could easily and successfully, be transferred to some GM tomato crops. However, they did acknowledge that great care, monitoring and segregation of crops would be essential to ensure that no 'crossing' occurred. Also it was important to the plan that these special medicines did not find their way to the supermarket shelves posing as common tomatoes. In an incident in the late nineties involving a GM medical exploit there were tragic consequences. When a bacterium was modified to produce an amino acid for purported health benefits, thirty-seven people died and a large number of others became seriously ill as a result of being exposed to the particular product. Though the cause was not established, it was said that something had gone wrong in either the genetic engineering of the product or in its processing.

Another fear associated with GM food was that of toxicity. For instance, it was said that most domestic crops like potatoes, parsnips and tomatoes, which belong to the nightshade family, have poisonous relatives or descend from poisonous ancestors. It was thought that GM crops might still contain the genes that make toxins dampen down, rather than lost. In this case, if an alien gene was parachuted by genetic engineering into the genome of a potato, or a tomato, the ancient genes of toxicity could well be reawakened. However, it would take many generations for the outcome of a gene recombination through sexual reproduction to be witnessed. But then, time was of the essence to the agro-chemical companies who were developing GM crops, for this costs money. They could not hang around for generations waiting for their products to be proven not harmful to the earth or its occupants.

There were 369 sites running trials for GM crops in Britain in 1998, and 500 sites in 1999, all of which were registered with the Department of the Environment. However, these experiments were transient inasmuch as just one test might be all that was needed to prove the crop a success. This meant that the harvest of the next planting would qualify to enter the food chain. Groups of environmentalists, protesting their fears about the safety of GM crops, surged the testing fields where they grew. Here they wrenched out the genetically engineered maize, sugar beet and potato crops that were undergoing government approval tests. The opposition to such actions said that people who destroyed test fields were stupid. After all, they said, how could safety features be measured if experimentation did not take place?

The testing of GM crops in Britain was instigated by a giant American agro-chemical company. In America this company was already marketing this type of produce and exporting it to other countries (including Britain). In 1998 American farmers planted about 20 million acres of soya beans, thirty per cent of which was genetically modified. When harvested, the conventional and GM varieties of soya were mixed together. The American suppliers refused to separate the two, saying that to do so would be impractical, and so costly that the growing of modified crops would be unviable! Unfortunately the people of Britain, and other countries, were not aware that they were buying food containing GM soya, for no labelling policy was enforced (nor was there any intention of introducing one). The disconcerting fact about soya is that it is an ingredient in about sixty per cent of processed food, from biscuits to ready-made meals – including baby milk and the bread, soup and pasta which sustains an infant in its formative years. Another fact that people were ignorant of was that most animal feed contains GM maize. Once again it was said that this feed is so cheap to buy that it is not worth segregating GM from non-GM.

It was not only crops that were being genetically engineered by the large US agro-chemical companies, for so too was the herbicide that is designed to kill weeds. If this particular weed killer was sprayed onto a field of GM crops, these plants would be resistant to it down to their roots because of their pest-resistance quality. Hence, where would the unabsorbed poison go to if not into the earth itself, where it would cause environmental havoc? When the question, 'Can GM pesticides affect the environment?' arose, the short answer was, 'Nobody knows'. However, there did come a warning from the government's scientific advisor, Sir Robert May, who said, 'The more successful we get at growing crops, the worse the news for wildflowers, insects, birds and the countryside'.

Then there were GM seeds to consider. In 1998 the Minister of Agriculture proposed changes to the law which would shorten the testing procedures for these seeds. The idea was condemned by the environmental group Friends of the Earth, which accused the government of cutting corners with food safety by seeking this change. A spokesman for the group commented, 'It is essential that something as novel as GM crops should be fully tested'.

Genetic engineering did not stop in the fields when it came to food production, because the scientists of 1999 were working on animals too. The transgenic creatures, which were destined for dinner plates – pigs, cattle, chickens and fish, were being produced with genes that sped growth and improved the quality of meat. The scientists revealed that the closest to reaching the market were transgenic salmon, which grew faster than conventional varieties, and cut down the time a farmer had to look after them before they could be sold.

Perhaps this type of animal farming would in time produce new species of animals to replace those which were at risk of extinction. For, in 1999, a survey carried out by the United Nations Food and Agriculture Organisation revealed that, of the 5,550 breeds of farm animals worldwide, thirty per cent of them were likely to cease to exist.

Maybe those who had been concerned about food safety issues during the nineties, such as:

- the method of supermarket farming, whereby crops were to be produced quickly with a guarantee of pristine quality (meaning that the bagged salads, vegetables and fruit which arrived at the shops were so unblemished they resembled plastic); and
- the means of factory farming, whereby the slaughtered animals which found their way to the butchery departments for slicing were all the same size (which meant that the weight of every portion offered for sale was uniform)

should cease to worry. Perhaps too they should forget that:

- the same crops were planted in the same soil time after time instead of being rotated, and were 'forced' to grow. Also that twenty chemicals were sprayed onto the plants to retain their 'good looks'; and
- the animals raised in factory conditions were fed hormones and antibiotics – the first to swell their flesh to uniform size in uniform time – the second to limit the risk of infection which could be caused by the appalling conditions in which they lived.

It could be that they should also forget incidents like the one that happened in 1996 when phthalates (which are chemicals used to soften plastic) had been found in baby formula milk (with the food ministry saying there would be no danger to babies' health!), for perhaps these things might measure tritely against futuristic food production where geneticism walked hand in hand with gain.

Health

With over 50,000 patients on hospital waiting lists for two or more years in 1991, the government of the day was obliged to review the workings of the National Health Service in order to effect sweeping reforms to the system. With the promise that the government's programme was to improve and modernise the delivery of service to the public, whilst continuing to reaffirm the fundamental principles of the NHS, the Patient's Charter was launched. This set out the rights and expectations that patients would be afforded, together with the proviso that more emphasis would be placed on health promotion and prevention than in the past.

During the years of the nineties many changes were observed by the public. At GP surgeries people no longer had to sit for long periods in waiting rooms and wait their turn to see a doctor. Instead appointment systems were put into place whereby patients would be allocated a time and date when a doctor would receive them. Unfortunately, however, the system proved impractical for those who wished to consult a doctor quickly. For example, if one was feeling unwell on a certain day, a telephone conversation with a doctor's receptionist might reveal that the GP had no free appointments until one or two weeks hence. Then, because they were not entitled to be registered with a GP, as they did not have a fixed abode, homeless people could not, in theory, make appointments to see a doctor anyway. On occasions when they needed medical attention and could not find a doctor, who had the kindness and time to see them, they were advised to attend hospital Accident and Emergency departments.

It was to a doctor's surgery also that a patient would go to undergo minor operations that were previously performed in hospitals. And, in further attempts to reduce hospital waiting lists, patients were redirected to specialist units where minor procedures and operations were carried out. Here hospital nurses, who had been trained to use specialist investigational equipment and extract tissue samples for biopsy, released valuable time for the surgeons who would have otherwise performed these tasks.

When a revised Patient's Charter was released in 1995 it appeared that the new regime was working well, for it was proven that hospital waiting lists had reduced. The document revealed that nearly half of all NHS patients were admitted to hospital within five weeks of their consultant having decided that they needed treatment. However, it did not state how long the other half had to wait, but suggested that nobody would wait for more than two years. Categorical waiting times were given for hip and knee replacements, cataract operations, out-patient appointments and clinical referrals. These were: a guaranteed eighteen months for the operations; an expected thirteen to twenty-six weeks for the appointments. Then, to be seen within thirty minutes of specific appointment time at out-patient clinics. However, complying with the political correctness of the Patient's Charter caused many a headache for hospital administrators, whose job it was to honour the rules. For instance, if a specialist consultant was called away from his out-patient clinic on an emergency errand (or indeed, if he fell ill, etc.) there would not be another consultant waiting in the wings to replace him. Hence the clinic would automatically go into a 'running late' mode when patients might complain that their wait was more than thirty minutes. As far as the waiting list time for operations went, it appeared that some hospitals had found a solution to the problem of compliance. According to the gossip of the late nineties, it was said that some people, after being told that they needed an operation, were receiving hospital confirmation letters telling them that their names *would* be placed on the waiting list at a later date – not that their names *had* been put onto the list.

In reality, how could hospitals be expected to cope with the ever-increasing demands for their expertise? After all, pioneering operations were still abundant in the nineties and included:

1991 – a first implant of an artificial lung;
1994 – a first implant of a permanent artificial heart;
1994 – a first six organ transplant (with a 3 month stay in hospital for the patient);
1999 – an ovary tissue transplant (great for premature menopause).

Then transplants in general were increasing, and to confirm this kidney transplantation had doubled over the years of 1978 to 1990. It was said that if there were more organ donations there could be even more transplant operations performed. The question was, however, how, when the operation system was already stretched to capacity? There were times in the nineties when hospital facilities and staffing capabilities were being utilised to saturation point, forcing administrators to announce that hospitals were unable to receive any more patients. In cases like this it was said that the hospital had closed its doors. This meant that the ambulance crews, who recovered victims of emergency, were obliged to seek out other hospitals which might admit their patients. Sometimes this involved their having to travel maybe hundreds of miles, either by road or air.

Not only did hospital personnel carry the heavy responsibility of restoring good health to one and all, their obligation was also to maintain high levels of safety to patients. Unfortunately, as hospital staffing did not operate on a one-to-one basis (one carer to one patient), there were inevitable occasions when patient injury occurred because of the unavailability of a pair of watchful eyes. Regardless of any amount of vigilance that existed in the hospitals of the nineties, there was a monster that lurked there that could not be captured. By the end of the twentieth century, 5,000 patients a year were dying from coming into contact with a bacterium called MRSA (Methicillin-Resistant Staphylococcus Aureus). Whilst this was called a 'hospital superbug' what most people didn't know was that it was already present in a large proportion of the population, often carried in the nasal passages. (The bacteria are usually harmless, but when introduced into the bloodstream through surgical wounds can cause disastrous effects, including death). Scientists of the time feared that the bug could escape its confinement to roam freely within society. However, they said that only the passing of a further ten years would prove if it had, or had not.

Particularly so after undergoing surgery, patients were also at risk of picking up other infections which happily wandered hospital wards. As far as cross-infection was concerned, it was thought that doctors and nurses were the cause, as they did not wash their hands patient to patient. However, the public was assured that they would greet the twenty-first century with clean hands. The NHS was also looking at schemes to educate the public into acknowledging that they too had a part to play in preventing hospital infections occurring. For example, many visitors would sit on beds to possibly deposit outside germs that might convey to patients. They may also visit whilst suffering diarrhoea or colds, etc. Also, the chances of their transferring infections to vulnerable patients through unclean hands was great.

There were areas, other than health and safety, which commanded hospital administrators' attention, for the public in general felt it their right to expect the services of the National Health Service to embrace all of their needs. Hence complaints were received about matters ranging from the non-friendliness of various staff, to the non-existence of a toilet roll in a loo. Perhaps the most popular protest made against hospitals was the lack of car parking facilities. When entering these places folk would rage at staff, complaining that they could not find a space to deposit their vehicle in the grounds. When wards were earmarked for rebuilding many pairs of public eyes would sparkle as they witnessed demolition crews, and their bulldozers, clearing areas of land. With excitement they would ask, 'Is it going to be a car park, because there's certainly a shortage of them?' At times, when the pressure on hospital administrators to provide car parking facilities reached crisis point, answers had to be found. As hospital land was at a premium, in favour of medical facilities, the only solution in many cases was to build multi-storey car parks on existing sites. However, this meant that car parks had to be closed whilst construction work was carried out. Alas, this did not suit the general public who screamed louder than ever about the non-existence of car parking spaces.

The scientific medical research of the nineties revealed these things:

- inherited Alzheimer's Disease is caused by a genetic mutation; and
- a gene believed to play an important role in the susceptibility of smokers to lung cancer was isolated.
- seven brands of contraceptive pill were more likely than others to cause thrombosis.

The scary health news items which emerged during the decade told of:

- two heart surgeons being struck off the BMA register after being found guilty of serious professional misconduct, after twenty-nine babies died during heart operations from 1988 to 1995;
- admissions to Alder Hey Hospital being halted after an outbreak of TB which killed a four-year-old patient;
- Britain's Chief Medical Officer stating that, despite a cluster of cases in Gloucestershire, there was no evidence to suggest that this incidence portrayed an increase of Necrotizing Fascitis (a flesh-eating disorder!);
- a woman who had received fertility treatment becoming pregnant with eight babies (she miscarried three of these and lost the remaining five later);
- the European Parliament approving the controversial Life Patents Directive, allowing the patenting of biotechnological inventions; and
- the drug company Glaxo withdrawing its antibiotic Raxar which had been linked to seven deaths worldwide.

An indication that all was not well with the nineties folk who lived in Britain was the existence of a well-developed drug culture. Amongst the younger generation of the day there was a natural assumption that drugs were an essential ingredient for concocting fun, relaxation or escapism. Hence the consumption, smoking or inhalation of illegal narcotic substances was deemed intrinsic to their lives. For some youngsters their habit began in the school playground, where unscrupulous dealers, not caring that their punters might be under the age of ten, peddled their wares.

It was not only illegal drugs that were abundant in the marketplace, for the land was awash with those lawfully prescribed by physicians. Spured within a nation of pill-poppers was the notion that doctors could give them potions which would cure any ailment that happened along. If an illness was not debilitating enough to warrant a visit to the doctors, then a journey to the nearest pharmacy might do the trick. For here the shelves were lined with drug companies' newly-discovered miraculous remedies, which were guaranteed to cure anything from a mole to a migraine. Even if one did not feel particularly unwell, there were pills to be purchased that could enhance one's well-being (to the point of one being able to perform somersaults and cartwheels all day long). In 1998 even an anti-impotence drug was introduced to the marketplace, prompting males with penile erection problems, to lick their lips in anticipation of the return of some sexual frolicking. However, they would have to pay for their fun themselves as the government announced that the drug Viagra would not be available courtesy of the National Health Service.

Opening a home medicine cabinet in the nineties might have indicted the people's reliance, and ultimate faith, in modern-day drugs, for many bulged with bottles and boxes of every size and shape. It was unimaginable to believe that anyone who consumed so many pills, on a daily basis, would not rattle. But then, most medically prescribed drugs were issued to prevent illnesses occurring, not to cure them. Those who had suffered, and recovered from, a major health scare seemed to be in a position where they would have to take drugs to prevent their illnesses returning, for the rest of their lives. However, it was known that many preventative drugs could induce illnesses, particularly organ damage. For this reason doctors regularly took blood samples from those who took these medications, to check for any malfunctions which might have occurred in their bodies. It was also known that drugs prescribed to subdue one cancer, could in fact cause a new growth to appear in another part of the body; and that some heart and blood pressure drugs might bring on other ailments. Unfortunately, when GPs prescribed such drugs to patients, they rarely advised them of the perils that may occur through taking them. Because of this, patients were not afforded the choice of deciding whether they wished to accept the medication prescribed, or decline it.

The modern epidemic of the late twentieth century was depression and nervous breakdown, with one in ten British people suffering with either condition. With approximately 22 million prescriptions per year being issued for antidepressants in England alone by the end of the century, it followed that drug companies hawked their versions of this single class drug with gusto. After all, in Britain as a whole, the bill for these drugs was approximately £296 million a year. However, doctors were becoming increasingly aware of another epidemic that was engulfing psychiatric patients, who relied on the use of strong antidepressants. This was that they were developing twitches and mouth ulcers, etc.

An illness new to the day was the one created by the obscure naming of human idiosyncrasies and emotions. This was particularly so where children were concerned, for they were labelled with a tag if they portrayed signs of acting outside a role considered 'normal'. This may have been that they craved attention, were shy, slow to learn, inattentive, hyperactive, naughty, over-imaginative or simply unique in personality. The labelling system operated to broadcast that children with behavioural problems were suffering illnesses which merited titles. Whilst these varied according to symptoms, the vital requirement seemed to be that the letter 'D' was embraced to define the problem. Therefore, children chosen to be labelled carried a tag that stated they had a disorder, dysfunction, deficiency, or even a combination of all three. In many cases, where physicians proclaimed that brain malfunction was the cause of their illness, prescriptions would be written up for the drugs that would nullify the child's mental activity and render him or her quieter, and therefore more acceptable to society.

There had been no drugs discovered that could alleviate the suffering of many residents of modern Britain. AIDS, for instance, was still proving incurable and claiming the painful deaths of numerous victims. It was estimated that worldwide the number of people affected with AIDS was approximately 40 million, and that in Africa one thousand patients a day died from the ailment.

Then there were those who chose to end their lives because they could not cope with the complexities of them. The Samaritans, a society that was founded in 1953 for the purpose of listening to the problems of those in distress and giving emotional support, published the number of suicides that occurred in the UK and Eire in 1999. They were:

Wales	–	330
Scotland	–	874
Eire	–	439
Northern Ireland	–	154
England	–	4,828

An analysis of these figures show that male suicides outnumbered female by around three to one.

Perhaps one of the most disturbing untreatable illnesses in the nineties was the one which caused people to frequently self-harm. They would throw themselves downstairs; slash their arms and legs with razor blades; cause injury to their heads by banging them on walls; insert knives into their bodies; and so on and so forth. It was estimated that over 150,000 people a year had to be hospitalised after having punished themselves this way.

It appeared that in the latter half of the century there was an abundance of ill health in Britain's land of plenty. Included in the equation was the list of illnesses and diseases previously unheard of. Whilst many of these new ailments have been mentioned throughout these pages, there are some which have not. For instance, a particularly worrying newcomer to the age was the one which rendered folk allergic. Tests on those who had suddenly become violently ill and collapsed into anaphylactic shock revealed that they were allergic to particular substances. Contact with the man-made product latex for instance could prove fatal to those who were allergic to the material. Even an innocent touch of a balloon made from the stuff might induce severe illness to someone with the allergy. Nuts, too, were a source of horror for there were people who could not even touch them without being taken ill. The actual consumption of nuts, in any form, could result in rapid death to those hypersensitive to the produce. Whilst the people who suffered this fearful condition took great care to avoid nuts, there was no guarantee that this could be achieved, for many products contained nuts, or their oils, without indicating the fact on the packaging. Also as small, or even minute, quantities of nut particles were used in the preparation of many recipes, it was quite easy for someone with a nut allergy to eat them unknowingly. For this reason sufferers were obliged to carry adrenaline and a syringe so that an immediate injection could be administered should anaphylactic shock occur. Sadly in the last years of the twentieth century there were isolated incidents when people, after having eaten food containing nut products, died before reaching hospital, where they would have received drugs to counteract their allergy.

For some, even an allergy to drugs themselves could prove fatal. In particular, before doctors prescribed penicillin they would ask patients if they were allergic to the product, for it had been known that those who had taken seriously ill after taking penicillin, and had not reached hospital in time to receive life-saving antidotes, had died.

According to Department of Health statistics asthma was taking the lives of over 1,500 people per year by the end of the century. Also, the number of folk who had to rely on a cocktail of drugs to control this condition, to maintain a reasonable standard of health, was approximately 5 million. From studies carried out it was revealed that asthma had doubled in Britain over the last twenty years and, that one in eight children suffered the condition. It was also established that asthma had rapidly increased since the 1960s, and that Britain had the highest rate in Europe.

Then there were the allergy ailments that, whilst not life-threatening, caused misery to many. Hay fever for instance was on the increase, with even people in their twilight years developing the condition. The same applied to the sinus problems that carried the label of rhinitis.

Housing

As 1990 arrived on Britain's doorstep it was seen that all was not well in the housing section. Following the boom of 1986, when thousands flocked to borrow the money that would buy them a house, there was now a situation where people were losing their homes. When people first acquired their mortgages they had worked out that they could afford to pay the monthly instalments based on the then twelve and a quarter per cent lending rate. However, the lending rate rose by two per cent in 1990 to fourteen and a quarter per cent, meaning that monthly instalment payments increased accordingly. Many people were unable to meet these further costs, and many realised that they should not have taken out a mortgage in the first place. This resulted in non-payment of mortgage repayments, and what followed was repossession. When mortgage arrears reached a certain point, the building societies and banks stepped in to take possession of the house, rightfully theirs to re-sell. Wanting a quick recovery of the monies loaned, the lenders would sell repossessed property at reduced market prices. There was no shortage of property scavengers waiting to scoop up these bargains and profit from someone else's bad luck. Those who were unfortunate enough to lose their houses had a double dilemma. Not only did they find themselves homeless, but discovered they had incurred a lifetime of debt. For, although the building societies and banks had recovered some of the original cash loaned, the borrower was still responsible for paying the interest outstanding and any balance of the capital remaining. The homeless people with nowhere else to go looked to the state to help them in their predicament. This caused a problem, as there was no surplus of public sector housing available. Councils had no alternative but to house those who had lost their homes and offered them bed and breakfast facilities in hotels. During the year the government pledged to give £15 million to alleviate problems of homelessness. By 1992 the housing market was floundering, making folk afraid to take out mortgages in case they fell victim to homelessness. The government stepped in again offering assurances. First, the Chancellor announced that stamp duty would be waived on properties up to the value of £250,000 until August 1992, meaning that buying houses would be cheaper. He also confirmed that building societies and banks would be contributing one million pounds to a scheme for cutting the number of repossessions in 1992. However, these promises did little to encourage people to buy and the housing market crashed during the year. To get the punters buying again interest was reduced to make 1992's lending rate nine per cent. Alas, still not much movement so, in the following year, it was lowered still further to eight per cent. Some picked up the gauntlet of cheap borrowing, and by the end of 1993 house prices started to rise. However not enough, and in 1994 the borrowing rate fell to seven and three quarter per cent. 1995 saw another drop – this time to seven and a half per cent and 1996, to a low of six and a half per cent. It seemed that people had not been tempted by low interest rates, because house sales in 1996 plummeted to reach 1992 levels. In 1997, however, fortunes appeared to be changing for the better for, despite the interest rate rising to seven per cent, house sales reached record levels since 1990. This high continued into 1999 when the interest borrowing rate dropped again to its lowest level of six and a half per cent[i]. Success for the money lenders had been achieved and, once again, house prices were soaring as people flocked to buy, buy, buy, envisaging handsome profits when they came to resell their investment. It was strange to observe that the working classes retained their ambitions to profit from buying and selling property regardless of the housing market crash of 1992 (and the negative equities that accompanied it). To add to this the mortgage obligations survey of 1999 had also revealed that as many as 440,000 people, at some time in the past, had to give up their homes because they couldn't keep up mortgage repayments, and of these one hundred and twenty thousand cases had happened since 1995. However, what their reasoning told was that if they had bought a house for 60,000 pounds, then sold it for 80,000 pounds after house prices had risen, they would have made a profit of 20,000 pounds on the deal. Sadly their greedy vision blinded them to some important facts. Firstly, that the said twenty thousand pounds would be greatly reduced if mortgage interest payments were taken into account. Secondly, that if they wanted to move into a house similar to the one they had sold they would have to pay the 'going rate' for it. This would mean that a mortgage of 80,000 pounds would need to be taken out which, at the current interest rate of six and a half per cent would cost them 162,000 pounds to repay over a period of twenty-five years. Maybe they should have asked themselves if they would have had more money in their pockets if they had stayed in their original 60,000 pound home, for had not their twenty thousand pounds 'profit' been lost to the tremendous debt they had now incurred? In reality, was buying and selling their homes the working classes dream of making money, or was it just an illusion that inflated house prices beyond their worth? And with higher house prices there came the need for increased borrowing. This, for many people, meant that they would incur debts that would last for most of their lifetimes, for if mortgage repayments based on a twenty-five year lending period were beyond the pockets of the borrowers, these would be reduced by extending the lending period to thirty-five years.

However, there were those who believed that investing in property would become more profitable than keeping a stock of gold. Property development had become so important to investors that land sites were at a premium. Deeply involved in the trade, the government was at odds with itself to identify the places where they would allow houses to be built. In 1997 the Planning Minister said that the government intended half of the 4.4 million new homes to be built by 2016, to be sited on farmland (a lot of which had been relinquished by farmers bankrupted by the outbreaks of foot and mouth and mad cow diseases which had lost them their herds) and in the greenbelts. In 1998 it gave approval for 10,000 new houses to be built on greenbelt land in the south of England. However in the same year a contrary statement was issued, stating that sixty per cent of new houses should be built on re-used, or brownfield, land and that developers would have to prove that no urban site existed before building in the countryside. Regardless of opinion from any quarter, the property developers of the nineties visibly engaged in seeking out all land that could be utilised for house building. Old derelict warehouses were converted into luxury apartments; empty church halls and shops were quickly bought up and transformed into houses, or apartments, and even places that garages and petrol stations had once occupied were cleared to make way for tiny dwellings. Supermarket bosses, too, were also keen to acquire large areas of land that could be cleared to house another of their stores. (It was wondered by some if one day Britain's green and pleasant land would be solely occupied by houses, apartments, superstores and pleasure outlets). Cash-buying builders rushed to purchase inferior houses that came onto the market to either refurbish them to sell at a profit, or retain them to rent out until market prices realised vast increases. Caught in the whirlpool of property profiteering, working couples starting a life together were struggling hard to buy homes they could afford, for as renting was so expensive this was the only option they had. Often, after taking out a mortgage, many of them took in lodgers to help finance their repayment obligations.

[i] Compendium of Housing Finance Statistics 1997 (percentages rounded to nearest one quarter)

CHAPTER FOURTEEN

The Nineties – M–S

Morality

Principles, honesty, trustworthiness and sincerity seemed to have been engulfed by the 'progress' of the nineties. So much so that it was felt by some that lives were being lived in a moral black hole. By now the ancient rules of life had gone and new ones had taken their place. These appeared to totally disregard the differences between right and wrong, good and bad, and encouraged the action of exercising individual free will. One of the aspects of this doctrine was that one must respect the actions and views of all without question. Another was that punishment was to be seen as cruel, admonishment as uncivilised, and death as something to be avoided at all costs. From this 'cloned' society of indifferent thinking came the belief that everything that everybody did must be right, if they wanted to do it. As ethical laws had been abandoned as the natural source of distinguishing right from wrong, it was the law courts that were given the task of deciding matters of controversy. According to media reports, some of their nineties decisions were as follows:

- a twelve-year-old girl, who was nineteen weeks pregnant, gained permission to have her child aborted without the need to ask for her mother's consent;
- a woman who wanted to be inseminated with her dead husband's sperm was denied the request because she had not obtained her husband's written consent (however she was told that she could do it in another country);
- a woman living in a lesbian relationship was allowed to adopt an eleven-year-old girl, despite objections from the child's natural mother;
- a court ruled that if a mother had chosen to abort it, an unborn baby has no

right to life! (This profound statement came after a man brought a case against his estranged wife who had chosen to abort their child, which she was carrying.);
- a recommendation was made by a court that more homosexual couples should be allowed to foster and adopt children; and
- (in an American court this time) a British male couple were granted the right to be named as parents on the birth certificates of their surrogate twin babies.

In the area of human demise there was a dilemma inasmuch as civilised people assumed the right to eternal life. It was deemed not right for anyone receiving medical attention to die. This standard placed a heavy burden on the doctors, and medical personnel, who had devotedly pledged their lives to the study and practice of medicine. Despite the medical skills they had acquired over many years, doctors were being denied the privilege of administering these in the best interests of their patients. Instead, they had the constant worry that, if a patient died, they might be accused of incompetence or malpractice. When brain death occurred because of severe damage to the organ, patients would often be attached to life support machines that would maintain the body by breathing for it. These machines could keep people clinically alive for indefinite periods of time, which meant another dilemma for doctors, for whereas they might know that life would never be restored to a patient, family members would contest the decision to switch off the machine. In other areas, too, doctors were at a loss to make independent decisions when it came to life or death situations and therefore had to turn to the law courts for the final say. The following examples are taken from media reports of the time:

- an Appeal Court ruled that a severely handicapped five-month-old should be allowed to die if he fell critically ill (apparently setting a legal precedent);
- a High Court judge gave doctors permission to switch off the life support machine of a three-month-old girl who was severely brain damaged (however he refused to lay down guidelines for such decisions);
- a Lord Advocate said that doctors in Scotland who stopped treating coma patients, deemed to be incapable of recovery, would be granted immunity from prosecution when patients died;
- the High Court ruled that doctors would be acting lawfully if they discontinued the artificial feeding of a victim of a football disaster who had been in a vegetative state since 1989;
- when social workers and doctors sectioned a woman under the Mental Health Act, so that they could perform a Caesarean operation on her, a

Court of Appeal ruled that they had acted unlawfully, even though her life and that of her unborn baby were in danger; and
- a High Court ruling made it lawful for a Caesarean operation to be performed on a woman, against her will, to attempt to save the life of her baby.

Even old age and vast bodily deterioration was determined no good reason for popping one's clogs in the days of the nineties. Hence, hospitals and nursing homes were crammed with aged folk who were without valid excuse for wanting to leave their earthly experiences behind them, for it had to be proven that modern medicines were capable of prolonging life. For this reason the many institutionalised old dears, who lay about in states of semi-consciousness, were given life-preserving pills to swallow each day. It was said by care assistants that, in their lucid waking moments, some patients murmured the words, 'Please, let me die'. Considering that it was not Mother Nature's intention for humans to live beyond their allotted time and reach this state of being, one could appreciate their desire for death. According to the philosophy of the Bible, it was thought that three score years and ten (seventy), was the average time span humans needed to fulfil one lifetime's goals. Regardless of religious beliefs, perhaps there is some truth in this philosophy, for when a human being's independent life ambitions have been achieved through sheer hard work; when this has taken a toll on their strength and determination, would respite not be welcomed without need to suffer more strife?

At the other extreme there were groups of people lobbying the government to legalise euthanasia in the belief that, in an advanced modern culture, no one should have to tolerate prolonged pain. The proposal was that mercy killing be executed on anyone suffering agonies associated with incurable diseases to bring a 'happy release' for the patient. The pro-argument of the groups was one that said that it was improper for Britons to have to travel to countries where euthanasia was legal, and then pay for their lives to be terminated when living became unbearable. An anti-argument however might have stated that it is wrong to take a life we cannot give. It may have gone a step further to pose the questions of pain which ask – could it be that a soul will recognise part, or full, perfection just by suffering the agony associated with prolonged pain? And is it wrong for human intervention to scupper life's plans for it?

In the nineties other clusters of folk were badgering the government to legislate on even more life control plans they had in mind. One of these was for cells to be taken from embryos to grow body parts. Another was for organ donation to be made compulsory (with the proviso that one could duck out of the scheme if one registered a written statement (saying no) to the proper authority). In 1997 the government accepted in principle that xenotransplantation (the transplant of animal tissues into humans) was a good idea. However, they felt that further research was required to ensure that there would be no risk of animal diseases being transferred to humans in the process.

In late twentieth century Britain it seemed that life had become so cheap that it could be either sacrificed, or bought at a whim. The women of the day were encouraged to put their own needs first when it came to childbearing. If an unwanted pregnancy came along, the first natural thought was that of abortion. Engaging in this act brought no remorse, for women were conditioned to believe that if it were inconvenient for them to bear a child at any given time, then the most natural thing for them to do was to get rid of it. After all, they were told continually, 'it's your body and it's up to you what you do with it'. Unfortunately, however, when women were advised to abort an unwanted foetus because it was her body it had invaded, there was no awareness of how this action may affect the way she would feel about herself for the rest of her life. Might she, for instance, sit alone and cry when she recognised that, although she was told it was a twenty-eight week old foetus that was to be aborted, if it were born prematurely at this stage it would be a baby. A baby whose life doctors, regardless of any bodily defects it might have, would frantically fight to save – a baby she had allowed to be killed. And how would her life be affected if it were discovered that the abortion had caused permanent damage to her reproductive organs to mean she would be unable to bear other children. When they were not approved officially, many abortions were carried out in private clinics where large sums of money would be exchanged. If there were funds available, then pregnancy also could be acquired through the privately run clinics specialising in life-giving techniques.

When it came to childbirth, age, circumstance or method mattered little to the women of the nineties, as modernity proclaimed that it was a woman's right to choose just when she wanted a child. In 1993 a fifty-nine-year-old British woman gave birth to twins after an implant which was performed in Italy. Then in 1997 a fifty-four-year-old woman gave birth to twins after in vitro fertilisation. In the same year a sixty-six year old produced a child, after receiving fertility treatment, and became the oldest British woman to do so (but she said she had lied about her age). In cases where a woman was incapable of carrying a child herself, it was readily accepted that a natural solution would be for her to pay another to perform the task on her behalf. Surrogacy enacted freely within family groups was also regarded instinctively fitting with mothers, sisters, cousins, grandmothers volunteering to act as host mothers to relatives' fertilised eggs. In one such case in 1996 a fifty-two-year-old woman gave birth to her daughter's baby after being artificially inseminated. Some couples chose to skip the options completely in favour of buying ready-made infants. For this purpose they would have to travel abroad to make their selection and pay their money. In 1994 a British couple were arrested in Romania, and sentenced to twenty-eight months' imprisonment, for buying a baby there and attempting to smuggle it out of the country.

Another example of the cheapness of late twentieth century living was that, if one had enough money, one could buy anything. Whilst in Third World countries people were dying daily in their thousands from lack of food, water or medicine, Western auction rooms were screaming an abundance of wealth. According to television and radio reports, these are some of the items sold at British auction rooms in the nineties:

- a painting by a famous artist – for £11 million;
- a volume of music – for £276,500;
- a twelfth century casket believed to have held the blood and bones of an infamous politician – for £4.8 million;
- the first edition of a famous book – for £4.6 million; and
- a famous still life painting – for £36.8 million.

Some might have wondered how so much money could have been accumulated by the folk who could afford to pay such large sums for the trinkets they wanted. Then there were others who didn't give the matter a thought because they were well aware of the intrigues that were not far away from moneymaking schemes in all walks of life. However, there were so many of them afoot that they naturally blended into part of everyday life, with only the monetary antics of politically-related persons being highlighted for all to see. Such as:

- a newspaper alleged that a family member of a former Prime Minister received £12 million in commission from a £20 billion arms deal with Saudi Arabia whilst his relative was in office;
- a Member of Parliament accused two junior ministers of accepting payment to ask questions on behalf of a Westminster lobbying committee;
- there was an allegation suggesting that many peers were accepting payment for asking questions in the House of Lords;
- two Members of Parliament were suspended from the House of Commons for accepting money for tabling questions;
- other allegations said that Members of Parliament had accepted cash from the owners of a major international store in return for furthering their interests through their House of Commons activities; and
- nine Scottish Counsellors were suspended over allegations that they had accepted overseas trips in return for their support in important votes.

However, not all issues were concerned directly with political dirty money schemes. For instance, in 1998 an enquiry was opened which concerned the exportation of arms to Sierra Leone, despite the UN ban on the sale of weapons to that country. The manufacturers said that they had acted with the knowledge and approval of the government. However, ministers were cleared of knowing anything about the matter a couple of months into the enquiry.

Governments in turn were trying to stop the fraudulent misgivings of the public who were robbing the Treasury of millions of pounds per year by way of benefit payment embezzlement. At the top of their hit list were the gangs who made a profitable living from the organised stealing of benefit payment books. Then there was the individual swindler who took delight in playing the system because it was tailored to be played. Whilst genuine folk plodded to work each day, paying one third of their salaries to taxes, it was those with no intention of acquiring employment who reaped the benefits of their toils, for each week the latter received payment from government funds for the mere reason that they were without a job. It was not only cash that was forthcoming to the unemployed, for free housing, medical prescriptions, education, etc., was theirs to claim. On top of all this financial assistance, extra funds were available to those who could prove that they were unable to pay their heating bills, or furnish their homes. This was especially so when children formed part of a family unit, because it had to be seen that British youngsters were cared for by the state. Whereas the word swindler might be relative to the fact that a large proportion of benefit claimants were in fact bodily capable of performing a job, but chose not to because they were better off not working, the word took on literal meaning in other areas. For example, many claimants, whilst receiving benefit payments, were earning cash from a source which was dubbed 'working on the side'. These little moneymakers ranged from performing tasks for folk who paid on a cash in hand basis, to selling second-hand cars or stolen goods. Bearing children for the sole purpose of qualifying for child benefit payments, and all the perks that accompanied them, also ensured an easy life for the dishonest state scroungers. Perhaps the most fraudulent practice carried out by those with the know-how of cheating the state system, was that of pretending to be homeless and penniless. Here, house-owning couples (with one or more children) would deceive the authorities by telling them that their partner or spouse had left the relationship, leaving mother and children with no home and no income. From here it was known that the state would automatically provide housing and benefits for the innocent victims of the circumstance. So, whilst the authorities were busy organising the rescue plans for the family, the plotting couple were laughingly preparing their own. These were: let out the house which they owned, and charge a high rent; continue to live as a couple in the property now allocated by the authorities, but for the mother to claim as many benefits as she could on the pretence that her children were fatherless; and lie that the man who visited the house frequently was an 'uncle'.

Despite the labyrinth of immorality that existed in the Britain of the nineties, the desire to depict civilised status was paramount. During the last decade of the twentieth century there developed an etiquette, which grew to infuriating proportion, and was known as political correctness. The custom, which was spawned by obscure groups of people known as *they*, stated that due respect be accorded to all people, at all times, in all situations. *They* believed that some of the modes of language, and approach, which had been used person to person throughout the years of history, might now cause intolerable offence or hurt to a cosmopolitan, civilised society. Hence born was a catalogue of procedures for all to follow. Just a few examples follow:

- if one observed a man climbing a ladder to enter a building via a window, one could not shout out to him, 'Hey mate, what're you doing up there?' Instead one would have to say, 'Are you all right mate, do you want any help?' for it had to be assumed that the man might be the owner of the property but was entering it from a ladder because he had lost his keys. Using the latter phrase would ensure that the man could not proceed to sue for defamation of character;
- at work all employees had to be given their proper job title according to correctness. For instance, whereas the men who collected household rubbish each week had always been acknowledged as the bin men, they were now to be known as 'refuse operators'. As for the man who caught rats and was lovingly called the rat catcher; he was now to be dubbed 'pest control officer';
- when it came to being fat, thin, tall or small, revenge could now be taken on those who addressed anyone as 'fatty', 'skinny', 'lofty' or 'titch/tiny '. For a precedent had been set that those who did not describe folk who fell into this category as vertically or horizontally-challenged, could be sued;
- longstanding locational terms of endearment were a no-no. It was not thought fitting to address unknown persons as 'cock' (London), 'duck' (Midlands), or 'hen' (Scotland) any more, for this could present an inference that an addressee was an animal, whereas 'love' (the North) or 'darling' (North or South) might be classed as sexual innuendo;
- it was absolutely taboo to tell someone that they looked gay if they were dressed in bright colours, or say 'you're in a gay mood' if they appeared bright and breezy. For the dictionary definition of the word had been replaced with a new meaning – one that described those who practiced homosexuality;

- using abbreviated country titles to describe people who were immigrants to Britain was unacceptable. This practice was seen as racist behaviour that could reap serious repercussions; and
- the word 'freak' had not to be used in any context, and 'crazy' was definitely out (which meant that the games of miniature putting, which featured outrageous novelty fun shots, would have to be named something other than 'crazy golf').

Whilst those without employment could not be taken to task for failing to apply political correctness to their living, this was not so for workforces, for companies were bound to comply with the PC rules of the country. This meant that their staff must do the same. Applying wrong words and phrases to customers, colleagues or associates, or making impolite representation to them, might result in an employee being severely eprimanded or dismissed. In one particular incident a man (speaking in his local dialect) went into his boss's office and said, 'There's a bloke here to see you,' and was told by his red-faced employer, 'You can't say that!' It was particularly distressing for those who worked in the public sector, for they reached a stage where they were frightened of opening their mouths, in case the wrong words fell out. Regardless of the speech or manner they used, it was the public who determined an interpretation befitting their human rights. Hence, senior public sector personnel were forced to keep abreast of the PC structure of the day and badger their underlings to do the same. Without a doubt, these exercises created great stress for both parties.

The members of the public who were most familiar with their rights were the children of the nineties, who commanded unconditional respect. At school they were aware that physical punishment was against the law, and that shouting at kids was not permitted. This led to a situation when even a directive given by a teacher, or school helper, could be interpreted by a child to be a 'shout'. The following anecdote is one to illustrate the point:

A school dinner lady said that she dreaded going to work each day because of the insolence of the children there. She said that, daily, children as young as five, challenge instructions given saying, 'You can't talk to me like that.' On one particular occasion she asked a little girl to pick up the chocolate wrapper that she had deposited on the ground. The youngster promptly turned around and said, 'I'll get you sacked for this.' Although she did not lose her job this time, she said that it could happen if a child reported an incident of this nature to the headmistress or headmaster. She went on to say that other employees had already been suspended from their jobs because of such events. In this area it would seem that political correctness had created a role reversal between adults and children, whereby it was now the kids who gave the orders and grown-ups who followed them.

As the twentieth century faded out of sight what was left in its wake was a shrunken planet. For now, because of jet propelled air travel, the world had become 'globalised'. When journeying through the air at breathtaking speeds first came into being, it was recognised that no corner of the world was ever too far away to be reached quickly. Armed with this reality the powerful nations of the world seized the opportunity of promoting world trading, with the promise that this would boost the worldwide economy. From here it was necessary for them to survey underdeveloped countries to establish resources there that could be utilised to world trading advantage. With flimsy overtures to world ears that the people of these countries would benefit greatly from world trading, the lands of foreign places thudded with mighty humanitarian feet. However, despite the monies from the International Monetary Fund and World Bank which flooded their underdeveloped countries to swell prosperity, the poorest denizens there could only breathe in the aroma of the abundant wealth around them. This is because they had been plunged into deeper poverty by the conglomerate forces who deemed it appropriate to seize their livelihoods to clear the way for 'progress'. With the means of earning independent livings gone from them, the only way these people could survive was to succumb to offers of employment from the giant manufacturing companies that had commandeered their country's resources and workforce.

One particular country to undergo globalisation, at the expense of its occupants, was Indonesia. With the knowledge that three thousand islands of the Republic of Indonesia were awash with natural resources, such as oil and copper, it was acknowledged that here was a prize not to be missed. Hence the mighty nations, with the IMF and World Bank in tow, could not wait to move in. However, the then President of Indonesia, Sukarno, though not wishing to alienate newcomers, refused to accept loans from them which would rob his country of its independence. This did not go down well with the affluent and potentially do-gooding nations, therefore, they chose to replace him with another President, Suharto, who would be global economy-friendly.

What followed in the year 1965/66 was the need to eliminate those who stood in the way of progress (or big business), and to this end the killing of those who supported the views of the deposed President was instigated. The propaganda which met world ears was that these people were Communists intent on destroying the world economy. Hence this became the justification for the slaughter of up to one million people.

A British newspaper carried an account of the murderous events that later became known as Indonesia's bloodbath, the second greatest crime of the century:

- estimates of the total number of Indonesians killed in political massacres after the attempted coup of September 30th are being revised as fuller information comes in from outer regions. One western ambassador considers 300,000 to be a conservative estimate, and other compilations run far higher.

- a traveller, who knows the island of Bali well and speaks the language, describes mass executions and the annihilation of village after village in some areas. A consular official in Surabaja accepts a figure of 200,000 for Bali which has a population of two million.
- estimates of the dead in Sumatra also range around 200,000, and a similar figure for Java is generally regarded as on the low side. When the death tolls for other islands such as Borneo and Sulawesi are added, the total may well be upwards of 600,000. Just how many of these are communists is another question.
- it appears certain that the great majority of the dead were innocent victims of political hysteria. In some areas communist suspects were shot or poisoned, but usually the Muslim youth beheaded its victims with the parang – the heads were often impaled on fences and gateposts.
- rivers in many parts of the country were clogged with corpses for weeks.
- a European resident of Surabaja describes finding bodies washed up by the river onto his back garden.[i]

As the twentieth century neared its end, most Britons joyfully reaped the rewards of globalisation. If they wished, they could choose to work anywhere in the world without restriction. They could buy anything they desired from any continent. In the supermarkets there was a preponderant choice of worldwide delicacies and out of season produce for them to purchase. The marketplace was awash with the imported, cheap goods obtained by way of slave labour. And, as it was obligatory to believe in the one-ness which linked all continents of the world, there was the unspoken right for all to regard every country as an extension of their own, and to feel free to jet off for visits whenever they wished.

Whilst late twentieth century Western peoples enjoyed the benefits of world trading and world-hopping, the word 'globalisation' left only a bitter taste in the mouths of those who had paid the price of providing the privileges. (As the twenty-first century approached, one third of the world's population was living in poverty, with almost seventy million people existing in dire poorness. To these folk the sight of food, water and medicine would have far surpassed that of a faraway land, a motor car, or fashionable clothing.)

Again with globalised Indonesia, in 2001 a T.V. Documentary[ii] revealed the appalling working conditions the poor of the country had to endure. For example, providing designer clothing for the British and American markets young women slave in claustrophobic, unventilated factories where temperatures reach forty degrees centigrade. They have to work quickly without speaking and cannot leave their stations without permission. Should they need to go to the lavatory during working time, and their bosses say no, then they stay where they are and shit in their pants. These ladies have no say as to the number of hours they work and, if a designer order needs filling quickly, then shifts of thirty six hours are expected; and all for a mere dollar a day, perhaps just enough left to buy a little food for their families needs after water supplies had been purchased.

In 1997 another facet of globalisation caused havoc in Indonesia. As rain forests had been logged to capacity to provide the Western world with hardwood, such as mahogany, it meant that drought conditions became intolerable. Whereas a natural rainforest, because of the dampness there, can withstand drought, one that has lost many of its trees cannot. Hence in the waterless autumn of the year, when the heat reached maximum temperatures, the debris from logging and unwanted young trees lining the forest floors became so dry that it ignited. The raging fires that followed caused a smog so dense that many people were taken ill and had to be rushed into hospital. Those who were not affected immediately had to wear masks as a preventative measure. Also, because of the smog, an aeroplane crashed causing the deaths of hundreds of people, and two ships collided killing twenty-six. Then, probably because of the heat of the ground, an earthquake occurred and thirteen people died. It was said that the pollution of the air, because of the incidence of smog, was so bad that it changed the direction of the trade winds and that it would affect the whole of the world.

As far as supplying hardwood (mainly to English timber companies) was concerned, the trade in Indonesia was a lucrative one. However, it was said that these business ventures were so very poorly managed that great risks were taken. Then there was a strong allegation that there was a lot of corruption relating to the trade, in which even government officials were involved.

As the Western world gazed towards the twenty-first century with futuristic images of continued wealth, perhaps many poor Indonesians could only visualise the memories of the past, and dare not think about tomorrow. Also, as they observed the peoples of Britain, America and Australia flooding into Bali to bathe in luxurious holiday-making, maybe they could only recall the sight of the thousands of bodies which once lay dead on the ground that hotels and car parks now occupied.

As the Western world shouted loudly of its fears of terrorist attacks on its domain as the twentieth century neared its end, were not Indonesians, and the peoples of other Third World countries, who had experienced the wars of globalisation, pondering the noise?

Shopping

During the last ten years of the twentieth century a majority of people had been transformed from human beings to consumers. Excitedly these beings would wake up each morning ready to scan the horizon to look for inspiration. Alas – not the kind that might promote goodwill, good health or good vibrations, but the sort that might jog the memory into recalling the promotions that day at the supermarkets. Conversation amongst this new species revolved around prices, and the quality and availability of goods at various emporiums. And for the people who enjoyed the best of everything, and the cheapest of world goodies, consumer chatting reached a high as word was spread as to where one could rush to acquire items which were free. The buy-one-get-one-free offer was something not to be missed by any devotee shopper (even though the product might be one that they did not like anyway). Consumers spent millions of pounds daily as they trudged around the shops buying not what they needed to survive, but what they believed they could not miss. The avid bargain seekers made sure they reached the shops before they opened – making sure that stocks wouldn't run out before they got there. From early morning opening to late night closing, shopping trolleys, loaded to overflowing, passed through exit doors. Of course bulk buying meant bulk payments, and bills totalling £100-£300 were not uncommon. However, when it came to checking the bill, to ensure correct pricing, speed prevented this. In a race against time one had to unload purchases from the trolley and place them onto a conveyer belt, quickly put them into bags when scanning was completed, move swiftly away from the till area then rush the contents to a waiting car, there to be crammed into every crevice. In the flurry of all this, the poor bill would be banished to the waste bin at home without being given a second glance. As many non-bulk shoppers could verify, many, many pricing errors were made by supermarkets. Those who did check their bills often found that the price charged at the till was sometimes higher than the one shown on the shelf. Then, in some cases the cashier might scan an item more than once. As for special offers, these very often appeared on the computer scanning systems at full price instead of the reduced one. It might have been wondered how many overcharges had helped swell the pre-tax profits announced by two leading supermarket chains in the late nineties. One of them boasted a £750 million figure and the other £756 million.

With smaller retail outlets having been forced out of the marketplace by the bulk buying supermarket and department store barons, chain shopping had become a way of life to the average British denizen. Super selling marketing strategy was of little concern to consumers. They didn't give a thought to the way that supermarkets were set out. For instance, to reach an item one wanted to purchase, one would need to walk through every aisle of the store. On the way to the destination there would be special offers on display; colourful advertising for new products; posters stating low priced and so on and so forth. Having come into the store to buy a needed jar of coffee, one might leave the premises loaded down with bagfuls of unintended purchases that were too good to be missed. To stop consumers becoming too accustomed to the store's layout, the supermarkets had a plan: they moved the goods around from time to time to make customers look afresh at every shelf. Sometimes stores would decide to change their layout completely to make customers think a new venue had appeared! Late twentieth century people were oblivious to their exploitation as consumers. Instead, they felt certain that it was they who were beguiling the sellers of not-to-be-missed bargains.

From their early beginnings supermarket owners had recognised so much success from their marketing of groceries that they determined to sell every other possible product that customers needed. By the end of the nineties (despite the Monopolies Commission) they had reached monopoly status. They sold newspapers, magazines, fruit and vegetables, fresh meat, fresh fish, clothes, shoes, haberdashery, crockery, petrol, home-made cakes and pies, cigarettes and lottery tickets. One could also go to a superstore to get shoes mended, or clothes dry-cleaned, or films processed and to the in-store pharmacy to have a prescription made up or acquire medical aids. What was more; there was no need for consumers to endure the inconvenience of having to visit their banks to withdraw money any more. Paying one's superstore bill with a debit card entitled the holder to ask for cash back. The cashier would ask how much money was required and hand over the cash there and then. From here the customer's debit card account would be charged, and the store reimbursed and paid a fee for its services. One leading superstore went as far as entering the world of finance in its own right, when in 1986 it announced plans to launch its own bank. In 1997 it went a step further and, in conjunction with a leading insurance company, launched mortgage lending facilities. One might wonder if superstore house selling would come next.

Shopping on Sunday had always been taboo for the people of Great Britain. The day was regarded as the Sabbath when even God himself took a day off. (This idea was begotten from the Bible, which taught that God had made the world in six days and that on the seventh he rested.) Even if one was not religious and therefore skipped Sunday church-going, it was nice to practice the day of rest part of the doctrine and enjoy a day out from daily routine. Hence the tradition of not working on Sunday had always been observed by generations of people. However, in 1991 four supermarket chiefs got together and made a decision to set new precedents. They announced that they would open their stores on the four consecutive Sundays before Christmas. Local Councils sought injunctions through the courts against the companies and succeeded. However, the companies objected and approached the Court of Appeal. This judged that local authorities, seeking injunctions against shops illegally trading on Sundays, would have to compensate the shops if restrictions on Sunday trading were eventually found to be illegal. The European Court ruled that existing restrictions on Sunday trading, under British law, did not contravene EC law. Probably because no-one could make head nor tail of the law anyway, the powerful and mighty supermarkets created a new one that said that Sunday shopping was here to stay. Having won the victory of gaining an extra day for profit-making, the supermarket chiefs decided they wanted more. Longer opening hours was now their aim, and as the nineties progressed so too did trading hours. By the end of the century consumers could make purchases at superstores from 8 o'clock in the morning until 10 o'clock at night – and for twenty-four hours at some stores.

Sunday trading and long opening hours were also the order of the day for out of town 'shopping cities', where designer chain stores were housed together under one massive roof. These were the places where delighted shopaholics, after travelling many, many miles by road to get there, could skip from shop to shop without having to worry about weather conditions outside, or the possibility that all their shopping needs would not be met.

With shopping having become the new religion of the age, consumers were oblivious to anything other than their devotions. Walking around shops and supershops was a dangerous occupation, for one could easily be maimed by those who pushed to reach something they wanted from the shelves, or who drove their trolleys into one's back or legs in their haste to grab wares. Supermarket management named the latter trolley rage, and recognised it to be an aggressive action. However the fact was that people seemed genuinely unaware when they did strike other people with their trolleys. Because of this oblivion, supermarket car parks could be terrifying, for Mr and Mrs Consumer forgot that they were in charge of killing machines as they searched for parking spaces. Their eagerness to find vacant plots blinded them to people, vehicles and shopping trolleys. It did not get much better as they brought their cars to a standstill either, for they (and their children) would bound across the car parks without bothering to check for vehicles in motion. Then, with future generations of shoppers in mind, supermarket marketing made sure that little eyes, and little hands, were able to focus on items that would appeal to them. Whilst mums and dads were busily reaching up to the shelves for the shopping they wanted, the kids were down below picking out their wants. Some superstores even provided miniature trolleys for 'trainee shoppers'.

Sport

Violent behaviour was not confined to British streets, for the green, green grass of football and rugby pitches were splattered with blood too. Over the past ten years there had been twenty incidents of football hooliganism, including both fans and players. On one occasion a man was killed when a marine distress flare was fired at him. Another man was killed by an opposing fan before the start of a Football Association match. And, of course, many injuries resulted from hooliganism. The government decreed that police should have the final say on whether football fixtures should go ahead if violence was envisaged. Also, the Football Task Force had come into being which, at the end of the nineties, published a report on tackling racism in football. Who would have thought that Britain's national sport would have needed this political intervention? Who would have thought that the word 'corruption' could ever be associated with the game? But events showed that it was when two incidents of match fixing came to light, and it was revealed that a football manager had received £425,000 following transfers of European players to his club.

Transfers, fees, deals – there was no ceiling to the football cash flow. In 1994 a record transfer fee of £5 million was paid for a player, and by 1996 this record had reached £15 million. The Premier League football clubs accepted £743 million for a four-year deal with two satellite TV companies to screen their games. Another deal was bonded when the Football League agreed to accept £125 million from a cable TV company to broadcast some of their Cup matches for five years. However, a committee of the House of Commons recommended that satellite and cable TV should not be allowed exclusive access to big sporting events. Would this have been their opinion too as they heard the news of 1998 whereby a TV company made an agreement to buy a top club for £625 million?

Whereas the game of rugby was not in the same league as football, it too had its moments. For instance, a rugby player died after being punched during a match. As for financial matters – well the Rugby Football Union too had an offer from a cable TV company. The deal here was that they be paid £87.5 million for the exclusive right to screen matches for five years.

Anyone for cricket? Well, nothing untoward happened in the nineties to render Britain's gentle game anything but that. The only deal the England and Wales Cricket Board accepted was from a mobile phone company to sponsor their wares for four years. For this they received £30 million.

Corruption seemed to have erupted in other sporting arenas too during this decade. The World Professional Billiards and Snooker Association was asked to hold an enquiry when it was suspected that there was some match fixing going on on the snooker tables. Then there was the report that the Female Athlete of the Year award had been rigged. Halfway through the nineties the government recommended that events sponsored by tobacco companies should not be shown on TV. A couple of years later the government imposed a ban on sponsorship of sports events by tobacco firms. However, there would be an exemption from this ban for Formula One motor racing! It later came to light that a £1 million donation had been made to the government of the day from the Vice President of Formula One racing.

In horse racing, MPs voted to lift restrictions on betting on Sundays, which would pave the way for Sunday racing. In the middle of the nineties the first Sunday horse race meeting took place with legal on-course betting. It followed that, for the first time, betting shops opened on Sunday.

Sports people found guilty of taking drugs to enhance their performances came from nearly every area – cricketers, athletes, cyclists, snooker players, boxers, rugby players. Strangely enough the only sports personnel who were not convicted of drug taking in the 1990s were footballers. Those taking drugs, without knowing it, were the unfortunate racehorses that had the things rammed down their throats by their trainers. There were one dozen convictions made for this offence, but who knew how many more poor animals had been drugged for the past ten years without their persecutors having been brought to justice.

Space

During the nineties worldwide space teams continued their quest to discover potentially habitable planets outside the Earth's atmosphere. Spacecraft zoomed the heavens depositing probes as they went. The unknown worlds to receive these uninvited visitors were Jupiter, Mars, Saturn and the Moon. NASA scientists were thrilled with the images that the probes transmitted back to Earth for they indicated signs of life. For example, pictures showed large amounts of frozen water on the Moon. Then, Jupiter's moons showed that icy floes on its surface could be floating on slush, or water.

By way of telescopes, Earth-bound astronomers discovered goodies too. It was found that a star named Pistol, which lived in the Milky Way, was 10 million times brighter than our Sun. And, photographs revealed the first planet ever to be seen outside the solar system and this was christened TMR–1C.

Without the aid of probe images, or telescopes, another discovery was made by scientists. This was that a meteorite found in Antarctica was believed to have been ejected from Mars millions of year ago. The exciting feature of the find was that it contained structures likely to be microfossils of bacteria – thus providing the first evidence of life on the planet.

The mishaps which occurred during the space decade were these:

- a Russian cosmonaut was delayed on space station *Mir* for four months because of financial problems with the Soviet-British mission;
- a space rocket named *Arianne 5*, which had taken more than ten years to develop, and was carrying cargo worth £500 million, veered off course after taking off from France and was blown up for safety reasons;
- the space station *Mir* had a computer failure which caused it to lose orientation, and a rocket launched by Russia was sent in to carry out repair work;
- the space station *Mir* was damaged when it collided with a supply ship whilst practising a docking manoeuvre. Later it temporarily lost use of its oxygen generators; and
- the Russian space probe Mars 96 failed two hours after launch and crashed into the Pacific Ocean.

i Nicholas Turner, The Guardian, 7th April 1966
ii John Pilger ITV documentary 'The New Rulers of the World' July 18th, Carlton Television

CHAPTER FIFTEEN

The Nineties – T–W

Telephones

Without exception every 'civilised' person in the world who needed to contact another for immediate response, communicated by telephone. By the end of the twentieth century Britain's top telecommunications company had just over 28 million subscribers who rented landlines from them, and delightedly used the services made available to them during latter years. For example, the answering machine, which appeared in the early eighties, was welcomed with open arms by the busy people who were not able to man their phone all day long. Now they could purchase a machine that would record messages to enable them to call back when they had time. This was a bonus for the telephone company too for, instead of earning revenue from the cost of one phone call, monies would now be collected from two.

When the automatic call steering and call queuing systems were introduced in the late eighties, to the mid-nineties, businesses were clapping their hands, for here was the opportunity for them to save money. Instead of their having to employ people to answer incoming phone enquiries at all times, this computerised system would take over the task. It would respond immediately to a ringing phone with a robot that would try to establish the nature of the call, offering a customer a menu from which to choose to reach his or her enquiry destination. Then, by pressing certain numbers on the telephone keypad (as advised by the robot) the call would, hopefully, be transferred to the desired destination. Alas, direct contact with a human being was rare as, in most cases, a transfer to another department meant listening to yet another menu from which to make a further choice. Even then the customer's chance of succeeding in his quest to talk to someone was unlikely, for at the end of the rigmarole the robotic voice was frequently heard to say, 'Your call is being held in a queue – please hold' (some messages even quoted the length of time it would be before a call was answered). However, all was not lost, for the designers of these automatic systems had captured a method of preserving customers' well being. This was to programme music for them to listen to when the call system had said all it needed to say. As they stood for long periods listening to the classical melodies that seemed to reach their ears via an unearthly quarter, many believed that they must be the only survivors of an earthly disaster. Once again the communication companies were quids in because of the system, for customers had to pay for the call regardless of whether or not they had spoken to a person!

The paramount directive of communication companies in the nineties was to inveigle the public into using their phones to capacity. Selling bulk telephone time to large organisations was a sure way of ensuring this. For instance, during the screening of some television programmes, watchers would be given a telephone number to ring to:

- give their comments;
- vote Yes or No to a particular question; or
- choose the artist they liked best in a talent show.

Then, with the offer of prizes to be won, people would be given a number to ring if they thought they could answer a question posed during a programme. Occasionally this might be one when only an avid sporting enthusiast could give a correct reply, but generally it was observed that any five year old would be able to get the answer right. However, to give the public the option to decline the chance of winning a much-desired prize, the inflated cost per minute telephone tariff would be shown alongside the question.

Still in the area of prizes, there came the idiot-proof letters that dropped through letterboxes daily, telling recipients that they could win cars, dream holidays or vast sums of money. However, qualification of ownership of such desirable prizes came only if one picked up one's telephone and dialled a given number. From here came a long, drawn-out confabulation that terminated only when the bottom line was reached. This usually told the caller that unfortunately this time he or she had not won a major reward, but that a pen (or some such trinket) was his or hers to claim. As the small print of these database-produced letters was lost in the boldness of offers, it was only the headline that received the attention of eager would-be winners. Therefore, on receiving their telephone bills, many were flabbergasted to find that their newly acquired pen had cost them several pounds. There were also database-produced phone calls that cost their recipients not money, but precious time and annoyance. These came from silver-tongued salespeople who promoted the quality of their not-to-be-missed inexpensive wares. At the time of the intrusive telephone call one could be cooking a meal; mourning the death of a loved one; having an argument; rushing out to catch a train; in the middle of dressing, and so on and so forth.

The chat lines and lonely heart services also generated high revenue from selling telephone time. Here, through TV and written media advertisements, lonely (or just 'fun seeking') people were offered the opportunity of meeting new friends simply by calling a given telephone number. The exaggerated charge per minute for these calls ensured that telephone bills rose tremendously for those who used the services. When bills totalling hundreds of pounds dropped through some people's letterboxes, they were astounded. These folks were the parents of offspring who had frequently used their phones to talk on the chat lines.

But then, by the end of the twentieth century, nearly every child in Britain owned a mobile phone. In 1991 just over one million Brits were proud possessors of this versatile gadget, which could be carried in pocket, briefcase or handbag. By the end of the decade, the mobile had become the toy of the century, with over forty million subscribers playing the game. One of the 'fun' features of the gadget was that, instead of delivering a plain ringing tone, it could sing out a robotic tune (of one's choice) to summon attention. This meant that wherever one roamed there were the inescapable, maddening noises which assaulted one's ears, followed by the unwanted conversations of other people. Strangely, it was observed that those who contributed to flaunting their own voices on their mobiles were those with nothing to say. For example, one might hear a flurry of words explaining, 'I am in the supermarket and then I am going to the toilet.'

Another novelty feature was the texting facility. For a minimum charge one could send a text message from one's own mobile to another. This system was used to convey jokes, tell someone what had just happened, ask a question, tell someone what was thought of them, etc., etc. When two mobile phones lived in the same house, text messages were useful for making requests – for example, asking a partner to bring an item from one room to another; telling him or her that the dog had escaped; begging the other to pass the sauce across the dining table. This system was also an avenue of entertainment for those who wished to inflict uninvited provocation on others. One might switch on one's phone to find a pornographic message waiting there, or a threat. Messages might have been relayed by telephone but not necessarily so, as computers could also convey texts to mobiles. It seemed that teenagers in particular were bombarded with such messages, so much so that many killed themselves because of it. The problem became so acute (as it was with mobile phone robbery) that the crime became a top priority in the law enforcement agenda of the UK. Not an easy task, for at the time there were 55 million text messages sent each day.

The toy of the day was portraying itself to be the most anti-social, time-consuming, offensively dangerous little gadget of all time. Regardless of social occasion, proceedings would come to a halt when mobiles tolled out their ghastly tones of beckoning. Without preamble the recipients of calls would proceed to chat to the instruments, attached to their ears like growths, completely ignoring the friends, family or colleagues who might be present. Alternatively he or she might vacate a room to speak privately to the caller, indicating that it was the latter's company that took preference.

By the end of the nineties concerns were being voiced as to the medical dangers that accompanied regular mobile phone use. It was thought that the radiation emitting from these miniature time bombs could cause brain cancer in young children because their brains were not fully developed. It was also envisaged that it could contribute to the development of Alzheimer's disease. Mobile phone experts were keen to say that their products emitted far less radiation than an x-ray. However, how much danger would there be from x-rays if people were exposed to them every day, and for long periods of time, as mobile phone users were? There were radiation risks also from the transmitters that enabled mobiles to function. Ironically, whilst everyone desired the use of a portable phone, no one wanted masts to be erected in their areas. Regardless of government announcements saying that phone masts were safe because they complied with European guidelines regarding magnetic field perimeters, the public were still concerned about the microwaves they pumped out twenty-four hours a day. Community groups protested when it was rumoured that a mast was about to be erected near to their homes. However, land and property owners were pleading with mobile phone operators to host the large, ugly transmitters, because of the money they would receive for accommodating them. UK renters could expect to generate £30,000 to £35,000 a year for siting masts. Sadly, many of the sites chosen for mast erection were those where the most vulnerable of society frequented, like schools, children's hospitals and maternity units. Whilst mobile phone operators were saying that there was no conclusive evidence making a link between exposure to radio waves, transmitter masts and long-term public health risks, many people were not convinced. Some parents withdrew their children from schools where masts had been erected, fearing that not enough was known about the emissions from them. They were not prepared to sacrifice their children's health for experimentation purposes at any cost. As the century drew to an end there were 20,000 masts erected in Britain and during the last couple of months of it, 400 British schools were approached by phone firms to site just one transmitter on their land. The reward for this would be up to £8,000 per year.

Apart from the possible health risk associated with mobile phones, there were definite ones to consider too. For example, the frequency waves created by these gadgets can greatly affect other equipment. If used in a hospital a mobile phone can stop electrocardiogram machines from working, cardiac monitors from functioning properly or render other machines and computers unworkable. On aeroplanes an activated mobile phone could well interfere with the sensor equipment, causing a pilot to believe that the plane's engine was malfunctioning. His endeavour to correct the assumed fault might then result in his creating a potentially dangerous legitimate failure in the mechanical system. Then, at petrol stations the presence of a functioning mobile can cause enough static charge to ignite fuel vapour.

Like other gadgets of the age, mobile phones were subjected to the technological updates which rendered them more desirable to the public. By 1999 possessing a mobile phone, for the sake of convenience, was not the ultimate objective of modern society. Instead, its aim was to possess the miniaturised and more attractive versions of the machine that offered a range of functions, other than those of providing voice and texting facilities. Gleefully phone operators churned out new models with gusto, and flooded the advertising media with marketing gimmicks, for success would be theirs when the younger generations of customers flocked to buy the wares that would retain their street cred (which means – the need to be seen in possession of the latest technological and clothing fashions).

Transport – Rail

Britain ceased to be an island when, in 1994, the newly built Channel Tunnel was officially opened and the first passenger train went through. There was speculation as to whether the United Kingdom would now be more accessible to people from other countries, eager to enter the country illegally. There was also concern that the animal-carried disease rabies, which proved fatal to humans, would no longer be contained.

During the nineties there were fourteen rail accidents that caused the deaths of fifty-three people, and injury to 743. It was being said that the railway network was dangerous since its privatisation in 1996, and that maintenance work on the lines was being neglected. In 1999 a railway company was fined a record £1.5 million by a criminal court over safety failures that contributed to a crash in 1997. However, at the end of the decade, when it was announced by the railway companies that major work to increase rail safety was to start in earnest, there was an outcry from the British commuting public. They were complaining that this would lead to train cancellations, or delays, which would cause them inconvenience!

Transport – Air

There were plenty of incidental mishaps and near misses in the commercial aircraft industry in the nineties, but as far as crashes were concerned only three occurred in the ten year period. Fortunately, too, there were no deaths or injuries associated with these incidents. However, in the private sector, and the Royal Air Force, aeroplane crashes accounted for the deaths of more than 15 people.

In the 1980s the government of the day greatly encouraged air travel and holidays abroad. During the ten year period air movements from just Manchester International Airport rose from just over 83,000 to almost a 155,000, an increase of eighty-six per cent. When the government approved that a second runway be built at this airport in 1997 there was much protest from residents of the area. Already they had to tolerate the constant noise and pollution that aeroplanes caused, particularly so as aircraft movements had increased so much over the years. They protested and shouted, 'No, No, No!' – but to no avail. An environmental group of protesters too were beaten to the ground by the determination of the government and aircraft industry to increase air travel. This group put their lives at risk by tunnelling underground in an endeavour to stop the building of a runway above them. Some also made their homes in the surrounding trees to halt the felling, clearing the way for the runway. The protestors made their voices heard for a couple of weeks, before security personnel in their hordes evicted them forcefully from the site.

At the end of the nineties there were over thirty international airports operating in the UK with approximately nineteen others dealing with island-bound flying. In the year 1999 there were approximately 1,500,000 air movements from just ten of the international airports of the country, with passengers numbering nearly139,000,000. And, whereas air tour operators numbered only ten in the early seventies, by the end of the century there were hundreds of them. Over the past forty years air travel had increased by approximately 450 per cent, and although aeroplane fuel taxes were nil, the Treasury would always be busy counting the money received by way of airport taxes which had to be paid by every person heading towards the skies. And, not surprisingly, there were very few people who could resist the temptation of doing this, for holidaying abroad, by courtesy of an air tour operator, proved less expensive in the nineties than erecting a deckchair on British shores for a week. It was said that sometimes it cost more to travel to an airport to board a plane than the actual air ticket.

During the last decade it had become apparent that aeroplane travel could cause DVT (Deep Vein Thrombosis) a condition that could prove fatal. It was said that one in twenty people carried an element in the blood that might cause thrombosis to occur, and that sitting in a cramped aeroplane for hours on end could well trigger an attack of the condition. In particular, the risk of developing DVT was said to be high to those people undergoing long-haul flights in economy seats where movement was restricted. Also, it was stated that women taking the contraceptive pill were more likely than anyone else to contract it when travelling by plane.

As the noise of aeroplane engines filtered their drone into the last moments of the twentieth century, and swamped the atmosphere with thousands of tons of carcinogens, the government was joyously awaiting the next hundred years. This was due to the fact that it had planned for there to be more and more aviation movements over this period. Initially it was envisaged that falling prices of forty per cent would bring about a four percent per year increase in air travel, up to the year 2030. To accommodate the swell of tourists and globalised business travellers who would take advantage of the cheaper flights, there would need to be more aeroplanes with more space for take-offs and landings. The government's promise here was that five new runways would be built.

Transport – Roads

During the latter half of the century the number of motor vehicles on Britain's roads had risen from 3,970,000 to 28,368,000. To cope with the volume of traffic more and more roads had to be built and obviously this meant the added sacrifice of the countryside. During the nineties there were six demonstrations of opposition to the situation from the public. The details and outcomes follow:

- when a group of people protested against a motorway extension, six of their number were imprisoned for twenty-eight days;
- 300 people who were protesting against the construction of a motorway link road barricaded themselves in three houses but were forcibly ejected;
- seven protesters were arrested for obstructing workmen who were clearing trees in readiness for a new bypass road;
- in an endeavour to block the path of a motorway extension, people built a treetop village but were forcibly evicted from the site;
- bailiffs evicted people who had made camps on the site of a proposed bypass and thirty-four were arrested for their part in the process; and

- when road improvements were planned to take place a group of people made their protests heard by tunnelling under the ground of proposed sites. They stayed there for a whole week before being forcibly removed by officials.

The efforts made by these people to indicate the public's concern about the environment were once again quashed. It seemed that whatever the government and big business decided to do, they would do it, regardless of opposition to their plans. In a so-called free country there was little opportunity for the people intent on protecting the planet from further damage, to speak freely.

In the middle of the nineties there came a couple of statements that should have made everyone stop and think. The first was from the National Environment Research Council that told of vehicle emissions having affected air quality even in rural areas. The second was from the Transport Minister who was appealing to the public to use their cars as little as possible, because air pollution was being exacerbated by a heat wave. Because the government was well aware that vehicle fumes cause pollution, during the decade several promises were made to combat it by:

- making catalytic converters on cars obligatory on all new cars by 1993;
- freezing carbon dioxide emissions by the year 2000 at the 1990 levels;
- stabilising emissions of carbon dioxide by 2005;
- cutting carbon dioxide emissions by 20% by 2010.

The catalytic converter promise did come to fruition and, in the last couple of years of the century, there was a massive incentive for people to buy new cars. This meant that the land was awash with cheaper second-hand cars (without converters) ready to be driven away! This caused there to be even more cars on the road, so it was hardly likely that the government's target 'freeze' would happen. Then, even if it did, surely the carbon dioxide levels of 1990 were not acceptable to the well-being of the planet. As for the government's 'promise' to cut carbon dioxide emissions by twenty per cent by 2010, could one not ask, 'Twenty per cent of what?' And what of catalytic converters? Well, the notion was that these were environmentally friendly because they emitted less carbon dioxide from the exhaust system. However, apparently these systems did not function on short journeys, and, it appeared that the residue of spent oil emitted into the car instead of into the air. Then there came a couple of suggestions that went like this:

- the Royal Commission on Environmental Pollution recommended that the price of petrol should double over the next ten years, and that public funds should be switched from road building to public transport; and

- the Secretary of State for the Environment published a consultation document outlining options to achieve an integrated transport policy that would reduce the use of private cars.

The reality was that the motor car had become a necessity, rather than a luxury, by the end of the twentieth century. The local shops, within walking distance, were gone; families no longer lived near to each other, and shopping centres and superstores had been built miles away from town centres. Companies, too, had been urged to move their businesses to industrial out of town estates which were linked to motorway systems and airports. Whereas the cry was to raise the price of petrol and put it towards public transport, there surely should have been a surplus of road tax revenue available for this purpose, for in 1999 the road tax for cars alone was £155 per year (and there were over 22 million of them trundling along at this time).

But then even if there had been an integrated transport system, as there was before privatisation of the rail and bus networks, who would have used it? For one thing supermarket, or superstore, shopping meant bulk buying – where one needed a vehicle to ferry goodies home. Without personal transport there would have needed to be a continual fleet of buses (fitted with trailers) to ferry the millions of people (and their purchases) to and from superstores. Then, everything and everyone was placed so far away from each other that the motor car was still proving the quickest method of getting from A to B for those with essential travel needs. The House of Commons Environmental Select Committee seemed to be aware of the travel problems facing the country, and recommended a moratorium on the building of out-of-town superstores. Also, it suggested that the building of suburban retail warehouses should be restricted further. The government thought about these matters and announced that their policy in future would favour new shops being built in town centres, rather than large out-of-town developments. All very well, but the deed had already been done. Were the out-of-town superstores and retail warehouses, which monopolised the UK, to be demolished in favour of new shops in the town centres? Or would the multi-million pound developers who had created these monsters leave them to die a natural death out there? Neither option appeared realistic in the real world.

On the other side of vehicle necessity came the problem of mis-use. People, especially those of the younger generations, would hop into their cars to travel to destinations which might be just around the corner. This applied especially to those who insisted on ferrying their children to schools, regardless of them being within easy walking distance of their homes. By the end of the nineties there were one million car journeys per day made for the purpose of the school run. Then boys not old enough to drive would steal cars for the purpose of joyriding, whereby they hared around the roads at speed to put their own, and others, lives at risk. Others who indulged in this pursuit were the thousands of young unemployed (nevertheless able to afford to own a car) who had nothing better to do than to amuse themselves this way.

The age of the motor vehicle showed us more signs of madness and selfishness than ever before in history. With seventy-four per cent of the UK population owning motor cars, life on the roads was hectic. Sitting behind the driving wheel of one of these metal killing machines, people engaged in a variety of stunts. At speed they would wend their way in and out of ongoing traffic, disregard weather conditions, ignore road hazard warnings, and generally fail to anticipate the risks of their recklessness. Hence multiple pile-up accidents occurred frequently on motorways, especially when there was fog or torrential rain. Another strange thing about the drivers of the day was that if it started to rain their madness seemed to increase, for if the fall was a heavy one they would drive faster (as if avoiding getting wet!) and switch on the vehicle's headlights (making visibility even worse).

There was a code of practice in the UK for road users on which questions were asked when one applied for a licence to drive. However, as the twentieth century neared its end it seemed that everyone had forsaken the rules of the Highway Code. Swinging a vehicle into a road, or pulling out of a parking space, without looking whether another vehicle was already travelling that road, was common practice. At roundabouts drivers would hare around the bends at top speed, challenging other motorists to join the racing circuit at their peril. At these venues there was much horn-blaring, light-flashing and heart palpitation. The latter symptoms also occurred when one's vehicle narrowly missed being hit by another whose owner was driving one-handedly (as he or she needed the second hand to hold his or her mobile phone). Maintaining road safety by parking a vehicle properly had also been abandoned. Drivers would leave their cars wherever there was a space, without considering the hazard caused. On residential roads in towns and cities, where the only place to park vehicles was on the road itself, much aggression was seen. It was a common assumption that owning a house meant owning the part of the road on which it stood. Hence, if a neighbour or visitor deposited a vehicle in front of someone's property, verbal or physical abuse might occur between the parties. The seriousness of where to park one's car was such that many people opted to sell up in order to move to properties where driveways were a feature. Considering that there was so little space for car parking on the roads, it might have been thought reasonable for every resident to take up just enough space to house his or her vehicle. Alas not – with a quick getaway in mind people would take up two car parking spaces. This procedure was adopted in public or supermarket car parks too.

As far as late twentieth century selfishness was concerned, there was no one more suited to illustrate the situation than the average motorist. An anecdote to depict this follows:

In a public car park a young woman was heard to be shouting at two little old ladies. As she stood beside her stationary 4 x 4 (a large fuel-guzzling vehicle which was a must for families with two or more children) she waved her arms about as she hurled abuse. Apparently the ladies' crime was that they had parked their car in a space reserved for 'mother and child'. One of the ladies responded by saying that they held disabled parking permits and could not find anywhere else to park. 'That's not my problem', shouted the young woman, 'you're occupying my space, just move your car'. Both ladies hobbled up to the large vehicle and peered at the young healthy occupants jumping about inside. Leaving the scene one of the ladies turned to the young woman saying, 'Think yourself lucky that you and your children have the use of your legs.' As the couple were leaving the car park I heard one say to the other, 'What kind of selfish world are we living in?' There were tears in her eyes as she spoke.

During the years of the nineties there were a few occasions when it was rumoured that oil shortages were imminent. Immediately the general public flew into panic and rushed to fuel stations, eager to grab as much as they could. Within hours, roads were jammed with queues of vehicles waiting to get to the pumps to fill up tanks, and cans, to capacity. It took only a day or so for fuel stocks at petrol stations to be exhausted and for 'closed' signs to appear. Obviously the demands for replacement fuel could not be met immediately as production of the stuff took time. Even if the refineries held vast stocks they did not possess the fleet of vehicles, or the staff, required to execute fuel deliveries to every station in the land at the same time. Needless to say, the only fuel crises to follow the rumours were those created by a selfish, greedy nation of people.

Television

Perhaps one of the most destructive pieces of technology invented in the twentieth century was television. Even in its early beginnings TV was seen to be transforming human society, inasmuch as people were changing from doers to watchers. With this they stopped thinking also, and allowed those who appeared on TV to do this for them. The mind bending had begun, with the need to think, to talk, to make any effort whatsoever gone. The instrument soon took over people's lives completely. They were being told by the little box that sat in the corner of the living room what to eat, what to buy, where to go, how to get slim, how to handle money, what was bad for them, what made the world go round (the latter information being gleaned from scientific research). Folks were running hither and thither obeying the instructions given them.

Social lives were becoming a thing of the past with people leaving gatherings with the excuse that they had to get home to watch their favourite TV programme. Either this or they would ask their host if they might switch on his or her television as they had forgotten to set their video recorders before leaving home. In the homes of television addicts the picture boxes were switched on first thing in the morning and didn't go blank until the last thing at night. On visiting one of these households it was difficult to have any conversation, because all ears and eyes were focused on the TV. If one did manage to squeeze in a few words here and there, one could never be sure if one's words had got through to the hosts, because of their involvement with the box. Television sets had become the monopolising focus of life in the sitting room. The result was that families stopped talking to each other – and visitors either did not call often, or stopped trying to communicate when they did. Playing with one's babies or children had faded away too. Babies' amusement now came in the form of being placed in a baby bouncer, and plonked in front of the television set (where the brain scrambling began). It was not uncommon either to hear mothers say, 'Oh – this is his or her favourite programme! Young children were usually positioned to sit on the floor beneath the TV. Very often, too, this is where they were handed food to eat. To ensure that television viewing was not disturbed, many families as a whole spent their mealtimes sitting on settees or chairs struggling to stop their plates of food falling from their laps. From a survey carried out in the late nineties it was established that over fifty per cent of British families did not even possess a dining table.

And of course owning the best equipment money could buy was paramount to the TV'ers. They liked their television cinema-style with sounds coming from the sides, the back, and the front of them. So they were always up for it when the latest TV technology came along. They didn't even worry that acquiring the most up to date set would bring them more debt – all they knew was that they had to have it before anyone else did.

As the art of box-goggling became more and more popular, it was seen that people were slipping into a world of unreality. During mists of mindless conversations that happened along, one could hear folk saying, 'Oh I know that's right 'cos the television said so', or 'the television said that salt's bad for you', and so on and so forth. Then one might hear an acquaintance saying to someone, 'Wasn't it awful about Fred, what a way to die'. Thinking that perhaps another acquaintance had met his demise without one knowing, one might ask, 'Who is it that's died?'

With the answer came the realisation that the person who was being talked about was just a character out of a television soap opera. To add to the fantasy of this non-existent world came TV advertising. Here images depicted talking motorcars; singing food; loquacious lavatory pans; dancing settees, etc., etc. (All of which were imitated by folk in their everyday living.) Then there were the programmes that encouraged aggressive competitiveness. In situations resembling those when early Christians were thrown to the lions in the arenas, participants of competitive TV programmes would be asked to strive to become the winner. There was no ruling against dirty tricks being used to outwit one's opponent. In fact, this seemed to be the purpose of the show to appease TV audiences, for it appeared that there was nothing they liked better than watching a winner triumph over a squirming loser. Another favourite of the people was quiz programmes, where competitors could win motor cars, holidays abroad, or large amounts of cash. Audiences would be whipped into a frenzy as candidates gave correct answers to questions and went on to win the coveted prizes. Their enthusiasm was such that it seemed it was they who would actually profit from the effort. Ironically the shows that folk seemed to like best were those named reality TV. Here groups of people lived together under one roof for a period of time and were filmed as they did so. The idea was that they be themselves and interact with each other accordingly, with the aim of proving themselves worthy enough to stay on the programme. The test of this came at the end of each week when the public, after having observed the intimacies of all members of the household, were invited to vote (by expensive telephone call of course) who should be evicted. What made reality TV even more exciting to watch was when celebrities took part in the farces, for here was the chance for the public to see their idols as they really were (supposedly). And again, by picking up a phone, it was the public who decided the fate of the competitors. Other reality programming involved the filming of the interaction between people as they lived out their normal lives at home, or at work. There were also shows where families were invited to interchange with each other. For example, to swap wives, husbands or children for a week and, be captured on screen living with these newly acquired strangers. The most disconcerting evidence that proved that TV had created an unreal world came from the people who lived alone. Often one could hear these folk say, 'Oh the television is company for me – when I switch it on I feel as if there is someone else in the room with me.'

Great attempts were made to safeguard children from adult material, which might include violence, or pornography. These programmes were scheduled for screening after 9pm (when it was thought that children would be in bed), and bore the words 'not suitable for children'. However, in the nineties a great many children had the facility of a TV in their bedroom (which they could switch on at will!)

In the early nineties satellite TV was launched and this would offer two hundred channels. As with cable, the more money one paid, the more programme choice one would have.

In the middle of the decade the government published proposals to create new radio and television channels using digital technology. Government and television? In 1998 the first digital TVs, which worked by placing a box on top of the TV set, went on sale to the public. After the initial purchase of the box, there would be no extra to pay for the increased channels available. In this instance there would be thirty channels for the viewer to choose from, instead of the five current analogue ones. An added feature of digital TV would be that one could interact with it. For instance, by pressing certain coloured buttons one would be able to recall sections of TV programmes, vote when asked to do so, or access additional information. Time once again to get out the cash and credit cards and rush out to buy this new phenomenon. The government announced that when ninety-five per cent of viewers owned digital TV, that analogue services would be discontinued. This being the case there would be five per cent of TV viewers who would be forced into going digital (like it or not) or give up TV.

War

In 1990, under a United Nations resolution, British troops were called upon to go fight a war. This time they were to be shipped out to the Middle East where the Gulf was awaiting them. The reasoning for the encounter was that the ruler of Iraq was mercilessly slaying the peoples of neighbouring Kuwait. Hence, Britain and America decided to go to the rescue. It was feared by these Allied Forces that Iraq possessed weapons of mass destruction, and factories where chemical and biological weapons were being developed. There was no doubt in the Allies' minds that the ruler of Iraq would not hesitate to use germ warfare against them and the whole of the world. For this reason the troops sent in to fight in the Gulf War were given a cocktail of drugs before they left, to combat any monstrous agent they might encounter. As the British Government felt one hundred per cent sure that Iraq possessed the chemical weapon anthrax, and would not fail to use it, British soldiers were given an anthrax vaccine to protect them from the real thing. With this came a hundred per cent assurance from the government that this vaccine was safe to use. Of course the government was well aware of the devastating effects of anthrax, because Britain itself had already carried out experiments with this type of germ warfare, hadn't it?

When one thought of the Middle East encounter it might have been better described as a massacre rather than a war for, unlike any other war, the weapons used by Allied forces were high technology missiles that were expelled from many, many miles away. Programmed to hit designated targets, the missiles would fly silently through the air until their goal was reached. The rulers and people of Iraq were powerless against these weapons of destruction, and didn't get a chance to either defend themselves or fight back. There seemed to be little concern as to how many innocent people would die in the wake of the missiles' path, or which buildings they would hit should they stray from their designated targets. The death toll incurred during the short attack on Iraq was as follows:

- 110,000 Iraqi troops
- 10,000 Iraqi civilians
- 343 Allied troops

There were also five thousand Kuwaiti casualties.

The consequence of the action was illustrated in a declaration which proved a hundred percent success in wiping out all the factories said to have been manufacturing chemical and biological weapons, and those of mass destruction. After the conflict was over it was established that the deaths of Allied forces had been caused not by the enemy, but by their own hands. At an inquest in 1992, into the deaths of nine British soldiers caused by American 'friendly fire' during the War, the jury returned a verdict of unlawful killing.

Skulduggery was also revealed in the same year when a British weapon-making company, Matrix Churchill, was accused of exporting military equipment to Iraq between 1984 and 1990, in breach of a United Nations embargo. The company was taken to court for attempting to export arms without the required permission of parliament. However the weapon-makers stated that parliament was aware of their transactions. An enquiry was set up and the findings were released in 1996. One of the main problems highlighted in the report was 'the decision of the government not to inform parliament of reforms to arms export laws for fear of public outcry.'[i] The Ministry of Defence was also accused of malpractices in 1996, when the Armed Forces Minister said that MPs had misinformed the Ministry over the extent to which troops had been exposed to organophosphate pesticide during the Gulf War.

Despite the pronounced one hundred per cent success of wiping out weapons of mass destruction, and chemical and biological weapons in Iraq in 1991, a British aircraft carrier was ordered to set sail for the Gulf in 1998. The reason? There was increased tension in the area because Iraq was placing restrictions on United

Nations weapon inspectors. 'If Iraq did not co-operate with the diplomatic procedures of seeking out weapons in the country,' said Parliament, 'then force would be used against them'. This in fact did happen when the British and American Operation Desert Fox began. Once again cruise missiles were launched at military and security installations in Iraq. Later RAF Tornado bombers joined in the air strikes on the country. When Operation Desert Fox was over, Britain's Prime Minister was happy to announce that serious damage had been caused to Iraq's military capabilities.

After the war on Iraq it must have been thought appropriate for the government to take a look at Britain's own arsenal, for two announcements were made. The first was in 1995 when they agreed to give up the right to carry out underground nuclear test explosions (a date was not given as to when this might happen). Then in 1997 the government said that Britain would destroy its stock of anti-personnel landmines by 2005. No mention was given to the chemical Ricin, or whether bombs containing this substance were still being manufactured in Portadown (as they were during the Second World War).

The twentieth century did not end without further conflict between Britain and Iraq. When an Iraqi fighter plane breached a No Fly Zone in 1999, six RAF Tornado bombers were sent in to attack an air defence site in Baghdad. When Muslim demonstrators in South Africa protested against these air strikes, police opened fire on them.

The Weather

By the time the nineties came around it was obvious that the weather wasn't the same as it used to be. Now spring, summer, autumn and winter seemed to have merged into a oneness that could produce warm, hot, or cold days at any time. Other facts that were obviously noticeable were the increases of wind and rain. Whereas strong winds had always been associated with winter months, gusts were no stranger now to days of sunshine and cloudless skies. When the rain started it appeared to flow through a broken tap which, once turned on, couldn't be turned off. In the nineties (as in the eighties) Britain witnessed gales, hurricanes and torrential rain which claimed lives, land and property. Strong winds too caused havoc at sea. On one occasion huge waves breached a sea wall in Wales and flooded a town.

Flooding had become such a serious threat to Britain that, by the end of the twentieth century, a special government agency had been set up to deal with the problem. In flood-prone areas advertisements saying, 'Be prepared for flooding – call

Floodline' were being displayed. However, in the eyes of some the government were not doing enough to prevent flooding. They maintained that the environmental department was failing to give ample warning of heavy rain approaching. But then, the government could only rely on the Meteorological Office to supply this information. They in turn could only rely on equipment in place to give them accurate forecasts. As it had been established 'officially' that climate change had occurred, some mocked the Met Office by saying, 'Treat weather forecasts with suspicion as meteorology can be affected by the weather'. However, this agency had become the nerve centre of preventable doom, as far as people in general were concerned. It was expected that they predict exactly where and when rain was going to fall (and how much); when the wind was going to blow (and how strong) and when the sun was going to shine (and how hot). People had reached the stage when they could not get on with today without knowing what tomorrow would bring. If the sun shone on a day when it was not forecast, folk would not accept it with joy in their hearts. Instead there would be murmurs of, 'They said it would be chilly today.' When going out on a sunny morning commenting to passers by, 'Isn't it a lovely day?' invariably the reply would come, 'Ah, but it's going to rain this afternoon.' On rainy days people would say, 'They said it would be sunny today.' When rain occurred on the days 'they' said it would, people seemed to take great delight in pronouncing, 'It's going to be like this all week'. What a heavy burden the Met Office carried in a society doomed to live life according to the predictions it made.

Climate change and unpredictable weather had become a much discussed subject. In 1990 as many as one hundred and thirty-seven countries were present at a World Climate Conference. It was here that an agreement was made to negotiate (by 1992) a convention to limit the emissions contributing to global warming. It was also said that developing countries would have to be provided with scientific and technical assistance to help them meet the requirements of said convention, without losing the benefit of industrialisation! In 1992 a European Commission agreed to end the production, import and use of CFCs in member states by 1995. 1997 recognised another agreement as a United Nations convention on climate change produced a treaty for reducing emissions of greenhouse gases, by an average of five point two per cent between 2008 and 2012. Once again five point two per cent of what? In the mid nineties came two staggering statements – one from the World Meteorology Organisation, stating that damage to the ozone layer over the Atlantic had reached a record. The second, from a British Antarctic survey which reported that a massive iceberg had broken away from Antarctica and that almost every ice sheet there was melting. Evidence of global warming came in 1998 when average world-wide temperatures registered that July was the hottest month ever recorded. As for a winter climate, Britain's Worcestershire witnessed a temperature of 19.6 Celsius on a February day in the same year – once again the hottest mid-winter day ever recorded. However, as the generation of the time expected constant heat, the day would have passed unnoticed. It was only when temperatures fell to say nine or ten Celsius that they acknowledged the climate, and then they would say, 'It's freezing'.

---

i News, bbc.co.uk/onthisday/hi/dates/stories/February/15/newsed2544000/254435

CHAPTER SIXTEEN

Where We Ended

At the end of the twentieth century there were good people and there were bad. The land was awash with millionaires and the status of being poor was gone. The latter had been achieved through the presence of a social state which ensured that no one in the country be without the necessities needed to sustain them.

According to the scientists of the 1990s the time was 'the most intellectual period of man's history'. However man's actions seemed to suggest that the contrary applied. Obsessed by the miracles that his technology had effected, and the wealth it had procured, he believed that his powers were supreme and therefore qualified him to claim dominion over life itself. To this end he chose to gobble up the rules of living, and the wisdom and knowledge that had steered the human species to survival for millions of years, and spit out the pips. To his mind only a new world of his own creation would remain and this he would govern in accordance with his rules. However, despite the glaring truths that his technology had caused great damage to the Earth, and therefore the environment, he planned to carry his activities into the future with increased vigour. Hence the twentieth century ended as no other had done with evolution having seemingly transported *Homo sapiens* to the very edge of insanity.

Strangely, however, in this new world was the overwhelming desire to rediscover the very thing that had been annihilated – the past. The land was swarming with experts and scientists who frantically searched the earth for signs of the life that once might have been. Discoveries of bones, earthenware, scrolls, trinkets, coins, cloth, boxes, stones, etc., were subjected to experiments that would determine their origin. Then all information collated would be fed into computers to produce an accurate picture of events before, and after, the invention of the wheel. Not only were the experts one hundred per cent confident of the authenticity of the results of their findings, they were pretty sure too that they knew the life and speech patterns of those long since transformed to dust. The most staggering information to be revealed to the public was that, by way of scientific experimentation and the miracle of computerisation, the exact moment of the Big Bang (the beginning of the universe) could be established. Folks were astonished by the news and enthralled by the ubiquitous cleverness that existed in their world of superior knowledge.

However, much of the knowledge that emerged from the media, via scientific exploration, was the kind that a primitive caveman would have known by instinct. For instance, that:

- babies' development depends on the nutrition they receive;
- breastfeeding is the safest way of feeding baby; and
- drinking milk increases bone formation in children.

Yet it took many years of study for these obvious facts to become clear to a superior intelligence. If a primitive caveman had heard that scientists were endeavouring to discover why males and females are attracted to each other, he would have laughed uproariously. He would have wondered too why it was so important for scientists to discover why the sky was blue, why one mountain was bigger than another and whether animals can communicate with one another. Whereas the caveman knew by instinct, observation and sense that he was a lesser wonder of the Earth, and therefore accepted whatever nature offered, new twentieth century man felt it essential to prove that it was he who could explain every facet of life. Before the century ended, scientists even declared that their tests had revealed that a foetus (a baby) in the womb cannot feel pain up to twenty-four weeks after its conception.

Perhaps the most arrogantly odious notions of late twentieth century science was the futuristic idea of how humankind could be created in another form. Whilst the practice of nanotechnology was in its infancy as the twenty-first century approached, it was envisaged that within twenty to thirty years the science would have developed to such a high degree that it would propel man to the height of his superior intellect. The outcome would be that he would manufacture electronic bodies to which would be transferred the human mind. Nanotechnology scientists were proudly boasting that these robots would replace the human race!

Until this great feat was achieved it was, however, recognised that existing human beings, with bodily functions, would need to be maintained to maximum functioning levels. For this purpose the advancements of the medical science that had been developed in recent years, would be put into practice.

Gene therapy, for instance, would be essential. This practice involves changing the genes of unborn babies in the womb. Any number of genes could be altered for reasons of taste – for example, choices could be made as to which hair colour or eye colour the child should have. More determinedly, genes that may cause deformity, disease, learning difficulties, etc., could be removed. Even the genes that supposedly caused criminal tendencies in human beings, could be snipped out to stop their development. As far as the future was concerned, life would not be so jolly for those who did not belong to the perfect master race, for geneticists would be on their tail. Cleverly they would be able to predict which illnesses people were going to get by conducting genetic tests, and from here it would be a downhill journey for some, for people diagnosed as being at risk of illness would be unable to acquire mortgages or life insurance because of their condition.

But then, all hope was not lost for these people because, if any of their organs did begin to malfunction, they could be replaced. Whereas at the beginning of the twentieth century the body-snatching boom had abated, it was the seizure of organs that mattered most by the end of it. Because organ failure was so common at the time the British public were besieged to donate their bits and pieces when they died. To this end, responding donors were issued with a card that they carried with them. If unexpected death occurred, a discovered donor card would give surgeons the permission they needed to extract all healthy organs from the body. However, because demand here exceeded supply, other organ harvesting schemes were to be used. For example, there had been several occasions when organs had been removed from dead bodies without permission, that is, without either a donor card being found, or consent being asked from grieving relatives. Then there was the importation of organs. As well as there being a supply of parts for sale, retrieved from the dead of foreign places, those still living were prepared to sell parts of themselves also. In underdeveloped countries, where people starved to death, it was not uncommon for individuals to sell one of their own kidneys in order to eat.

But still, supply did not quell the demand and there needed to be a more reliable method of obtaining organs. Before the century ended scientists discovered an organ manufacturing process that should solve the problem. This would function by courtesy of animals, whereby pigs would become organ donors. Under the heading xenoengineering, leading to xenotransplantation, the animals would be specially bred in laboratory conditions to ensure that their hearts and livers were of the calibre suitable for humans. As the organs to be extracted would only be in the torso of the animals, it would be unnecessary to create fully-fledged pigs. Instead scientists proposed to breed them to be born headless and legless. The people involved in these pursuits believed wholeheartedly that organ transplants should be made on request, and bragged that their industry would bring a lot of money to Britain's economy.

Another contributory component important to the maintenance of the master race that was desired, was cloning. All through the twentieth century scientists had been besotted by their god-like desire to create life. Their work succeeded when, in the latter years of the century, they produced both a man-made rabbit and a sheep. Eager to expand their life-giving skills they envisaged further miracles, one of which was to clone human beings (their desire since the onset). Their theory was that, once they had got the practice right they could enhance it further. For example, it was envisaged that they would be able to implant one of two identical eggs into a womb, and freeze the other. If the child born by way of the implanted egg ever became ill and needed organ transplants, then the second egg would be brought out of the freezer and grown so that its organs could be extracted and transferred to the defective body.

When remembering twentieth century history we might recall the Holocaust during the Second World War. To recap on the comments that were made in its wake, it was said that the atrocities committed during the war were evil, the leader of the enemy was a monster and that the medical experiments carried out on innocent prisoners of war were odious. Promises were made, pledges were signed, and vows were made that never again would evil be allowed to reach such a peak. But now, at the end of the twentieth century, it appeared that the majority of society readily accepted, and condoned, the obscene immorality carried out in the name of science and progress. It never even entered minds that, during the forty years following the Abortion Act as many unborn babies were killed in Britain as the Nazis killed Jews. The masses had been converted into believing that science and technology had surpassed the quantum of human expectations, and had taken them into a world without boundaries.

Life in this new world had been given a dimension that was to lead to Utopia. The sixty million people who trudged around Britain's shores wanted for nothing so there was little need for the art of survival to be practiced. Instead it was advocated that UK residents strive only to achieve anything, and everything, their hearts desired within the long lifespans that were being promised them. Indeed, apart from there being new body parts for old available, there was the assurance that no one need ever grow older. This fact was compounded from the discovery made by scientists that the human body does not have a gene that causes ageing.

In the nineties people were greatly encouraged to believe that they had only one life and that this should be crammed with innumerable pleasures. Then there was the futuristic vision that all suffering that might affect civilised man would be eradicated, and that if all went to plan accidents would cease to be.

The results of these doctrines showed in people's attitudes towards life, inasmuch as they expected everything to be 'just right' for them. In cases of illness it was presumed that doctors had the power to restore health, regardless of the degree of disease or damage present in the body. The miracle-seeking public blamed doctors if they were unsuccessful in saving a patient's life, or even declaring that a patient's condition was beyond medical repair. In many cases people seemed to think that doctors were responsible for allowing illnesses to develop in the first place. Folk were so scared of dying that they had grown afraid of living too. Present in the nanny state, that Britain had become, was a tumultuous neurosis which prompted the public to wait anxiously for instructions from experts as to what they should either avoid, or indulge in, to preserve their lives and well being. If it were to be advocated that staying indoors all day without moving was the only way to guarantee the safety of life and limb, this is what would have happened.

Another foible of late twentieth century people was their inability to be satisfied with their lot in life. Regardless of the assets they possessed they always wanted more. They craved bigger or better houses, flashy cars, and the latest technological gadgets. It was essential that they acquire the most up to date housing and clothing fashions, and indulge in taking as many foreign holidays as possible. Their kids too needed to be equipped with the technology of the day to keep them abreast of their contemporaries. It also had to be seen that parents were affluent enough to fund expensive school holidays abroad for their offspring. What all this meant was that cash was needed – lots of cash. This was acquired from the moneylenders of the day who were more than eager to relinquish their stocks of sterling for a profit. At the end of the twentieth century the British public was in debt to the tune of nearly one trillion pounds and they seemed proud of it. It was the fashion to borrow money. Everybody did it they said. The idea was that if you wanted something, then you must have it without worrying about the cost. After all, wallets and purses were filled with little pieces of plastic that procured funds on demand. Brandishing a credit card, or a store card, seemed to lull people into believing that they were successful and therefore affluent. They thought themselves clever as they handled their plastic as a millionaire would thumb his bank statements. Very little thought was given to repayments and the massive interest rates demanded by lenders. It never occurred to these clever people that what they might be were fools, for in reality, what they were doing was paying for their acquisitions many times over – as they would if they paid a shopkeeper £20 for an item priced at £5. But the people of the nineties paid little heed to thoughts like this, as they were only concerned about the indulgences of the moment. Tomorrow did not seem to matter, nor did the consequences of their actions. They could not envisage that one day their credit limits could reach saturation point, when the whole of their salary would be consumed by debt. However, as the people of the day left the management of their finance to the banks, they were often oblivious as to when this might occur. For all money transactions in the nineties were operated via banking systems that controlled clients' accounts. For example, it was standard procedure for bills to be paid on the same day of every month by way of direct Debit. This involved the transfer of money from client accounts to creditor ones. Should there be no funds available to honour the transaction, then clients' bank accounts went automatically into overdraft mode where interest rates were incurred.

Because it was the culture of the time to turn to others to sort out any problems that might arise in life, those who experienced that day of reckoning hurried off to consult with debt counsellors. The advice given here might be to engage the services of a professional debt management company who would maintain the debtor's affairs. Alternatively, the suggestion may be for the heavy borrower to consolidate his or her debts, and transfer them to a credit card or loan operator who charged less interest than others. The purpose of this would be to acquire a loan which would settle all immediate debts, to leave the debtor with one loan to pay where repayments were lower than before. This method of obtaining credit might have been the incentive some people needed to clear their debts completely, but in general it was the opportunity to increase them.

However with faith in a spiritual god, a supreme power or even a soul, gone from the lives of the people of the 1990s, devotions had been directed elsewhere, with money rating as the greatest icon of them all. All life revolved around its power, and everything was measured by cost. Even in the wake of disastrous events, it was the price for clearing up that took precedence over the mourning for those who had lost their lives. Surely an indication that everyone knew the price of everything but the value of nothing.

After money came the worship of sexuality and the body. For the first it was promoted that sex was the pleasure in life that should not be missed. It was advocated that even people in their seventies, eighties or nineties enjoy sex to the fullest (to aid them in their frolics, centres were set up to give tips on the art of seduction). There were no barriers – no limits in the promiscuous society that applauded sensuality, pornography and sex at will. The belief seemed to be that Mother Nature had not invented the activity for the purpose of procreation, but for their unlimited pleasure only. Sex was rammed down people's throats so much that it was felt that indulgence in the sport was compulsory, and that the inclination to decline would signify abnormality. Because of this, young men in their prime bought Viagra to keep in their pocket in case they needed it whilst on a night out. This they did to prove their sexual prowess to every maiden who wanted to play the mating game.

As to the body, it was the fashion to seek out perfection. With trends to be thin, a vast number of people were persuaded to indulge in gymnastic pursuits in order to wear away any bulges they did not want. Along with this came dieting. There were hundreds of non-fattening products and slimming concoctions on the market. There were slimming clubs, and a range of diet plans to ensure total thinness for everyone who desired it. Even children as young as five were anxious not to put on weight, so refused food they considered fattening. By the end of the twentieth century eating disorders had become killer diseases. Those who could only see themselves as fat would, after eating, make themselves vomit or cause a bowel evacuation (by use of laxatives). The continuation of such bodily abuse often caused organ malfunction that sometimes resulted in death.

Then on the other side of the coin was the problem of obesity. Doctors were concerned that people – particularly children – were becoming so fat that their bodies might suffer ill health in time to come. In view of this the government feared that more money would be needed by the NHS should these fatties develop chronic diseases. Hence talks of operations to tie the stomachs of children, who were grossly overweight, became the order of the day. (Whilst Britons in general were already up to their eyes with the nanny state conditions of the country, many of them were appalled by this barbaric suggestion.) Maybe, too, the purveyors of fast food were sick of government interference, for they were asked to reduce the fat content of their products. (This was an incentive for some regular burger and chips eaters to attempt to sue fast food outlets for their overweight problems!)

The height of body enhancement was reached by those who underwent surgery to achieve it. Cosmetic surgery clinics, where people could go to seek operations to adjust their bodies to their liking, were abundant. They might ask for a new nose, because they didn't like the one they'd got already. They might consider their breasts too small, or too large, so alterations would be requested. Then there was the nip and tuck treatment which proved an effective method of ridding a body of excess fat. All the surgeons need do here was to cut out unwanted flesh from the body, then tuck in the leftover skin. For those with money enough to spare, or those who were happy to incur more debt, there were no heights that could not be reached as far as bodily enhancements were concerned. Lips, ears, cheeks, faces, necks, etc., could be renewed for a fee.

The people of the nineties were so conditioned to expect everything to be just right that even the weather came under scrutiny when it did not comply with the scheme of things. Folks bemoaned the rain, the fog and the wind, and utterly went into panic if snow started to fall and ice began to form. When hurricanes, floods, landslides and earthquakes occurred there were outcries of rage against the planet, suggesting that it was a cruel and violent place. The developed *Homo sapiens'* attitude was one that thought it all right for the species to inflict any amount of suffering on the planet, but it was wrong for it to retaliate. (In Japan there was even talk of action being taken against the government there because houses, and other structures, had collapsed under weather pressure due to its guidelines. What the people wanted was for it to ensure that buildings be erected in a way that would render them indestructible). In the case of flooding it was suggested that environmental agencies were ineffective in pre-warning the general public of the waters coming. If snow arrived, and driving was hampered by the event, it was town council officials who were blamed for the situation. It was said that they should have prevented the roads becoming impassable by applying grit before the snow fell.

Not only did late twentieth century people expect permanent sunshine, they wanted capacity warmth with it too. And constant heat was required in the home and workplace at all times. For this purpose, central heating boilers toiled endlessly to produce the heat required to keep temperatures high. At home folks dressed to suit their tropical living conditions and, if it became too warm indoors they would open all the windows to release the hot air into the atmosphere. This procedure would be operated at work too, with the proviso that electric fans could be switched on if it became unbearably hot. At work and at home, it never occurred to anyone to turn the central heating down if temperatures indoors became too hot. Also no-one considered putting on extra clothing, if they felt chilly, to eliminate the need for maximum heating. Though it was common knowledge that the planet was warming to unsustainable levels because of mankind's demand for energy, little thought was given to conservation. Whilst meek persuasions were made to encourage the general public to go out and buy low voltage electrical appliances to save power, it was not advocated that the shameful waste of the stuff be stopped.

Industry had been transformed during the latter years of the twentieth century. Whereas in the past the word had been commonly used to describe the places where the manufacture, or mining, of products occurred, it was now applied in a different context. With Britain's manufacturing industries gone, it was now non-productive activities that were dubbed thus. For example – tour operators, insurance companies, film makers, supermarkets and farming had become industries. Holidays, life policies, films, pre-bought goods and cattle had become products. And, of course, the newest industry there would be would be that of organ manufacture, with body parts as the products.

The death of British manufacturing was brought about by the capitalist fraternities of the time who sought to earn bigger profits from their goods. Around the middle of the century clothing manufacturers found it cheaper to import cotton, wool and silk from under-developed countries than to buy it from British producers. This caused a slump in these industries and, by the seventies, the mills which produced these items, and employed many thousands of people, faced inevitable closures. After this many rag trade bosses decided to withdraw their contracts with the British manufacturing companies who assembled garments for them to sell. Large British manufacturing conglomerates were the first to recognise that the Britons of the eighties were better off now, and not desperate to acquire work, which was poorly paid. Employed persons earned decent salaries, and there were easily acquired loans to be had. For those without jobs, the state benefits and payouts they received surpassed the levels of low wages. Hence, the exploitation of the British workforce was no longer an option, so the practice was transferred to underdeveloped, or third-world countries. Here the poor, underprivileged populations were willing to work for very little reward. There was no concern that many who complemented the sweat shops of foreign lands were children (a story similar to that of early twentieth century British kids). As far as exploitation went, it was not only the British clothing trade that chose to accumulate wealth in this manner, for many other manufacturing concerns had taken the same path. Lots of large companies had even transferred their administration processes to countries where wage costs were low, having trained the natives in the use of Western techniques.

Although the workforces of Britain had travelled beyond the realms of exploitation, the land still held pockets of people who were victims of the practice. For instance, it was reported that some groups of underprivileged Britons were working for no more than £5 per week. These people were those with learning difficulties and who worked in factories five days out of seven assembling items for re-sale. It was said that in some cases these people had to pay for the privilege of working. Then there were the folk who had entered Britain illegally and were desperate for food and shelter. Knowing their plight, many smaller companies would break the law and pay them a pittance to secure their unlawful employment. Supermarket bosses were careful not to engage in such pursuits, though they knew of a man who would. He was someone called the gang master and his job was to recruit masses of people to harvest farm crops designated for supermarket shelves. As payment for crop picking was to be kept to a minimum, to ensure low selling prices, the gangmaster would only recruit people prepared to work for very meagre wages. Asylum seekers and illegal immigrants fitted the bill. Also, because they had nowhere else to live, they were forced to take shelter in the squalid accommodation offered by the gangmasters. In many cases these were metal containers, tents or sheds with no running water. It was common practice, too, for some farmers to pay the passage to Britain of migrant workers wishing to participate in food harvesting. In many cases, however, the only reward these workers received was that of food and shelter. Other cheap labour was utilised by many other businesses that ignored the National Minimum Wage Act rules. Because there were thousands of overseas visitors who were prepared to work for small reward, their services were frantically sought, with the hotel and restaurant trades employing a large percentage of them. For the women who had no alternative but to work from home, their reward for their toil was scanty, as the National Minimum Wage Act did not even extend to this area.

With the death of British industry came the demise of unions. Although unions were still operational in the few large industries that lived on in the country, their voices had become inaudible. As working conditions had been raised to comfortable levels, and there was a National Minimum Wage Act in operation, Britain's workforces no longer had the need to shout about their woeful plights. Also the power of the unions had been diminished greatly by the actions of the 1980s government, which had removed the right for them to lead their members into mass striking and picketing. The long-lasting and violent strike of the coal miners in 1984 was an action that would never again be repeated in Britain. As far as coal was concerned, this British industry was a mere skeleton, with most mines having closed down. It was regarded unprofitable to retain an industry that was obsolete to demands. After all very few people burned coal anymore, nor did trains or other steam-producing machines. The greatest demand for coal came from the power stations and this need was fulfilled, as it had been for many years, by the importation of the fuel.

As the nineties dwindled to an end it was clear to see that Britain had become a wasteful and throwaway nation. If appliances ceased to function it was the norm for people to replace them, instead of attempting repair. (Also it was a fact that many items were manufactured to a non-repairable standard.) Not only were broken articles discarded, others in good working order were sent packing too. This was because it was the vogue to keep in fashion, in home and garden, by following trends set by television programming. This could mean that if a toaster, oven or microwave did not match newly-designed kitchen colour schemes, it would have to go. The same applied to every other room of the house whereby furniture, crockery, bedding etc would be slung out to make way for more up to date and colour-coordinated stuff. The result was that town tipping sites were filled with hundreds of tons of unwanted articles each day. On top of these were dumped the plethora of wrappings incurred by pre-packaging. For everything in the nineties, from food to computers, was factory-packed for safe handling. Electrical goods were bound in plastic, buffered by polystyrene blocks then fitted into strong boxes, as was the ninety per cent of flat-pack furniture that was bought. As the massive container lorries left the tipping sites daily, loaded with the refuse bound for landfill sites, it was wondered by some if the earth would one day consist of nothing but rotting rubbish. Then of course not everything thrown away by late twentieth century people would rot down. As long as the planet survived so too would man-made items such as PVC, plastic, incontinence pads, disposable nappies, etc., and millions of TV sets, unwanted because of new digital programming.

Although tipping facilities were provided in every town in the country, not everyone felt obliged to use them. There were those who chose to ferry their unwanted items to wastelands, parks or railway embankments and dump them there. Alternatively, in inner city and town areas, people would deposit their rubbish in the back alleyways of their homes. This procedure applied to household waste also and black plastic bags, filled to overflowing, were added to the debris. The result was that, as many bags were ripped apart by nocturnal food-seeking animals, litter was scattered everywhere. Apart from rendering areas unclean and offensive, this also posed a health hazard as it invited disease-carrying rats to visit. But, although it was known that the rat population was double that of the human count, and that bluebottles thrive in muck, little was done to stop the British public from dumping. There were anti-litter laws in operation, but they were not enforced because councils considered it too costly to bring prosecutions against offenders. Instead cleansing departments employed workers to go around with brushes and shovels clearing up the mess (which is exactly what the people expected of them). Streets and roads of Britain were deluged with litter too, for people thought it acceptable to either drop their waste wherever they stood or throw it out from car windows. Hence everything from fast food containers to disposable nappies were seen lining pathways waiting to be cleared up. (Ironically though, in many counties, people who dropped cigarette butts in the road were fined for doing so.)

In general the pride that used to be shown by displaying one's cleanliness had gone. No longer was it necessary to indicate one's self respect by maintaining the tidiness of one's living area, or one's country. Dignity was now pronounced by the array of assets and their condition. And, in this competitive area, it had to be seen that one's home featured the latest in trendy house gear in order to qualify for recognition of worth. The motor car too was symbolic of this notion with success achieved by those who inspired heads to turn at the sight of their top of the range vehicle. Regardless of demands on the use of their time, people (especially men) deemed it essential that their cars be cleaned and polished on a weekly basis in order to retain the admiration of their contemporaries.

Though the act of recycling did not come naturally to modern-day people, it was recognised that it would have to be reinstated into twenty-first century living. Fears that the Earth's resources were being drained to the point of depletion, meant that certain minerals would be unavailable in the future. Whilst other countries had realised this fact many years earlier, and had already installed recycling services, Britain had not. However, before the twentieth century ended many British town councils had provided ecocentres where items such as glass, wood, cardboard, paper, clothing, shoes, oil, building rubble, metal, plastic, garden waste etc., could be taken to be recycled. A few pilot schemes were also put into place whereby councils supplied containers to homes and, asked people to deposit their used cans, bottles and paper in them. The containers were to be left at front gateways every two weeks so that council workers could empty them. Alas, as neither of these recycling procedures was compulsory, only the handfuls of people who had pride and concern for their planet used the facilities. The majority continued to sling all their waste into the rubbish bags which ended up in landfill sites.

Even though the rag-and-bone man had long since ceased to characterise Britain's roads, rag merchants had continued their pursuit of cloth into the latter half of the twentieth century. However, their supply now came via other avenues – the main source being charity shops. It was common these days for folk to take their unwanted clothing, and nick nacks, to be resold at the shops which raised money for charities. If clothes remained unsold after a period of time, shop volunteers would bundle them up and pass them on to rag merchants for recycling. As clothes recycling facilities were now provided by town councils, the rag merchants' vans often collected there too. For those who wished to profit by selling unwanted belongings, instead of giving them away, the recycling options of car boot sales, newspaper advertising and the Internet were available.

Not only had the people of the time forsaken the duty of living their own lives by expecting others to do this for them, many had lost the innate instincts attributed to humankind. For instance, there were those who did not have a clue of how to handle babies, or bring up children, and had to attend classes where lessons on parenting were taught. Alternatively they would read books on the subject, pick up leaflets from baby clinics, or surf the Net for information. Similar lessons, or written suggestions, were offered to those who sought how to make their marriages work. Perhaps the most alarming fact to emerge was that children, on the whole, did not possess the basic ability to do what should come naturally to *Homo sapiens* – communicate. Because of this there came the need for kids to attend classes where they would learn the basic art of talking to each other. It was not only children who experienced communication problems, as getting through to people was proving more and more difficult. Often they seemed to fail to understand the simplest of questions, instructions or statements sent in their direction and might gaze before them with blank expressions. Proving too that memory functions were on the blink, people would forget what had been previously told them, with the consequence that repeat conversations occurred on a regular basis. Another indication was the thousands of silly notices that were displayed here, there and everywhere, to help people to get through their days successfully. For example, on car park entrances notices read 'IF CAR PARK FULL PROCEED TO ANOTHER CAR PARK'. Food labelling bellowed 'REMOVE PACKAGING BEFORE COOKING'. Suppository capsules were marked – 'REMOVE

CELLOPHANE BEFORE INSERTING' and 'DO NOT SWALLOW'. Whereas electrical lifts would warn – 'USE THE STAIRS WHEN POWER CUTS OCCUR'. Then, before using microwave ovens it was all-important to check that food was available to cook in them, for their notices read 'DO NOT PUT LIVE ANIMALS INSIDE'. Which meant of course that one could forget the idea of serving up the family budgies for dinner!

The working masses of the late twentieth century had everything they could want to promote happiness and contentment in their lives. However, despite their good fortune, this seemed to elude the majority of society, who favoured bemoaning their lot in life. In general, living had become a solitary function within a culture which advocated that one should consider oneself, and one's assets, above all else. To achieve the first meant that executing personal desires, over those of others, took precedence. For the second would be the need to secure one's belongings against theft by one's fellow men. Besides involving the installation of alarms, security lights, barbed wire, metal bars or guard dogs in one's home, there was also the requirement that window locks, and many door locks, be fitted. Locked tightly within the confines of their homes, people would wait tensely for sounds (or lights) that would indicate the coming of an intruder intent on stealing their possessions. Eluding the custodians of riches was the fact that the display of security systems on their homes was an indication that there were treasures within worth stealing. It also missed their attention that burglars would be happy to ransack their homes if they were out, because activated alarms were ignored by one and all (other than those who eventually would complain of noise pollution).

Whereas the century had provided a mass of nourishment and medical benefits to maintain people's good health, it could not be proclaimed that they were one hundred per cent well. Apart from there being an epidemic of depression, there was also one of a lethargy that shouted of weariness. Everywhere one looked mouths were seen to be yawning and people could be heard to say, 'I'm so tired', 'I'm too tired to think' or 'too tired to speak'. It appeared that energy levels were so low that all that lots of people (including children) wanted to do was to sleep, or slouch about. Before the century ended a study that had been undertaken to establish how tiredness was impeding work, sex and play, proclaimed that, 'fatigue was a phenomenon of modern day life'.

Whilst food, shelter, water and warmth had been the priorities that humankind had sought throughout the ages, late twentieth century people considered these assets a right. However, though their priorities had been shifted to the pursuit of pleasures and possessions, there seemed very little joy in many lives. The problem was considered so acute that in 1998 a twenty year study was commissioned to determine how happiness can be achieved.

PART THREE

And Then What?

CHAPTER SEVENTEEN

Life

'There are no secrets, there is no mystery, there is only common sense.'
North American Turtle Clan philosophy

With the passing of the twentieth century there can be little doubt left as to the accuracy of the prediction of 1854 which was made by North American Chief Seattle. However in his prophesy this wise old man did not forecast that the cleverness of 'the white man' would peak prematurely during the period to lose him many centuries of natural slow evolution, for no mere mortal could ever have envisaged this. With the event came worldwide revolution, both socially and environmentally, for man now possessed a mighty weapon that he had not yet learned how to use for the good. Therefore he used it to create technology that was capable of altering the pattern of life itself, and commenced to inflict more devastating damage on the earth, and its people, than had been inflicted during the entire history of the human race. Furthermore, because he believed that this cleverness superseded all else, it was decided that all the rules and codes, that had been passed down from generation to generation throughout the existence of mankind, be zoomed out into space because they were obsolete. Zoomed out too was the common sense of humankind for it was reasoned that this measured little against the extent of cleverness that existed.

With the absence of rules, codes and common sense, what most of us have are ponderous thoughts which ask; is there a true meaning of life, and where might evolution take us next? We may reason that the human race was created so it might be observed just how far it would go if cleverness increased to capacity. Then, if it would be automatically returned to a state of origin if man presumed that this gave him dominion over his creator - the Earth. However the march of evolution and its consequences are beyond human control and, therefore, should be of no concern to us. What should interest us is that we have the power to command happiness from our lives regardless of evolutionary circumstances. Why? Because this is the reason we are born to the Earth.

Amongst twenty-first century Britons there are those who plead for the causes of the lawlessness and immorality that exist in the land to be found. But is a search really necessary, for did not these things materialise when the rules and codes of life were abandoned during the twentieth century? We might then say that it is governments who are to blame for our plight, but consider this:- whilst politics are the voice of big business and it is mighty politicians who make this voice heard, it is we – the people – who take the major steps to put the words into practice. Because this is so, is it not true that if *we* have the power to make things happen we could, if we made the choice to, make them happen for the better under our own steam? Or will we instead choose to sit around for another ten years waiting for the results of the 'how to be happy' survey to be revealed?

Before I undertook to write this book I interviewed a large number of people aged between fourteen and forty to learn their opinions of life. Sadly the majority of comments I received were of dour, dismal and despondent proportion, with only a few indicating a rosy future. If we look at some of these comments with common sense, this might enable us to see life in perspective. From here we could go on to witness the hope of life that Mother Nature intended all human beings to experience.

Comments

These days – 'we live in a nanny state, and there's always someone telling us what to do.'

Facts

When the codes and rules of life were removed in the twentieth century it was, however, appreciated that there needed to be some rules in the new technological world. Hence, armies of scientists, experts, professors, specialists, etc. were enlisted to invent some. The trouble was though that most of the time battles raged within the ranks as members fumbled to reach the same conclusions. What resulted was an ever-increasing collection of mouths that opened to ooze words that said nothing. However, despite the fact that no one seemed to know in which direction they should be heading, there were times when some codes were established. Ironically though these often proved laughable, for after years of survey, study or experimentation, what the experts had come up with were old-fashioned codes that had been practised throughout the centuries, and not original ones to befit this new world. Nonetheless, regardless of the conflict of opinion that existed expert to expert, people became reliant on them to tell them how to live their lives. They wanted to know what might kill them; contribute to their hair falling out; make them fat; reduce their sex drive; help them keep slim; help them produce babies; ensure they enjoy sex; show them how to eat healthily and so on and so forth. It was also taken as a right to be advised what the future had in store. For example, to be told what the weather was going to be like for the coming weeks; to be advised of the sex of babies they carried in their wombs; to be notified if anything untoward was about to happen in other countries they were to visit, etc. Then, there was always a barrage of questions to be asked of those with knowledge of specialised subjects. For instance, when being interviewed for television or radio these people may be asked, 'Is there likely to be another earthquake in the not too distant future?', 'Why did the building fall down?', 'How near are you to finding the murderer?' ,'Could the incident have been avoided if there had been more vigilance?' And so on, and so forth.

But then, promises had been made that no western denizen need endure any of the hardships or strife that human beings had suffered throughout the ages. This, it was said, was because the miraculous benefits of technology would eliminate these things from life. Therefore it was not surprising that, in late twentieth century days, the demeanour of people was that of spoilt children who stamped their feet at anyone they could when things went wrong for them. By the end of the century so much of life's meaning had been lost that people no longer knew how to cope with it. What was left were painting-by-numbers lives, with the canvasses void of the splashes of colour and the erratic brushstrokes that create richness and depth. Gone was the oomph that constitutes the challenges of life; the oomph of natural emotion and self-motivation which are the embodiment of humanity; the oomph that provides substance on which to hold and essence of which to breathe.

Possibilities

We could choose to realise that we are all responsible for our own actions and resume the practice of making our own decisions by virtue of our own observations; decisions which we feel will bring the consequences that we would like to see. And to make us recognise that life really is what we make of it, we could renew the art of making the best of whatever challenges or cherishes the days bring. We could put an end to the nanny state by demonstrating our desire not to be nannied any more. But, as a whole, we won't.

Comments

'Because of our wonderful technology we are a more advanced culture than all who have gone before us.'

Facts

Perhaps the most nonsensical notion that carried over from the twentieth century to the twenty-first is this one. If we recall that we live in fear of annihilation, whereas our ancestors had no reason to have such a fear, we should be wondering if, because we have put ourselves in this situation, we are in fact inferior to them. If we were then to look at the reason they managed to survive their lives more successfully than us, we would need to acknowledge two things. The first; they did not have technology, but they did have the instinct to follow the fundamental codes of life. The second; we have technology up to the eyeballs, but lack the reasoning to tread the paths of life as they should be trodden. What is more, when we put our complete faith in the sciences of mankind, the people of the past would have regarded these as nought but a by product of the prowess of Mother Nature. A prowess that is the wealth of her knowledge, and which science is now probing to discover.

Furthermore, if we were an advanced culture we would have learnt how to revere life to practice only compassion, empathy and mercy towards all living beings regardless of their status. But we don't, do we? For instance, the majority of us do not scorn the painful misery that is inflicted on slave workers in overseas countries who toil to manufacture cheap goods for us. Instead we close our eyes to the facts that media coverage reveals of their circumstances, because our overwhelming desire to acquire these goods is greater than the one we have to see an end to the suffering of these people.

Then, although technology has provided mankind with clinical and epidemiological studies, cell and tissue cultures, mathematical, computer and mechanical models and audio-visual guides as alternatives to medical experiments on animals, we still continue to conduct them for the sake of financial profit. We also condone tortuous experiments being carried out on animals even though they maim or kill them, and all for the sake of testing products for humans to use. Do we do these things because we think we are superior to animals because of our cleverness? Well, from the feel of the earth and the touch of the air, wildlife can tell when tempestuous weather is afoot and will scurry from its path for safety, whereas man needs state of the art technology to tell him the same, but then waits until it arrives so he can watch! How clever is this? And, would any living creature be so stupid as to damage the environment that gives it life as Man does?

Possibilities

We could try to acknowledge the truth which tells that no culture will ever be a perfect one, regardless of the advancements that have been, and will be, achieved through evolution, for the one thing that has never, or will ever, change is man himself, because this is how it is supposed to be. We could endeavour to learn that no human being can derive happiness from being the source of suffering to another living being. We could begin to realise that without animals, insects, birds, fish etc. we human beings would cease to exist, for it is they who ensure our food supply and maintain the good health of our ecology. This applies even to the common earthworm, without which there would be no plants, or the insects that pollinate these both summer and winter to enable them to fruit or flower. But, as a whole, we won't.

Comments

These days, 'there's no discipline, people can get away with murder and it's not safe to go out into the streets'.

Facts

When we come to Earth as humans we are born with basic instincts that advise of the good behavioural paths we should tread through life, and consciences that tell of the wrongs we should not commit against fellow beings. These are given to help us to be self-disciplined human beings and, therefore, happy ones. However in an imperfect world self-discipline does not come easily, for temptations to pander to the selfish desires inherent to human nature are greater than the ones we have to restrain them. Therefore, until we absorb the boomerang effect of life and the importance of self-discipline, we must have the discipline of others to maintain our good behaviour. This is as important to our growth as the food that we eat and the air we breathe. It is the birthright we depend upon to provide our mental and moral training, and is the one we crave from the moment of our birth. However, rarely can discipline be acquired through instruction alone. Who of us has learned lessons of right and wrong just by listening to commands that advise what we are allowed to do, and what is not permissible? As naughty human beings the more we are told not to do something, the more we are tempted to try it. Therefore when we commit the same wrong over and over again the only thing that will make us mend our ways is the punishment that, in future, we will do our best to avoid. If we reflect on history we will see the logic of these facts, for only a very small proportion of people from the past were subjected to punishment, because the majority of them avoided its onslaught by obeying the laws of the land to the letter. Furthermore, up until the mid-twentieth century leather straps hung by many fireplaces to warn the children of the house that this would be used on them if their behaviour was offensive. Very rarely were they used, and seldom was there the need for parents to reprimand children with a cuff!

It may be said that discipline must not be secured through punishment as this is cruel, but surely it is more so to deny the right to be disciplined. After all, only those who have learned self-discipline in life will go on to find the happiness that accompanies it. If all this is doubted for lack of scientific proof, then common sense will tell us that we have this in the form of The Human Rights Act of 1998. With the Universal Declaration of Human Rights, which was completed in 1948, came good reason. This was to ensure that the kind of tyrannical actions imposed on many during the Second World War would never again be allowed to happen in worldwide society. (Unfortunately this declaration proved ineffective, for as the century progressed a catalogue of tyrannical acts were committed against the peoples of the world.) However, with the 1998 revision of the Act came a different dimension. Because, in late-twentieth century days, pockets of do-gooding people with loud voices insisted that only an inferior and uncivilised culture would subject the wrong doers of society to the punishments of old, its purpose was now to safeguard the rights believed to belong automatically to human beings of the developed world. Within the boundaries of the Act, however, there is still great confusion as it is found ludicrously difficult to define it. Therefore, folk kill and steal as if by licence to do so, for it is generally assumed that the Human Rights Act is to protect all people from punishment of any degree, or from discrimination. Children also ignore the directives of their superiors to shout, 'I've got my rights and no one can touch me'. As to the people who have become self-disciplined enough to honour the laws of life and the land, they are despondent of their efforts to prevent anarchy. As well as having to tolerate the reduced quality of life that lawbreakers cause, they also have to sacrifice any human rights *they* should have. The questions they ask are, 'If human beings deliberately set out to hurt, cheat, kill, steal from or lie to others, do they not forfeit all rights to receive respectful consideration from fellow beings? And should not the majority of people who uphold laws and offer only good-mannered behaviour be rewarded with justice?' Of course, in a just world the answers to these questions would be 'yes'. However justice has never automatically prevailed in the world, nor is this ever likely, especially so now when indifferences in the laws that govern the manufacture and use of firearms and other weaponry are present. Justice is the element of life which has always had to be pursued, and will always require pursuit, by those with courage enough to challenge injustice.

Possibilities

We could attempt to recognise that if we are disciplined we are on the right road to happiness, but if we are not then we are on the cobbled and miserable one to unhappiness. If the first applies we could try to feel empathy towards the undisciplined and offer them the example and instruction of discipline that they desperately lack. If the second is the case we could try to establish if it makes us feel good when we adhere to the lessons we receive from the disciplined. As far as nature's natural punishment of children is concerned, we could realise the truth that the abandonment of this will do nothing to prevent the beatings that 'monsters' inflict on them, irrespective of any law which prevails. But, as a whole we won't.

Comments

These days, 'you can't trust anyone, and it's not safe to let children out alone.'

Facts

Despite the fact that the strict rules of law and order (and therefore enforced discipline) have been abandoned, let's hold on to the positive aspect of life. This is that Mother Nature planned for there to be more qualities than faults present on Earth at all times. This means that there is more goodness in the world than bad, with more good deeds performed daily than bad, and this is how it will always be. Mind, the reason we tend to believe that our world is swamped with badness is that the media throws news of this at us unmercifully day in, day out. We are inundated with details of (it seems) every single incidence of mishap, injustice, accident and the like that happen around our shores, with the inference that someone has done something bad to cause them. To add to this, news items are thrust down our throats which tell of the troubles and terror that exist in other countries of the world. When there is murder afoot, especially so if this takes the life of a child or if a child is abused, the minute details of the incident are chronicled over and over again until our minds absorb the content to assume that our world is full of monsters. Therefore, a culture of fear has developed within society that promotes the notion that no one can be trusted. But this is wrong, and we need to become open-minded and aware of perspective to realise this truth. For instance, when, in early twentieth century days, bad people abducted children and women from the streets to bond them into prostitution, and murdered them if they tried to escape, did folk believe this cause to mistrust the whole of society? No they did not, because they were not brainwashed into accepting that the actions of the minority reflected the status of the majority.

As mistrust goes, perhaps the most shameful example of this is the doubt of the natural love and respect that can exist between older and younger human beings. Throughout the existence of mankind, bonds between the aged and the young have been regarded as naturally beautiful, as they reflect the greatest love and respect life can offer. To an older person the innocent actions of a child portray the trust, sincerity, enthusiasm and vitality that he or she once felt. To a child an older person is the book of knowledge that contains the wisdom they hope some day to have. The two are on the same wavelength and on a par unique to living. But, in the scourge of public mistrust the old are regarded as possible child molesters and, therefore, are scorned if they attempt to interact with children who approach them, but whom they do not know. How sad to think that the joy of seeing a small child offering a tiny pair of hands to an aged stranger attempting to rise from a chair, or climb a step, or of seeing the awe in a child's gaze as it listens to an aged stranger giving an answer to the question it had asked, is missing from life.

Mother Nature bestowed us with the task of learning to trust in others because it is of paramount importance to human development. If we go through life mistrusting all, then we will see nothing but the ugliness that this cynicism brings and happiness will evade us. On the other hand, if we recognise trust given gladly we will see the beauty of it and happiness will follow.

Possibilities

We could make ourselves aware of the fact that more often than not the victims of child abuse suffer at the hands of people they know. We could stop believing that every group of youths we encounter is intent on causing us harm, or that the clothes they wear are an indication of this; that all people who smile at us, or ask for directions or the time, do so because they intend to rob us; that all who smile at or speak to children are potential child molesters. We could switch off to a media intent on encouraging crime by broadcasting how this is committed. We could wake up to the truth that monsters have always roamed the earth, and always will, but that they are in the minority. We could switch off to the dreariness and negativity the media offers in the realisation that the human spirit can only take so much of this before succumbing to thoughts of doom. Instead we could switch on to the positive facts that never reach our ears, like; for every child murdered, kidnapped or abused there are millions of others who escape this; for each person who is killed, raped, robbed or beaten there are millions of other people who are not. We could learn to use television very selectively in order to recover our minds and prevent those of our children from being lost, for this is a mighty tool which has the power to make or break presidents, popes, politicians, and pollute the populace. But, as a whole, we won't.

Comments

These days 'nobody listens, people don't want to know, people only care for themselves, I'd like to live in a culture where people smile and speak to you, and everyone is so rude.'

Facts

With trust comes its bedfellow, comradeship, but it seems that this has disappeared. When people of the past worked together they laughed and sang to get them through the days; no one passed each other outdoors without exchanging a few kind words; there were always willing pairs of hands to help where needs be; should people fall sick or be involved in accidents, folk rushed to give aid; older people living alone never felt lonely for there was always someone checking to make sure that they were alright, and when cinema was born it was always films with happy and positive endings that were favoured. On top of all this there was a live and let live attitude amongst people. Whereas now, we live in a 'watch and be watched' society; people living alone are dying alone without anyone knowing; if anyone seems in need of help our tendency is to pretend that we haven't noticed; all echoes of communal laughter and song have disappeared, and speaking to strangers is taboo. As for lending a hand to those who are smitten with misfortunate in the streets, generally our feet will hasten past them to preserve our own wellbeing. Why should this be? Well, when dire circumstances prevail like war, or poverty, these innate emotions are practiced naturally as we lean one against the other for strength, love, comfort and support. In peacetime and wealthy conditions however, comradeship stagnates in us, as community oneness is no longer a requirement to survival. However, it is nature's plan for human beings to interact closely with fellow beings in order to exercise the emotions innate to the species. As human beings we crave to care, share and be cared for. We are a tribal species that depends on comradeship to bring out the best we have to offer. Is there proof that this is so? All we need do is to look around us to wonder. For example, when a person of fame dies it is fashionable for hundreds of thousands of people to flock together to mourn the passing of this someone they have never met. At every newsworthy event there are television or newspaper cameras on hand to capture shots of those who display the tears, or tantrums, of emotion that might provoke viewer empathy. Pictures of flower arrangements laid to express sympathy in areas where death has occurred by accident, or murder, are also transmitted with the same aim. When events are staged to raise money for charity, there are very few who decline the chance to participate in one way or another. It is often said that what these actions portray is mass hysteria, but is it? Or, could it be that these gatherings represent the chance to experience the sharing of emotional feelings with others? If this is so, is it an indication that we twenty-first century people are starved of the comradeship we need to survive life?

We might agree that we are, but proclaim that we have no time to devote to others on a regular basis. However, how could this be when we still have the same measure of time as there has always been, with sixty minutes in an hour, twenty-four hours in a day, seven days in a week, twenty-eight–thirty-one in a month, 365 days in a year, and twelve months in a year? We might explain that the majority of us have to go to work most days of the week, but as men and women throughout the ages also did the same, time depletion cannot be blamed on the need to work. We could say that childcare and household duties absorb so much time, but then it takes far less time to execute these chores now than it did when gadgets were unavailable to speed up the processes. So to where does our time disappear? Perhaps it would be more than fair to say that we spend far more time travelling now, because of the distance there is between ourselves and family, friends, workplaces, pleasure outlets, shopping venues etc.Then we could explain that because we move faster than nature intended us to do, we spend so much time rushing about that there are not enough hours in the day to do all that we need to. However, in all honesty, can it not be seen that the reason we don't have time to spare for others nowadays is because most of our spare time is donated to the execution of our personal needs first?

Possibilities

Instead of believing that donating time to others is a waste of our precious time, we could try to establish if this is so. By doing this we could come to the conclusion that it is not, for when we share a problem with someone; offer them a short period of much-desired companionship, or provide help that they need, what we feel is an enormous buzz of pride and wellbeing within ourselves. As to good manners, if we want these to take the place of rudeness we could set the trend by demonstrating that courtesy makes life far more pleasant to live. After observing the consequences of these actions, our children could then learn to offer respect to others as a matter of course. We could wake up to the fact that love and comradeship are the elements of life we cannot survive without, and that if we possess these precious assets there is little more we could want. But, as a whole we won't.

Comments

These days, 'it's all about money, we just go along with the flow believing that we must have everything everyone else does, kids want everything, we're aggressively competitive, and it seems as if the whole world is at war.'

Facts

It cannot be denied that we *are* selfish, but then we do live within a culture of selfishness. It follows also that we are greedy and live within a culture of greed, for the two are related. But this doesn't mean we are bad people, for remember there's no more badness in the world now than there ever was – there is just more ignorance of life than before. How did the gross selfishness and greed culture we have today develop? Well, in Britain during the 1980s there was lots of government propaganda promoting that we 'look after number one' and get all that we can from life. The implication was that if we didn't, we would be losers who deserved to be left behind. After all, came the assurances, globalisation meant that there was nothing worldwide that could not be ours. To flaunt this theory capitalist conglomerates spent billions of pounds and dollars on marketing campaigns to convince us of its reality (even the cost of a one day, full page, advertisement in national newspapers could reach £56,000). The brainwashing to ensure that we became fully-fledged consumers continued by way of the subliminal messaging and advertising that television afforded, and very soon people joined the 'got to have' zone. Also, the second generation of established 'got to haves' enthused over programmes that suggested how they might profit by investing in property, or keeping their winner image by being possessors of state of the art motor cars, technology, luxury homes, continental villas and so on and so forth. (The first generation of got to haves were those who had experienced poverty and war but who, after tasting affluence, decided that their children and grandchildren must have much more of it). So, for big business a utopian dream had come true, for all new products and original notions introduced to the marketplace would be greeted with cries of, 'must have', 'must do' from a newly invented consumer society that failed to realise that it was the most exploited in the world.

Sadly, there are always those who have to pay the price of greed born to others through illusion. As far as the twenty-first century goes, it is the younger generations of the day who must pick up their bill. Take housing for example; because one of the must have crazes of the late twentieth century was to own second homes, or to buy property merely as an investment, house prices peaked beyond buying capacity. The consequence of this is that the chances of young couples acquiring homes they can eventually call their own are rare. Those who do buy are sure of being saddled with a very heavy mortgage to pay for the majority of their lifetimes. The alternative is for them to sacrifice their right to build nests of their own by choosing (as many have done) to continue to live with parents in the family home where they grew to adulthood. In the seaside and rural areas, where the better-off second homes are sited, there is an even greater problem. Because most of the housing stock in these areas has been given over to out of town buyers, there are no houses left for indigenous peoples. Therefore many of them have to seek out new areas in which to put down their roots to hopefully gain housing and jobs.

Shop keeping has also become a no-no in some areas, for in towns and villages which are empty of people for most of the year there is no call for commodities. Alas, the plight of all these people seems of little concern to those whose greed caused the situation, for they continue to indulge in property investment. However, now that the British market has been pared to the bone, many now take to foreign countries where house prices are low enough to recognise massive increases according to must have demand. (Overseas land agents are those relied upon to furnish details of these cheap properties, and they are popping up on British high streets like mushrooms.)

As for the compensation culture born from greed, this has put great strain on life for us all. Because so many people seize the chance to make money by blaming others whenever accidents and mishaps befall them, misery escapes no one. In organisations directly involved with the public (especially hospitals), policies have to be put in force to safeguard against the chances of litigation being brought. When the sentence, 'I'm going to sue you for all you are worth' is heard, organisations have to be sure that these will successfully prove that they have not committed mistake, misdemeanour or negligence. What this means for the personnel of these organisations is stress, for as they endeavour to earn their living they are bound to uphold workplace policies that do not allow for any degree of human error.

Another of the mammoth tasks we souls have to face, as we deposit our human footprints on Earth, is to endeavour to conquer the selfishness and greed that is bestowed on us for this purpose, for these faults are a deterrent to happiness. If the validity of this statement is questioned then perhaps we should compare the consequences of poverty against those of wealth. For instance, when the primitive tribespeople of the world are being filmed by television camera crews, they either smile from ear to ear at their photographers, or laugh uproariously. From the images relayed, mindful observation will tell that these people are not putting on a show because they are to appear on television, but that they *are* genuinely happy. And why? Because they are contented with their lot in life, and with each other. We might argue that this is relative because these people have not been subjected to the temptations that westernised civilisations know. However, what can't be argued away is the fact that they *are* happy without westernised luxuries. Whereas million and billionaires never seem contented with their wealth, but instead always strive for more of it. Also, in these quarters family feuds have perpetually raged as to who will inherit the fortunes that are up for grabs due to the demise of their rightful owners. Another example of the happiness many wealthy people lack is this: in nineteenth and early twentieth century Britain 'money people' maintained that it was their duty to donate some of this to the poor in order to demonstrate acknowledgement of their plight. However, very few of the poor were beguiled by these benevolent gestures, for they knew it was their own bitter toils that enabled the fortunes of these people to be made. Therefore, they were not unaware that the charity offered them was to appease the consciences of the donors from time to time so that transient happiness could be experienced. But, regardless of the track record that unhappy wealthy people have, it seems insufficient to make us wonder if inner happiness only materialises out of poverty, for in the late twentieth century the majority of us felt the urge to follow in their footsteps. To this end we chose to lose sight of the true meaning of life so that we could grapple to gain the whole world. However the question is, have we become happier people because of this, or is there more unhappiness lurking in our wealth of today than there was in our poverty of yesterday? The results of a survey in 2006 suggested that this is so, for it revealed that unhappiness is rife within society and has escalated since people have become better off. Furthermore, where does our longing for money leave the children of today, who supposedly want everything? Do they really want to travel the world and possess everything available at an early age, or is it *us* who want these things for them? Would they prefer to be given the chance to gradually earn their privileges under their own steam, according to the right that children have to do this, instead of being left with nothing to strive towards in the future? If this were allowed, could it be that all they would expect us to donate to their cause would be the love, time and encouragement needed to get them there?

Perhaps a couple of anecdotes here could emphasise some of the important thoughts that go through the minds of children who live in a world of greed:

Recently I overhead two eight-year-old boys talking. One said to the other, 'My mum and dad are taking me on holiday and they're taking my bike with us too'. The second puffed out his chest to pronounce, 'My mum and dad love me, do yours?' With great pride the other happily replied, 'Oh yes'.

In a café, a short time ago, I observed a boy of about thirteen sitting at a table with an elderly female companion. Whilst they were waiting for their meal to arrive the young man gazed at a photograph on the wall beside him which showed a group of smiling people. Turning to his companion he asked, 'Why do they look happier than we are these days?' The lady peered at the photograph to note that it was dated 1940. She smiled at him and replied, 'In those days all we needed to make us happy was each other'.

Possibilities

We could start to question if we want to retain the culture of greed that we inherited from the first and second generations of got to haves, or if we would rather see it disappear. If the latter is preferred then we would need to ask ourselves if we could pluck up the courage to step outside the crowds to restore and practice the standards of yesteryear? We could try to see that money cannot buy happiness, compensate for the death of a loved one, or bring back health which is lost. We could wonder if, when we justify our longings to acquire lots of money by benevolently stating that we will make others happy by sharing our fortune with them, there would ever be enough of it, for how much money would it take to make us happy, and how much would others want to reach this state? We could ponder if money that has not been earned can sometimes bring unhappiness when it fails to fulfil dreams. We could even ask ourselves if we would be able to eat money to sustain us if all the animals, trees, bushes and plants were gone. And, if we were to examine the philosophies of the people of the past that told, 'you must learn to live without those things you cannot afford, and you must make the best of what you have to know contentment', we could perhaps see the truth of them. As to wars, we could realise that these are instigated through greed and are, therefore, integral to life, with no nation being free of warmongering leaders, or able to say that 'its' war is justifiably moral, ethical, humanitarian or innocent of misdemeanour. But, as a whole, we won't.

Comments

These days 'there seems to be something wrong with nearly everyone you speak to, and it has been said that the human species is teetering on the edge of extinction.'

Facts

Whilst there is evidence that the health of the public is on the decline, can we really believe that this is a sign that the human race is soon to become extinct? After all, Mother Nature had to wait 4.6 *billion* years before she could begin her skilful engineering of our species, for this was how long it would take to cultivate an ecosystem of perfection to support human life. Therefore, would she have hung around for so long, with blueprints in hand, if she thought that we – the human species – would quickly become extinct? Instead of succumbing to thoughts of inevitable doom, maybe we should look at the reasons for our sickliness.

Firstly, there can be little doubt that the air we breathe into our bodies is clogging our respiratory systems and damaging our internal organs. This is because it is so polluted that the oxygen content of it, which aids our breathing and regenerates our cells, has been reduced. Then, we are not as robust as we used to be, as we now have machines to do the work that we once carried out with the physical effort that enhances bodily strength. Even our mental and spiritual vigour has depleted by way of the technological advancements that have robbed us of the need to exercise our 'grey matter'. It might be true to say that we are also far too clean nowadays, for whereas human bodies are strengthened by conflict with the odd germ or two, we are obsessed with wiping out any bacteria that attempts to invade our space. The bodily functioning that Mother Nature endowed us is also being unnaturally altered by man's hand. The natural immune system for example, which comprises of armies of healthy living organisms that fight to destroy unhealthy ones that invade to deposit disease. In this area medics are sceptical of whether or not a body can survive an illness whilst the immune system battles to cure it. This is because the fight can be a long one. Therefore antibiotic drugs, that are known to kill off bad organisms within the body quickly, are administered to ailing patients to speed up recovery to acceptable modern day levels. Unfortunately however, little heed is given to the fact that whilst these drugs merrily go about their business of killing off bad organisms, they wipe out the good ones at the same time, and that internal organs cannot adequately process unclean matter that passes through them with the rapidity that antibiotics promote (children in particular are more at risk of developing organ damage as their livers are undeveloped and, therefore, do not function at adult capacity).

The immune system is also under attack by way of the preventative medicine schemes devised by western civilisations to stop people becoming ill or dying. For example, one of these is the yearly inoculation programmes that involve injecting people with a small dose of the virus which is thought likely to attack the population in winter months. The plan? To fool the immune system into believing that a legitimate enemy has entered the body that it needs to kill off. The trouble with this is that the immune system will start to malfunction if its natural functioning experiences interference. For example, whilst it will work flat out to kill enemies that enter the body, if the same one, or similar, returns on a regular basis it will believe that the body has accepted it as an ally and will, therefore, ignore it. What this means is that if a real disease struck there would be no immune system on hand to come to the rescue. Another implication is that when immune systems do not work properly, there comes the invitation for some bugs to develop into superbugs whilst roaming unchecked within a body.

Another are the preventative drug programmes designed to deter reoccurring illnesses. When people suffer an illness and are cured by way of drugs, instead of this bringing an end to the problem the same drugs, or similar, are prescribed to a patient on a semi-permanent basis on the surmise that these will minimise the risk of illnesses returning. However, whereas the natural healing system of the body will accept medicines that will help it to cure a current illness, when this has been achieved it will see no reason for their continual return and will, therefore, ignore them. With the drugs of today that are strong enough to cure illnesses quickly there is also a downside, for it has been recognised that they can also damage healthy organs and bodily functioning. The consequence of this is that many people, who initially received treatment for one illness, develop varying malfunctions that require lifetime drug maintenance.

Then, there are the preventative drug programmes aimed at trying to stop the natural bodily deterioration associated with ageing. Perhaps one of the most common of these is hormone replacement therapy (HRT). Here drugs are prescribed to ladies who have reached the menopausal stage and are, therefore, thought to be at risk of developing osteoporosis (brittle bones) because of the depletion of the hormones known to maintain strong bones. Its other use is to fool a body into believing that it is menopause free and, therefore, vacant of associated symptoms. The point is, if there were a drug capable of altering the natural functioning of a woman's body, would it not also interfere with other functions to cause them damage?

Unfortunately, alongside the preventative medical schemes there comes a further downside with which patients have to contend. This is the pressure which is put on them to either obey medical instructions given, or risk losing their lives. Naturally this ultimatum throws patients into immediate panic and, therefore, they go away either clutching prescriptions for preventative drugs, or with arms throbbing from needle injections. What they don't appreciate, but what doctors should, is that they are leaving the surgery, or hospital, with something else too. This is, the negative messages of possible doom that have been lodged in their subconscious minds by their medical practitioners, messages that will keep returning to haunt them with fear for their lives and wellbeing. However, blame for this cannot be put solely on medical personnel, for they are under pressure to comply with the dictatorship that government has over the supposed healthcare of Britons. As an example; when vaccination programmes are the order of the day, GP practices are given a governmentally ordained target to achieve. If the practice fails to inoculate the number of patients that constitute 'the target', then maximum state funds as a reward are not forthcoming. So whereas the people who study long and hard to qualify to practice medicine, and undertake a Hippocratic Oath to pledge their care to the sick as the title of Doctor is bestowed on them, what faces them in reality is the requirement to devote their expertise to the practice of preventative medicine rather than curative. When governments are questioned as to why preventative medicine must be practised, the answer given is that this conserves some of the vast amounts of money that is spent treating illnesses. Can it not be wondered though if the opposite applies, for when our immune systems are weakened through inoculations and preventative drugs, are we not more likely to develop illnesses that require medical attention?

In the area of surgical operations there are some factors that are seldom considered. The most important is that human bodies are sterile units which are purposely sealed against infection. Another is that they depend on the elasticity of internal organs to allow them to function as intended. However, when they are cut open so that operations can be performed to correct, or extract portions thought to be malfunctioning, or to insert replacement parts – they are at risk. This is because the hands and instruments that are inserted into the now unsealed units are liable to cause damage, or movement, to cells and organs strategically placed to ensure their accurate functioning. Also, more often than not, surgical procedures cause scarring to develop on delicate tissues, which damages elasticity and, therefore, performance. Hence, it is not uncommon for patients who have undergone an operation to need further surgery at another stage of their lifetime.

It is generally accepted that so many advances have been made in the medical field that miracle status has been achieved. However, might we not wonder if mankind is not overstepping his cleverness when he claims dominion over life and death? For has it been forgotten that it is Mother Nature who creates the miracle of human life, and ensures that all able bodies operate with the precision of 'state of the art' machines? Because medical technology and technological advancements have offered mankind the opportunity to explore the inner mechanisms of the human body, to observe its functioning, does this give him the right to think he knows more of human physiology than Mother Nature and is ready to supersede her? Does not this arrogant assumption ignore the fact that mankind can neither match nor emulate her creation, but can only attempt to copy it? Another vital function that Mother Nature has is her quickness to notice when sections of her creation need adjustment because of evolutionary development. For example, did she not shorten human arms and curl up tails, then tuck them away in the base of the spine, when tree swinging abilities were no longer required by the human species? Has she not, over time, minimised those organs of the human body that have ceased to serve a vital function because of evolutionary changes in lifestyle? Then, after observing that human animals are now experiencing problems with their respiratory systems, because of their inadequacy to filter the foul air that enters them, will she not be currently working on a plan to expand their functioning? What will she make of man's inspiration to create a master race of humans who will, by way of genetic engineering, suffer no disease? Genetic engineering that will require there to be more and more organs and body tissues available so that experiments can be carried out in order to prove his theories. Then, what of genetic engineering generally? When geneticists categorically claim that they can isolate genes that make people what they are, are they not entering a territory which is beyond the boundaries of scientific proof? When they state willy nilly that humans are equipped with a God gene, and that this is why humankind invented God, or that 'XYY' chromosomes in boys mean that they may grow up to be criminal, are they not treading on consecrated ground? Why? Because as human beings our souls have to execute the karma they have taken on board and need the help of Mother Nature (or life if you prefer) to do this. What I suggest here is that every gene in our bodies is there for a very specific reason, and that the removal or replacement of them will dramatically change the course of the plans our souls have made.

In his evolutionary march, should not Man be mindful of what his medical prowess might indicate to Mother Nature? For example, will she wonder what to make of his fumblings to replace human organs with those of other animals? May she assume from these that he is asking her to convert human physiology to a four-legged state? Confirmation of this may come to her as she watches mankind conducting intermingling experiments betwixt himself and other animals for the sake of acquiring cheaply-produced medicines – for the first, through the second. Then how will she regard his attempts to create human organs from human sources? This was achieved at the end of 2006, when scientists succeeded in growing a liver from stem cells taken from embryonic blood. (Stem cells are retrieved from embryos – offspring of animals before birth – a supply of which comes mainly from IVF clinics where fridges there bulge with a surplus of them.)

The question is, will Mother Nature play along with mankind's desire to create a master race of humans who, by way of organ and joint replacements and genetic engineering, can live forever, or will she resume her rightful control of human fate to cause his ingenious plans to backfire? Perhaps we should consider this as a prime example of her powers to do this:

> *Throughout the centuries children born with a condition now called Downs's syndrome were conceived only by mothers of advanced years. When modern culture proclaimed its aversion to allowing humans who were less than one hundred per cent bodily and mentally perfect access to the world, a foolproof plan was devised to stop further births of those who might carry this particular disability. This came in the form of a test offered to all pregnant women who had reached, or passed, the age of forty to determine if the children they carried in their wombs fell into this category. As the test carried a warning that it could cause miscarriage, only women who could not commit to bearing a Downs*

syndrome child, and would opt for abortion if tests proved positive, would undertake it. (Not taken into account was the fact that because of the test babies that lacked the condition might die). However, the foolproof plan showed itself no match against Mother Nature, for what happened was that those who would carry the tag of Downs's syndrome started making their entrance to the Earth via the birth channels of younger women, with eighty percent of Downs's babies currently being born to women under thirty-five.

The facts about life on Earth are that physical imperfection, and disease and death, are integral to its concept. For the first – this represents the burden that souls choose to carry through human life as an aid to acquiring perfection. For the second – no matter how many diseases are annihilated, others will spring up in their place according to environmental conditions, for death is the doorway through which souls pass to relinquish human life. Without this door the evolution of the human race would cease. Therefore, when mankind claims that his vaccination programmes conquer diseases, and always have, can we not see that we now have epidemics of diseases that used to be incidental? Furthermore, if we want proof of evolution in action, the newish big disease that is likely to claim one third of the world's population will provide this, for there are approximately forty million people already suffering with AIDS, and approximately sixty-five million with HIV. To add to this there are many different life-threatening illnesses which crop up but cannot be identified. They are, therefore, classified merely as viruses, bugs, allergies and the like.

Whilst it is obvious that human life is continuing to evolve as it should, there are so many people who live in fear of the big 'D', and believe that, in these days of miracle medicine, no one should die. Of course this fear stems from the belief that we have only one life, and that when it is over the final curtain closes on us. However, if it's immortality we seek what price are we prepared to pay for this, for though miracle medicine is available and longevity has been achieved, is our good health and wellbeing being sacrificed to its cause to maintain life artificially? If it *is* immortality that we yearn, should we not wonder if, as souls, this is ours already, for how many hundreds of lifetimes might we have to live before graduating to the perfection that brings ultimate human death?

Possibilities

When illness strikes we could decide to give nature the chance to heal us naturally, but slowly, first before consuming man-made concoctions that will restore us quickly, but unnaturally. We could also consider using the many natural remedies of healing that nature bestowed on the Earth's surface. Then, because of the common knowledge that the human body functions through the instructions transmitted to it from the brain, via the mind, we could realise that all human beings who are able-bodied have the capacity to maintain a fair proportion of bodily wellbeing by asking the mind to convey thoughts of this to the body. We could also come to the conclusion that human beings are not meant to live on indefinitely, but that the most precious asset we can have whilst we are alive is the natural good health that enables us to function happily. But, as a whole, we won't.

Comments

'The world is going to end in a big bang, our kind will perish in floods, fires, earthquakes and the like, someone's got to do something about the way things are, and the world will end if computer technology does.'

Facts

If we review the earth movements and weather conditions that have occurred around the globe during the first five years of the twenty-first century, we might wonder if what we are witnessing again is evolution in action. During these years there were fifty earthquakes, two killer heat waves, twenty-nine tropical storms, four typhoons, four tornadoes and fifteen devastating floods[i] - all of which claimed many thousands of lives. The biggest disasters to hit the headlines were these:

- 2002 – flooding across Europe was described in some areas as the worst in history.
- 2003 – blistering heat waves across Europe killed approximately 40,000 people.
- 2003 – an earthquake in Bam, Iran killed almost 30,000 people and injured over 20,000.
- 2004 – the world's biggest earthquake, which happened under the sea, spread from Indonesia through the Malay Peninsula, Thailand, India and Sri Lanka, and killed over 226,000 people and devastatingly affected over two million.
- 2005 – one of the most powerful and deadliest hurricanes to hit the United

States devastated the Mississippi coast just east of New Orleans and killed 1,900, and left thousands homeless.
- 2005 – in an earthquake in the Kashmir region of Pakistan almost 75,000 people were killed, and over one hundred thousand were injured.

Then, when 2006 ended, it was declared that it had been the hottest year in history. It was also proclaimed that even million-year-old glaciers were melting in some countries of the world. In Britain, even without this official news, mindful observation brought awareness that summer plants were blooming during the months of February and March of the year, and that bees, flies and butterflies were making a premature appearance. Also, that some animals were leaving hibernation in the misguided belief that their food supplies and habitats would be available to them because of the hot weather.

We might believe that the political, social and economic problems that the game of life has created through corruption and intrigue are our ultimate concern, but if we consider the problem that affects the planet which give us life, are they? Of course this represents the global warming that is a threat to all things living on the Earth's surface. The opinions of scientists as to how this will affect the Earth differ, with some saying that it will scorch it to the point of rendering it desert; others, that when the Antarctic ice melts into the oceans their levels will rise so tremendously that most parts of the world will be submerged under water; the rest, that as Antarctic ice continues to enter the warm gulf stream its cooling will cause another ice age to occur. (The latter prediction goes on to say that the country likely to receive this impact first will be Great Britain.) But what are we doing to try to halt global warming? Unfortunately very little, for this would mean our having to sacrifice many of the luxurious lifestyles we enjoy. Of course many people still deny that global warming does exist and proclaim that *they* (the government that all life revolves around) are making it up. Others say that global warming has happened before; some, that the world is going to end anyway so why not enjoy it whilst it's here; lots, that if the Earth has warmed so tremendously the damage that has been caused is irreversible. Then, of course some scientists proclaim that violent earth movement and weather conditions have besieged the Earth since its beginnings without putting it in danger; others, that it is not the burning of fossil fuels that is overheating the planet, but the radiation of the sun. The common sense truths about these issues, however, cannot be denied. These are: that it is scientific observations that advise the levels of global warming and not those of government. Yes, global warming has occurred before, but the last time it did almost every living thing on the Earth's surface was annihilated. Then, as the Earth has existed for billions of years, and has a mechanism that ensures its survival in its own right, it is not going to disintegrate just because of the damage mankind has caused it. And, the damage that we have caused the Earth does not represent irreversibility, for she will eventually repair her billion-year-old infrastructure, and the hole in the ozone layer, to restore herself to her pre-mankind state. Furthermore, though the Earth has always shuddered, slipped and shivered through earth movements and weather conditions, it cannot be denied that these are becoming more furious and frequent, and that for the first time ever the seasons of spring, summer, autumn and winter have merged into one. And of course, *it is* the sun's radiation that is responsible for heating the Earth, *but* before *Homo sapiens* happened along, a protective ozone layer covered it to prevent it from being damaged by the full rays of the sun!

No matter how much we try to wriggle out of acknowledging that global warming exists, and the reason why it does, *can* we? After all, is there any mindful person over the age of thirty who can honestly plead ignorance of the rapid and dramatic climate change that has occurred during their lifetime? Or, is there anyone who can not make the connection that fossil fuels have been burned to maximum capacity over this time?

Unfortunately many British people who do accept the fact that the Earth is troubled make statements of disgustingly selfish proportion. One example of this is, 'Nothing's going to happen in Britain because we are too far away from the equator'. And sadly, it is countries nearer this region that have in the past suffered the havoc that earthly disasters bring. And ironically too, the people of these countries who endure the pain and death associated with such events, are the ones who constitute the one third of the world's population who do not contribute to Earth-damaging activities. Another example is, 'I don't care what's going to happen to the world in a hundred years because I won't be here then'. (This thought is promoted by the scientific predictions that tell that it will be a hundred years or so before any big Earthly shake-ups, or downs, occur.) How sad it is to recognise that we have reached the point of selfishness where we disregard the wellbeing of future generations, especially if we consider that these will consist of children, grandchildren, great grandchildren and subsequent descendents. I wonder if attitudes would change if it were thought that it would be *us* who had to live out *our* lives on a planet submerged under water, swamped in burning sand or covered in ice? Well, as we are born to the Earth, over and over again, this will be so!

As to the hundred year prediction, how, when seasons are so intermingled that any one day can bring hot sunshine, torrential chilling rain, hailstones, high winds or frost, etc can this be made? Is not the climate so out of control that it can't predict its own events for the next twenty-four hours? How then can mere humans possibly predict what Earthly events will occur in a century's time? Furthermore, were scientists able to predict that in 2006 the islands of the Maldives, in the Indian Ocean, would be engulfed by water because of the rising seas attributed to global warming, or did this come as a surprise? And are they able to say that this won't happen to the seas that reach the British shores of Blackpool, Bridlington, Brighton or Bossiney for example? Even if it were in mankind's power to predict with certainty that the future might be bleak, would we heed the warnings to change our ways? Would we stop destroying those things that are capable of absorbing some of the pollution we create like the peat bogs, or the rainforests, whose trees not only absorb carbon dioxide but convert this into precious oxygen? Would we return to the seas the vast acres of the shores we have stolen from them, and stop building bigger and bigger sea defences to prevent them from claiming these back? Would we begin to learn that when the sea's natural courses are marred their waters are forced to seek alternative channels of escape, and that when this happens flooding and weather changes are the outcome? Would we look again at the damage that our luxury lifestyles are causing? I think the answer to all these questions would be 'no'. However, if we were questioned as to our intention to prevent further global warming, we would utter the current obscure phrase, 'We are measuring our carbon footprints' to justify our non-committal to do anything. In December 2007 a series of films[ii] were screened to stress the fact that our carbon footprints are already so deeply embedded on the Earth that these will cause many major climate changes. One particular piece of information told that there are signs that the ice in Siberia is beginning to melt. The scary thing about this is that the ice (permafrost) is over one metre thick and contains methane. As methane is a greenhouse gas which is twenty-three times stronger than carbon dioxide, this means that when the ice melts to release it into the atmosphere, that which is already there will multiply by a factor of ten, to dramatically accelerate global warming far beyond current predictions. This is based on the fact that Siberia, the coldest place on Earth, measures well over 9,500,000 kilometres (bigger than the USA) and that temperatures there are rising faster than anywhere else on the planet, with an increase of three degrees in the last ten years. The bottom line messages that were stressed throughout the series were these: by burning fossil fuels we have changed the very composition of the atmosphere and as a result have overheated the climate; the human race now moves more rock and soil on the surface of the Earth than all nature's processes put together; because our influence is now so great scientists have declared that a new geographical era has begun – the Anthroposy – the human era; we are now beginning to threaten the very conditions that have made Earth's recoveries from major disasters a special planet – a home to complex life.

If we apply sense to the theory that the world of man will end if computer technology does, we would have to be realistic and recognise that it has survived very well without this for approximately four *million* years. If we exercised this sense further we might wonder if the obscene experiments that are carried out to explore the secrets of the universe, to enable the expansion of computer technology, are more likely to end Man's world. What undoubtedly would end, however, is the mighty power that big business has globally enlarged by way of the many advancements that have been achieved in this field. Although it is true to say that there would be world-wide chaos with the death of computer technology, as all things revolve around this engine, this would force us to resume the ancient methods of living that ensure the survival of the mere human beings of the past. But, would this not be a good move, for after all is it not mere human beings that we are supposed to be? And as mere human beings we would then need to live by our wits, senses, physical abilities, characters, imaginations and arts to mean that these, frozen by the icy fingers of technology, would need to be thawed out as quickly as possible.

Possibilities

We could come to our senses and acknowledge that the damage we are causing the Earth is destroying the delicate ecosystem that gives us life – a system *4.6 billion years* in the making. Perhaps we could then begin to understand that it is not the Earth that is in danger but only us humans, and other animals, who are. We could go on to wonder if we have done ourselves any favours by raping the Earth to get at her resources, and trampling her unmercifully to satisfy our selfish demands, if the price we have to pay for doing this is the home that she provided us. We could then be spurred on to imagine the dilemma that Mother Nature has regarding the bad behaviour of the human species, and ask ourselves:- if it were us who had spent a year preparing our house so that we could accommodate guests who needed a home, would we be justified in throwing them out if, after only one day, they had set fire to the roof to cause a big hole to appear; removed most of the brickwork; dug up the foundations; ignored all the house rules, and filled the house with more people than it could support? We could even stop bemoaning the effects of climate change on account of our non committal to stop burning fossil fuels to capacity, for the immense rainfall that is falling worldwide represents the moisture, produced by the intensified rays of the sun, that is being held in a man-made smog of carbon dioxide; one which prevents its escape from Earth's atmosphere. As to the world's end we think that the demise of computerisation will bring, we could start to prepare for the eventuality of it's surviving this by losing our reliance on computers to think for us, be our constant playthings, and annihilate the need for us to live life through our initiative and participation, as human beings are supposed to do. But, as a whole, we won't.

★★★★★★★★

Comments

'There's no reason for us to worry about the Earth because when we have completely destroyed it we'll just move on to another planet.'

Facts

Those who choose to believe in this obscure statement feel that, because of it, it matters not if we continue to damage our environment. The space scientists who have convinced pockets of the general public that space hopping will become a reality, and try to persuade sceptics that once the idea of air travel was pooh-poo'd, also seem unaware of some important facts. The one that cannot be missed is that the human species evolved on Earth through the evolution of the planet itself, and is equipped with the physiology to suit the environment. Therefore is it not logical to ask how our species could survive on an alien planet, or if aquatic life could survive if *it* were removed from its own world, the sea, and re-housed on dry land (even if there were super-duper technology on hand to assist the transfer). Then, even though scientific conjecture states that there may be planets in other star systems that could support the kind of life that the human species requires, this is merely *conjecture*. The truth is that most astronomers and scientists who, after searching the universe for man-friendly planets for many years, have come to the conclusion that the Earth is the only home that mankind will ever have, and is where he must live out his life. (What space exploration has revealed, however, is that there are man-friendly minerals on other planets. What is planned for these is that they be mined up there then transported to Earth by way of the space vessels many years in the testing. On arrival they will be utilised to provide the power to keep the Earth fully illuminated and in working order. The nations to benefit economically from this exercise would, of course, be the ones that got there first.)

Why should we want to go planet hopping anyway, when we already occupy the most beautifully lush one in the universe? Then, what of the planets that space exploration tell might be suitable to support human life, and who of us would like to live there if we could? Take Mars for instance; when space probes discovered ice on the surface excited chatterings were exchanged as to the possibilities of there having been life on the barren planet at some point in time, for if there were ice there must have been water and, therefore, an existence of life. Armed with this knowledge it was envisaged that Mars could be adjusted to accommodate the human race. For instance, it was decided that plastic trees could be zoomed up there and prettily planted out to enhance the surface with a little temporary greenery. However, before this event the atmosphere of the planet would need to be warmed up if Man were to live there, hence greenhouse gases would need to be released into the air. So, even before the collapse of Earth the destruction plans of yet another planet were being conceived.

For those who believe that technology has the power to transfer the human race to another planet, perhaps the truth of the matter should be acknowledged. This is, that even if space occupation were possible it would be only the upper hierarchy of the human species who would have access to the limited number of space suits, breathing apparatus and spacecrafts needed to survive the transfer as Earth met its demise. All others would be left to fend for themselves.

I must confess my own fascination with American science fiction films based on space travel. My excuse is that I find it interesting to observe how Man views himself in a potential space age future. The first thing I notice is that, although the crews of spacecraft insist on proclaiming, 'We come in peace' to the alien species they stumble across, their vessels are jam-packed with weapons of mass destruction. Furthermore, that they never hesitate to use these if pushed. Then, every alien they encounter looks like a human, with the only difference being the variation of obscure heads they carry on their shoulders. Of course, when it comes to the differences of opinion that crop up between aliens and humans when matters of right and wrong arise, it is always the latter who insist that their ethics are the right ones and, therefore, must be followed. And then, it is always the humans who manage to correct any problems that alien planets and their inhabitants might have. Also, the funny thing is that although the stories are a projection of life thousands of years ahead, the scripted dialogue includes obscure phrases of twentieth and twenty-first century days such as, 'have a nice day, you're welcome, no problem, 24/7' and the like. My overall observation of science fiction fantasy is that it portrays the arrogant pomposity of the human race as a whole. Nonetheless, there is one important point that runs through the space series that is worth observing. This is; despite the technology that surrounds the space travellers to provide them with permanent good health, food at the nod of a head and state of the art virtual reality entertainment programmes, it seems that the most precious assets the crews possess are the love and comradeship they share with each other.

Possibilities

We could learn to believe that the assets of love and comradeship are indeed the most precious ones we could have to make life worth living. We could start to appreciate that we have a precious asset too in the beautiful planet called Earth which was provided to us to bring the same joy. But, as a whole, we won't.

Comments

'We live in a moral black hole.'

Facts

The reason we do live in this black hole is that we do not know which is the right way to escape it. This is because we have lost the ability to distinguish between right and wrong and, therefore, keep heading in the wrong direction to find the exit sign. And of course, this inability materialised in western society when an 'anything goes' attitude towards living was adopted in the twentieth century and the word 'wrong' took on the same meaning as the word 'right'.

But to whom can we turn to lead us out of the moral black hole where the purpose of life stagnates in its darkness? Is it world leaders who have this capacity as many of us believe? Well, let's look at the biggest moral dilemma the world faces – the depletion of the habitat of the human race – to discover if they do. In 2005, at the Kyoto conference, world leaders got together to discuss how global warming could be reduced. The outcome of their talks, after it had been decided that China was mainly to blame for the situation anyway, was that the solutions would be for industry to reduce carbon emissions and for economical light bulbs to be fitted in every home. The big carbon emission issues, however, were overlooked, for not a mention was given to the fact that a newly-licensed fossil-fuelled vehicle takes to the roads of the world every few minutes of the day; nor was a dicky bird said about daily-increasing aviation that deposits carbon in the Earth's atmosphere as it ploughs the skies burning millions of tons of oil. It might have seemed that these issues had taken a back seat in the discussion because world leaders were unaware that these vehicle movements do cause devastation to the Earth. But, when Britain's Prime Minister, Tony Blair, repeatedly advocated that no one should stop driving motor vehicles, or refrain from flying in aeroplanes because the fumes from these will become less pollutive when advancements in technology are achieved, his stupid admission told that the score is known full well. The confession that neither he, nor any world leader, would ever make is that sanctions to stop, or even reduce, the burning of the fossil fuel called oil will never be imposed by any country in the world. And why? Because this black gold is an economic stairway to riches. Nor will it be admitted that in oil-rich countries the people of them grow thinner and thinner to wait for death, whilst their leaders grow fatter and fatter in famine-free circumstances, or that the perpetrators of oil-seeking, and keeping, wars remain safe in war-free zones whilst soldiers and civilians go out to die for the cause. If we look at the profits made over the first three months of 2008 by Shell BP, which was £7.5 billion (over £3.3 million per hour), we might realise how high this economic stairway can reach. If we consider just how much the treasury of Britain profited from the massive taxes imposed on oil sales in relation to this figure, we might acknowledge this truth even more so.

Is it Mother Nature who can help us find our way out of the black hole, so that we can see the light again? Well, let's look at the simple plans she made to avoid our ever being caught in this trap. Her intention was that the human species evolve on a planet perfected through time so that it might learn how to reach the same state. By observing the functions and consequent wonders of the Earth, the idea was that the species would want to emulate its creator and offer her nothing but admiration and respect. And because the Earth is the mother of all people she deemed that all of her children have equal rights upon her. What of the plans to maintain the continuation of the human animal? Like every other species living on Earth the human variety consists of males and females who are endowed with the reproductive organs necessary to secure procreation and, therefore, permanence. However, because Mother Nature intended human beings to be born through love, because this is imperative to the development of the species, she designed a unique bodily function to allow couples to experience the very foundation of this as they engaged in sexual intercourse. And this is, the climax that is reached during the act when the body releases the eggs of the female, and the fertilisation sperm of the male, to create a glowing warmth of well-being to body and mind of both parties. Then, the bodily and mental makeup of men and women is different, with man – the intended hunter and provider – being of strong physique, and woman – the designed child bearer and home maker – having strength of mind. The scheme of Mother Nature here was for this equality in human status to bring equilibrium to family living and help children determine their own balance by observing the differing attitudes of parents who are male and female. As children, human beings are meant to learn from parents, and their contemporaries, how to honourably survive and respect life. As adults, human beings are intended to provide the lessons their children seek and also, to furnish them with security and love. When preliminary lessons are over and puberty is reached, nature's intent is then for young human beings to venture out into life in their own right as reinvented people where they will become solely responsible for their survival through their own efforts. With this in hand, what she expects of them next is that they extend this responsibility by becoming responsible to others, i.e. a spouse to whom they commit their lives, and a child, or children, to whom the pair pledge the same. And the responsibility doesn't end here, for there is a final plan she has up her sleeve for humans to enact during their life cycle. This concerns the role reversal of parent and child where, when parents become less able to care for themselves because of ageing, offspring provide *them* with the same kind of care that they themselves received in childhood.

Possibilities

We could realise that the last places we will find the guidance we need to get out of the moral black hole are the corridors of politics, for here the wellbeing of the people of the world en masse, and the earth, are wrongly disregarded. We could go on to believe that if we are to find a sign from this place that reads 'the right way out', then we must ask Mother Nature to define right and wrong to enable us to recognise it; to which she will reply – if you follow the instructions I have made for you this is the right way, but if you go in the opposite direction the wrong way is what you will have. Perhaps we could then begin to appreciate that the reason we landed in the moral black hole in the first place is that we have made a mockery of all the plans that life has set for us. But, as a whole, we won't.

Why, on the whole, will we *not* do all we can to make the world a better place? Is it because humanity is ghastly and was created by some superbeing in the universe who was obviously incompetent, or is there another reason? There is. This is that on the whole we *can't* make all the right moves because, whilst we humans are intended to be ghastly so that we can learn how to become less ghastly as we plod through our lifetimes, none of us will make the same grade at the same time together. When we arrive on Earth as first time human apprentices we possess more faults than qualities, because our test is to discover how to eliminate the first by developing the second. But, as developing the art of transforming bad to good does not come easily to human beings, it follows that our apprenticeships will spread over many of our lifetimes. What this means, therefore, is that during these times we will dole out more wrong to our fellow beings than right. However, the good news is that this behaving badly syndrome does not go on indefinitely, for once our souls begin their atonement plans to correct wrongdoings of the past, then less ghastly human beings start to appear. And of course these plans are those which cause suffering to us human beings so that we might recognise our priorities in life. We might believe that suffering should not be borne by us but, it is this that justifies the existence of humanity, for if there were none, nor would there be humankind. This is because the human species would annihilate itself through sheer selfishness and greed if it didn't have to suffer its way to love and giving. And to elaborate a point again, there *are* more people in the world who have found this love than have not. As suffering goes this comes to us in varying degrees in accordance with the plans our souls have made to move on to higher levels of purification, through life experiences. Therefore, the steps upwards could be of minor, intermediate or major proportion depending on the level of life education already possessed. An example of a major step a soul might undertake to make in a future incarnation could be this. If it had inflicted horrific suffering on others during one, or several incarnations, it would choose to atone for this wrong doing by undertaking to suffer the same perils itself. However, to bring this plan to fruition it would have to depend on there being other souls present on Earth who were capable of administering the type of suffering it was seeking. It would also need the presence of souls who had already completed the same purification process so that it could lean on them for comfort and support during the gruelling test. If the help of these souls were unavailable, then the first would drown in the deep pools of unhappiness it had constructed without ever knowing the wonders that happiness can bring. So, what all this indicates is that it is essential that at all times there are souls in the world who can help one another achieve atonement targets by virtue of their different levels of learning. It also demonstrates that, as a whole, the human race was never intended to reach perfection. What is intended is that we strive individually to complete the major task of acquiring perfection through imperfection and, the ultimate one of learning to forgive those who have yet to recognise this truth.

With this in mind, we should acknowledge that the suffering people endured during the twentieth century, as in all other centuries, was meant to be, for this pain represented the atonement plans their souls had brought with them into their reincarnated human lives (this is how it will be in all centuries to come, too). What we may have noticed, however, is that there appeared to be *more* suffering in this century than in any that had gone before, but there is an explanation for this. This is, that there were more people on the planet then than the total who had lived before. Hence larger scale suffering was necessary to enable so many souls to complete the tasks they had undertaken to move along the path to perfection. And, necessary too was the increased number of souls who were called upon to inflict this suffering. But let's not forget that the souls who had the capacity to offer love, empathy and comfort to the sufferers were present in great numbers also. And so it is to this day.

The only people who will, and do, commit to avoid damaging themselves, their habitat and their fellow beings, are the ones who have learned enough about life to know that the only way to personal contentment is through a clear conscience. And, whilst they appreciate that their efforts will do little to bring about the uniform changes needed to make the world a better place, because they are in the minority, what they do know is that their attitude towards life has created a better world for themselves. Also, even though they are aware that nature has the almighty power to take the human species to the point of evolution where it belongs, they know that wherever this may be their contentment will travel with them. This is because they have learned that the good they put into life will be returned to them to be retained eternally.

---

i Compiled from Whittakers Almanacks 2001–2006, A & C Black Publishers

ii Earth – Power of the Planet, screened 20/11/2007 to 11/12/2007, BBC2

CHAPTER EIGHTEEN
Living

Since the word go man has had the need to believe in something that has the power to make everything in life right for him. After observing clouds banging together until they burst, wind bellowing harshly around them, the earth shuddering under their feet and potentially fatal lightening flashing from the skies, early human beings could not fail to believe that there were supernatural powers present on earth that could determine their destinies. Their reasoning told that these must be a collection of gods, with each one governing a particular aspect of life. Therefore, they concluded that if they wanted the weather to be kind, and all to be well for them, they must aim to please the gods, instead of offending them, to receive only their wrath. To this end they performed rituals to them, to beseech forgiveness for anything they may be doing wrong. Also they offered up gifts of sacrificed animals or people to prove their devotion to 'the cause'. As evolution progressed and the world's population increased, there came a split of 'religious' beliefs in so much as, where some cultures retained their faith in a collection of gods, others came to the conclusion that there was only one god. However, within the confines of this latter belief the same theory of the first applied, i.e. that if people behaved as they should all would be well for them, but if they behaved badly punishment would be inflicted on them. With the advent of the civilised world, worship to please the one god replaced the barbaric rituals that were used to appease the many. As in other countries of the world, the Christian religion that supports the theory that there is only one god is the one that Britain adopted as its own some two thousand years ago. Whilst this religion did not deviate from promoting the ideal of there being one almighty god, it did, however, also advocate that faith in this god might be expanded if people could learn to believe in themselves too. Proffered with this titbit came the suggestion that within the core of the human being is a soul which is eternal. The acceptance of these beliefs was going very nicely until the latter part of the twentieth century when a religion was formed from a material god called technology. This religion taught that nothing should be believed unless proven by technological prowess, to mean that all presumably unprovable beliefs of the past be thrown out as gobbledegook. Therefore, gone was the faith that had inspired generations of people into believing that there is more to life than just being born, living and then dying. What was offered in its place was the suggestion that faith be put into the conception (ironically unproven) that there is no purpose or reason to life other than to enjoy the one-off experience to capacity by any means. The trouble with this theory, however, is that it did not expand to offer suggestions as to where faith should be put when sad things happen in life or happiness eludes people despite their wealth of luxuries. So, by the end of the century there were hordes of people desperately searching for an alternate god who might furnish advice in this direction. Because of this, the marketplace became swamped with those who, for a fee, offered to guide folk to the place this god might be found, and so it is to this day.

However, could it be that we should look no further than ourselves to find a god in which to put our faith? Perhaps so, for as the Earth is in command of its own destiny by virtue of the powers it has been given to make this so, human beings are also provided with powers that can procure the same situation. Whilst the powers we possess are many, the most important of these are the conscious and subconscious minds which respond to the instructions we transmit to them. As to the conscious mind, this is the one which comes into play when it receives requests from us that require immediate action, but the subconscious mind stores the non-urgent information it gleans from us to activate at a later date. For example, if we repeatedly think, 'No matter what time I go to bed I always wake up at 3am' then our subconscious mind will make sure that it gives us an alarm call at – yes, 3 am Then if we say:

'I feel as if I am going down with something,' or
'I get sick in cars,' or
'Nothing ever goes right for me,' or
'Everything will work out fine,' or
'I will feel better tomorrow,'

then our subconscious mind will aim to please. It will also take on board suggestions made by someone other than ourselves. For example, if we hear someone else telling us:

'You don't look well,' or
'You've put on weight,' or
'You've got a couple of bumps on your head,'

by the end of the day we will probably feel poorly and see only an enlarged self with a pair of horns as we look into the mirror.

On the other hand if we are told that:-

'You do look well,' or
'I always feel better for seeing you,' or
'You are so funny, you make me laugh,'

then the day will probably end with our feeling happily thrilled to little mint balls. In a nutshell, if we think negative thoughts, we will get negative results; if we think positive ones, positive consequences will be ours. So we need to kick out negativity and make room only for positivity. When someone tells us that whatever we're doing is bad for us, we need to replace this suggestion immediately with the positive thought that says – it is good for us. If a person plants an idea in our minds that we are not capable of performing a particular task, then straight away we need to tell ourselves that we are. If we should doubt our own abilities in any field or are tempted to say, 'I can't do that,' instead we should proclaim, 'I can if I want to.' For more often than not we say, 'I can't,' when what we should be saying is, 'I don't want to.'

The truth is that we can, if we have the courage, do anything we have a mind to. But most of the time we apply the 'I can't' phrase to get out of attempting challenging situations.

To become optimistic we have to talk to ourselves constantly, making sure that we say the right things. For example, if we experience a pain we should tell ourselves that it will go away instead of signalling to our subconscious mind that we fear the worst. If we want something good to come to us then we have to convince ourselves that it will. One of the ways of achieving this is to repeat sentences over and over again in our minds. If we want to succeed in anything then we should let our subconscious mind into the secret. So, we would inform it:

'I will do well in my exams,' or
'I will pass my driving test,' or
'I will get the job,' or
'I will decorate the lounge perfectly,' or

'I will learn how to paint,'

and so on and so forth. We might choose to talk to ourselves during quiet moments of daytime solitude, or when we lie in bed waiting for sleep. Should it be the latter, then our day will close with positive thoughts. A really effective night-time lullaby to induce sleep is the one which repeats the words:

'Hour by hour, day by day, I am growing stronger in every way.'

And what better first waking thoughts could we signal to our subconscious mind than these:

'I am well and I am happy.'

One of the most exhilarating lessons we can learn from living is that we do have great power within ourselves. The human spirit is like a plant that reaches out to touch the light that ensures its growth, for rooted in dark places it struggles for life. Therefore, if we flood our spirits with only dark thoughts we confine ourselves to the dreary greyness of the nothingness they create for us. How many times have we noticed that people who spurt out words such as, 'With my bad luck nothing ever goes right for me', are unhappy ones? On the other hand, how many of us know, or have heard of, folk who have achieved happiness and success in their lives despite carrying the burden of a bodily disability. How? They ensured that their handicaps became secondary to their sheer determination to have happiness and success in their lives. And of course, this is all they needed to make it so.

Many years ago I stumbled upon a poem, written anonymously, which inspired my continued faith in the power of the mind. This is how it goes:

I will succeed, I simply cannot fail
the only obstacle is doubt.
There's not a hill I cannot scale
once fear is put to rout.
Don't think defeat, don't talk defeat
the word will rob you of your strength.
I will succeed, this phrase repeat
throughout the journey's length.
The moment that 'I can't' is said
you slam a door right in your face.

Why not exclaim 'I will' instead
half won then is the race.
Don't close the door to your success
by entertaining one small fear.
Think happiness, talk happiness
watch joy then coming near.

I have kept these words by my bedside since I found them as a reminder of two things; that life is a journey, not a destination, and that my happiness here depends on me.

For many of us living is not easy, but the sooner we learn that it was never intended to be, the better we will cope with the task. It might also comfort us if we try to remember that the Earth is a testing ground for our souls, and that it is they who set the exam papers. With this in mind we then need to understand that our lives on Earth are planned before we arrive here, and that our souls have organised for all manner of ill-fated events to transpire during *our* lifetimes so that *they* can conquer them. Therefore, to master the art of living we need to appreciate that it is futile to think that we can chart our destinies so that all the downfalls of life can be avoided. All that we can do when these do occur is to fight with all our might to conquer them by making the most of the situations they present. This also applies when our plans do not work out and leave us despondent. (It has been discovered by some that when they did make the best of what life had given them, they found such contentment that they began to wonder if they could have been any happier if their plans *had* worked out. And the words they said in response to this thought? 'What will be, will be'. However, our souls have also arranged for there to be large chunks of joy and laughter floating about to bring equilibrium to our living. (How sad it would be then if we allowed any of these to pass us by). If we can learn to trust in this theory we may be truly amazed by the reassurance the concept brings, and the courage it can inspire in us to battle our living alongside our souls. We might also be encouraged to believe that our lives are very important, meaningful and individually unique. When I was growing up this theory was my heritage. In particular, I remember one incident which inspired my adolescent mind. My friend, who did not like his recently acquired job, was at odds with himself about his future. He did not know what he wanted for himself and doubted his own ability. For a week or so he had neither eaten nor slept properly and was beginning to look a little ragged around the edges. One day I called at his home to find him sitting in a chair with his head in his hands. As I was looking at him, his mother walked into the room and said, 'You've been put on this Earth for a purpose, so stop moping about and get out there to find what it is. And never forget, we've all got to do things we don't like to do. I'll tell you something else too, steel isn't proven until it's gone through fire.' He did go on to become a successful businessman.

As our lives go by we could reach the point where we believe that the more we understand, the more we will trust and the less we will fear. However, until then we have to cope with the day-to-day emotions that come our way. Irrespective of any beliefs we hold, these cannot be eradicated, for human beings are meant to function by way of senses and feelings. Those which can sink us from the heights of exhilaration to the depths of despair, or raise us from an abyss of gloom to the peaks of hope, depending on the circumstances of the moment. But we have to try to remember that this is the test which is meant for us. We are endowed with emotions to learn how to find equilibrium. However this is hard to do when our feelings are out of control and render us incapable of thinking straight. This is where a little help from our friends is so important. When we share thoughts with other people, not only do we exorcise our negative emotions by talking them through, it is also possible to gain clarity through others' viewpoints of the situation. Perhaps the most comforting outcome there could be would be to hear them confess to having experienced the same feelings as ourselves (or would do if a similar situation presented to them). Therefore, we must never be afraid to discuss our feelings with others on the assumption that our emotions are unique, because no man is an island.

Human nature is such that we rarely ponder how we would cope if we lost the blessings we had. Therefore, sometimes we need to experience the emotional events that might rob us of these to teach us how to appreciate them. For example – who could suffer the emotions related to surviving a life-threatening experience without realising that the most cherished asset we have is life itself? Who could develop an incurable and debilitating illness without becoming aware that possessions measure little against good health? Then importantly too, other people have a great part to play in helping us discover ourselves and our priorities, for whilst we believe that it is they who can determine our happiness, or heartbreak, we will eventually learn *through* them that happiness is manufactured within ourselves, and is not a product of others. The bottom line fact about living is that we are all in the same boat struggling to find our way through the maze of life, not knowing why we are here; where we are going; what makes us feel this, or makes us do that. And, the only way we will find these answers is to get to the end of the maze, for that's where they are hiding. But we'll never do it without the most powerfully earthly education we could receive – the lessons that our fellow beings teach. Because this is so we should never underestimate anyone else's capacity to help us establish our priorities. However, as humans we have a most debilitating fault which often hampers our process of learning. This is, we egotistically believe that we can convert other people to our way of living. So we constantly badger partners, family or friends to try to think as we do, behave as we do and share the same emotional feelings as we. In other words, we fail to establish empathy towards other people's way of living. We do this in the wholehearted belief that life would be easier for us if everybody acted in the right way – which of course would be our way. However to everyone's mind their way *is* the right way because we all only know what we know. And what we know is determined by the number of times our souls have visited the Earth and, how many lessons they have learned. Which means that unless the people we know have had similar learning experiences to ourselves, we cannot always expect to view life 'eye to eye' with them. Therefore, when we boldly attempt to change other human beings to act in the way we want them to, it would be wise for us to recognise that this is impossible. Instead we should learn to accept others for what they are in the knowledge that they are unable to effect personal changes to their current lives, unless their souls decide this should be. Perhaps a more positive approach of attempting to change things for the better would be to wonder if it needs to be *us* who should make the adjustments required to bring about acceptable equilibrium. After all, the power to effect change lies only within ourselves.

As far as people go, we couldn't pass any test at all without them. However, we are born to the world alone and depart from it alone, leaving the interim period free to establish our worth. Whilst other people can help us determine the path we should take to lead to this, they cannot walk it for us – we have to do this *alone*. What others can offer is the support that one human being needs from another when tackling this important task. To ask for more is futile, for the only certainty that any one of us can know is our own happiness or unhappiness. Therefore if we are dependent on others to provide our contentment and worth or, have total addiction to another person for the same reason, this will mar our growth. The reason for this is that when we live our lives this way we forgo the challenge to explore our self-worth for ourselves. In these situations we hide behind the faults and failings of our 'idols' and blame them for the unhappiness we feel ourselves. And there it stops, for we do not even attempt to find our personal happiness after this. We also find it necessary to conceal ourselves under their skin so that people will see us, not in our own image, but as a reflection of the other. Often when those who are co-dependent are asked, 'If your partner, husband or wife makes you so unhappy why do you continue the relationship?', more times than not the answer will be, 'Because he or she needs me.' This is difficult for others to comprehend, especially in relationships where one partner is the victim of physical abuse from the other. Who could not wonder here why a woman, who was constantly being beaten by her partner, would keep going back for more despite pleas from others not to do so. Or why a man in the same situation would do the same. There would seem to be no sense or reason to it – but there is, for nothing happens in life without good reason. To make sense of this we need to remember that we are souls with bodies and, it is they who set the learning curriculum for us humans to follow.

I believe, like many others, that we become involved with certain people for a special reason and that we meet them when the time is right to do so. Though we, 'the bodies', will not be conscious of this, our souls will, because it is *they* who have set it up. If troublesome relationships result from these arranged meetings then there's only one explanation. This is, that the souls of the humans concerned have debts from previous lifetimes to settle between themselves or, didn't learn enough from each other the last time round. Which means that it is *us* who will know the pain or heartache that battling souls inflict on each other. However, this does not go on indefinitely because once our souls feel that they have settled their debt with another, or learned a lesson from them, they will let us know that enough is enough. From here on in we will move on to know so much self-worth that we will vow never more to allow others to treat us with anything other than respect. (What has to be recognised is that outside influence to resolve the problems of parties suffering conflict with another is futile, for it is only the souls concerned who can bring resolution to their own plights.) If we pondered our bad experiences with other people what might we see as the outcome? Might it be that we have changed many of our opinions because of them; grown through them; gained more confidence because they happened or, established self-worth by virtue of the occurrences? If this is so might we not admit that much good can develop out of bad and, that everything does happen for a good reason? It might appear that the folk of old believed in this theory, for when they recognised that a thing or two had been learned through conflict with another person, they would say, 'These things are sent to try us'.)

When we reach the point in our lives where we believe we have moved on by having developed strength of mind through hurt, there is something more we need to do to enable us to move on further. This is to try to find it in our hearts to forgive those who caused it. Why? – because this is the ultimate test that life sets for souls to attempt (and eventually achieve). A dear lady I know asked of me: 'If we forgive people for their wrongs against us, will they not treat us as doormats?' The simple answer is no. The explanation? Whilst we have forgiven them in our hearts, they won't know this. All that they will spot is that our attitude towards them will have changed to indicate that their disrespect is not acceptable. She also asked, 'How do we know when we have forgiven someone?' The answer is – when the people we have forgiven no longer have the power to hurt us.

However if we do develop the art of forgiveness, by appreciating that we have learned lessons that they have not, it does not mean that we need suffer the company of those who offend us. On the contrary, we should always aim to spend our time with people with whom we can share pleasure. Also, we should avoid those who have the capacity to bring out the worst in us, for this is detrimental to both our health and our progress.

Not all souls are hell-bent on paying debts or learning the hard way however, for there are some who have only debts of kindness to repay others they have known before. In these cases there can come loving relationships that may last for a lifetime. This might apply particularly to souls who had lost each other by way of early demise in previous incarnations. So then, it might well be that the people we grow to love may have been mothers, fathers, sisters, brothers, aunts, uncles, husbands, wives, daughters, sons or friends to us in past lifetimes. My own conviction is that if it were a child who had departed life prematurely in a previous lifetime, then that soul would certainly plan to return to give all love possible to the parents who had grieved so much for its passing.

Although death became a taboo word before the twentieth century ended, the fact is that death is integral to life. As souls we need to die as much as we need to be born. But what about us, the human beings who lose those we love because they need to leave the Earth; where do we stand in the equation? What we have to do is suffer one of the most devastatingly human emotions there could be – bereavement. Nothing could compare with those feelings that submerge us to the depths of despair when someone we love dies. We wish that we could have gone with them; we don't know how we can face living without them; we can't bear the thought that we'll never see them again. Life stands still. We could scream at those who tell us that 'life has to go on', or quote 'to live in hearts we leave behind is not to die', or say 'you'll get over it in time'. For only we can feel the pain in our hearts that hurts so much. We appreciate that life has to go on, but how? And although we know that our loved one will remain in our hearts forever, how do we bear the thought that we will never be with them again? And how does someone who has lost a loved one ever get over it? The fact is that we don't. Whilst it is true that they leave behind a memory of themselves that will live with us always, they also take a large chunk of us away with them. Our mourning does not cease with passing time but only tends to get worse. There come times when we might think we are getting on with our lives, when the reality of the death can hit us like a brick. Perhaps when a memorable tune captures our ear, or we see a film that we know our loved one would enjoy, or their birth date comes around, or we pick up a photograph to see them staring up at us. Then the biggest whack shatters us when we pick up the telephone to speak to our loved one, or enter a room in the house to look for them. In great gulps of breath we remember, they've gone – died – never to be seen or held again. Then we weep the tears we thought we could weep no more. The only comfort we can know at such times is the one that makes us think that the spirit of our loved one remains on Earth to be with us in another form. The following anonymous poems are from the minds of those who had obviously gazed hard into the clouds to look for those they had loved and lost.

Do not stand at my grave and weep
I am not there, I do not sleep.
I am a thousand winds that blow
I am the diamond glints on snow.
I am the sun on ripened grain
I am the gentle autumn rain.
When you awaken in the morning's hush
I am the uplifting rush
Of quiet birds in circled flight
I am the soft stars that shine at night.
Do not stand at my grave and cry
I am not there, I did not die.

If I had spoken before I died
these are the words I would have sighed.
Goodbye my family, my life has passed
my love for you will always last.
Weep not for me but courage take
and love each other for my sake.
As time goes by and you grow older
my hands will rest upon your shoulder.
Those you love won't go away
they walk beside you every day.

After reading these poems we might conclude that their Western authors believed in the Chinese T'ai Chi philosophy that tells: we are of the same universe as the natural elements, and have the same life force passing through us. If this is true then perhaps it can explain why the image of our loved one might appear before our eyes shortly after their death and why their presence can be felt around us for a period of time.

During mourning there often comes remorse, for who of us has not felt regret that we did not act differently to our loved one in life. We ask – could I have done more; might I have prevented his or her death; why was I so inconsiderate to him or her?; I wish we had not argued so much; why did I not see him or her more often? – and so on. And sadly in some cases this can haunt us through life to the point where we might develop a guilt complex that will mar our happiness. To try to prevent this from happening we need to remember that we are just human beings who are meant to make mistakes as we trundle through living, so that we can learn how to correct them. As far as death is concerned it can be a great aid to learning, for when we lose someone we love we usually take a look at our own lives to rethink our priorities, values and perhaps our beliefs. Perhaps too the death may alert us into reflecting that loved ones should be cherished in life – despite their foibles.

For parents whose child has died however, their remorse will not allow self-forgiveness, for they automatically assume blame for the death. Who, who has not also lost a child, could ever know the agony that these parents suffer because of this belief and, how could parents begin to accept that this is not so, for the death of a child signifies that its soul has opted to take a short human span this time round to fulfil its tasks. However, before embarking on the journey, this soul would have chosen special souls to give it human life. Those who themselves had very important tasks to undertake to aid them to human perfection. When a child died in days gone by people would try to offer parents comfort by saying, 'It's only the good who die young'.

Though man boasts his control of life and death, this is not so, for only souls have this prerogative. It is they who determine when the time is ready for them to come to Earth, and, when the time has come to leave it. Some might choose to stay until earthly bodily functioning reaches expiry date, but others will need to depart before, or well before, this time arrives. For the first, death will usually present by reason of natural causes. For the second however, the souls who need a quicker release from mortal life have to find alternative avenues to achieve this. Which could mean that war, disaster, starvation, illness, accident or murder will cause their deaths. It is said that souls who choose to undergo the violent suffering that death in any of these circumstances causes will automatically acquire part, or final, human perfection through the experience. 'They'll go straight to heaven,' said people of days gone by of those who died tragic deaths.

In the cases of suicide however, where death is secured either by one's own hand or by euthanasia, there is doubt of this. Souls who choose to withdraw from strenuous earthly tests, by killing their bodies this way, will have to tackle them again the next time round. Which means that the same problems, and the same suffering, will be there waiting to be conquered when these souls reincarnate to Earth. Again, it would seem that this is something folks of yesteryear believed by instinct. They reasoned that their god would take a good look at the size of people's shoulders to assess how much of a load they might be able to carry through their lives. Then he would place the appropriately sized packages on their backs and instruct them to carry them safely to the journey's end. The proviso was that if they dropped the cargo they would have to return to the beginning and start the process all over again. In a bottom line summary they would say, 'God never gives us any more than He knows we can carry'. So, whoever or whatever their god represented, it inspired them to believe that they could stoically cope with everything that living threw at them. On top of this there seemed to be an understanding that, at the end of it all, there would be something worth having waiting for them. However, these positively inspired folk would not have felt so confident of their beliefs during the actual times of their suffering. Like all human beings, they would have experienced the despair that trauma causes. Which is to wonder how we can survive the pain our problem brings, or to feel that death would be preferable to it. It is only when the time has passed, and we realise that we have survived, can we begin to understand life's plan for us.

When we look at our lives to observe our happiness, what we should be asking is – 'am I happy with myself?' If we are then we will possess self-worth; if we are not then we've probably got a 'dragon' in tow. If we recall that this monster represents the fear we have of ourselves, we might ask why we have it. The simple answer is that we have not learned how to believe in ourselves for who we are. Instead we continually doubt ourselves by believing that it is other people who have defined this. What we're talking here are hang-ups. These are the things that we develop through the words or actions of our superiors as we struggle to grow up, and which carry with us into adulthood. They create great problems, for instead of our trying to establish our own identities as re-invented adults, we live life in the shadow of the past, where others determine our characters. At this time they may have convinced us that we were unlovable, brainless, shameful, deceitful, bad or utterly worthless. It could also be that they impressed us with their own attributes and expected us to impersonate them. On the other hand, maybe all they wanted from us was to succeed beyond our own limitations – for their sake. When our hang-ups take control of our living we easily forget that we are individually unique, with the need to prove this to ourselves. Instead we find it easier to believe that we need to prove ourselves to the world. To do this we will engage in pretentious behaviour to impress others with our wealth, success, style, breeding, education, superiority etc. We hope that from this we will glean the love and respect which is missing from our lives, without ever wondering if this could be earned by demonstrating how much room there is in our hearts, instead of how many rooms there are in our houses. When we act this way however we blind ourselves to the fact that our contemporaries may get the measure of our worth when they look into our eyes. This is true also of the times when we boast of the successes of family members so that we can bathe in their glory. Apart from boring the pants off our listeners, we take the chance of convincing them that we have no glory of our own in which to bathe. Do we really want to travel through life in the shadow of other people because of our hang-ups, or do we desire to stand up tall and shout, 'I am what I am', and be proud of it. If it's the latter then we need to have guts and patience for we will have many years of hard work ahead. Our main objective will be to try to put the past in perspective. To do this there will be need for us to talk logically to ourselves to determine the reason for our hang-ups. Here the most important point we should recognise is that the people who impressed our young vulnerable minds with their opinions of us were no more than mere human beings. Whilst they had the right as adults to express their views to us, we must recall that these were based on their priorities, their beliefs, their prejudices and their values. Let's not forget also that they probably had 'dragons' in tow. If, as adults, we want to move on to develop our own priorities, beliefs and values and leave the influences of the past behind, then we need to appreciate these points. Perhaps we would also like to consider the fact that most things said to us in childhood are not deliberately spoken to cause us hurt, but are offered as gestures of helpfulness in accordance with the speaker's views. Very possibly too it might be that, in our early days, we misinterpreted the words or actions of others when we were not then mature enough to decipher their meaning. Or, it could be that our sensitivity sometimes rose to the fore and allowed us to see teasing banter as condemnation. Time to sort out the wheat from the chaff so that we can get things in perspective.

If it is parents we blame for our hang-ups, are we going to lay this burden on their doorstep indefinitely, or will we have the guts to face up to the responsibility of shaping our own lives? Perhaps the commonest blame attributed to parents is the one which accuses them of a lack of love towards us. When we feel that we were unloved as children this causes a devastating effect on our lives, for we enter adulthood convinced that no-one else will love us either. If we are to eradicate this thought from our minds we have to come to terms with what is probably the truth of the matter. This is, that whilst our parents may not have loved us as we expected to be loved, they loved us in the only way they knew how – *their way*. Should we feel unloved because we were either rejected or abandoned by parents, then this memory is far more difficult to wipe from our minds. However it can be done! If we know the circumstances that led to these events we could ponder the legitimacy of the actions taken by them, and go on to look at our predicament in a different light. If we find that we cannot justify their actions on any account, then to raise our self-esteem we must tell ourselves that we are *not* unlovable but that our parents were only capable of loving themselves. Following this would come a very important lesson to learn without delay in order to find love and good health. It is – the only person in the world who can love us as we deserve to be loved is ourself, for this is the greatest love there is to quell the desperate need for that of others.

It may be that we are haunted with guilt because of bad things our parents committed. Because guilt is an emotion that will hinder our growth and may cause illness to develop in us, we have got to kick it out of our lives. To do this we will need to recognise that *we* are not responsible for our parents' wrongdoings – *they are*. If we feel shame on their behalf and believe that this will remove their misdemeanours from either our lives or theirs, it won't. All that this shame will represent is wasted energy and time. Time that we could otherwise consign to our own well-being. If our main concern is that other people judge us in accordance with our parents' follies, then we should try to be realistic, for if they do then we are already superior to them. And who of us would want to be associated with folk who did not assess us on our own merits anyway?

Really heavy hang-ups can develop if we were victims of abuse, whether at the hands of parents or of others when we were growing up. How can we possibly remove the trauma of the sexual or violent physical abuse we suffered in childhood, for all that we feel is shame of ourselves because of it. The task ahead here will be a very arduous one and may last many years, but it can be completed. What we must continually convince ourselves of is that *we* have nothing to be ashamed of because *we* did not do anything to bring shame to ourselves. Then we should shift the blame to the rightful owners – *the offenders*. After this we have to try to do the seemingly impossible – forgive the person who has caused us such suffering. But how could we ever forgive monstrous actions like these? Indeed a very difficult thing to do without our being super-human. But, at least we should give it a try if we want to free our lives to the future. To attempt forgiveness we must become aware that those who committed their crimes against us are bitterly unhappy people, people who can never know a moment's peace, unlike ourselves, who do.

It may be that we have a hang-up regarding our physical appearance. If we were bullied in childhood by contemporaries because of our height, weight, colour of hair, shape, disability, etc. it is likely that we have become sensitised to seeing ourselves as they described us. This can develop into a dangerous situation as it can lead to our taking drastic measures to attempt to change our natural features; those which constitute our very being. There is an escape from this nightmare, but it will only present when our self-worth is established enough to render all other than this unimportant. However until this wonderful asset materialises inside us we need to think logically. If we do we will realise that bullying stems from the inadequacy of people, for those who lack self esteem to a high degree believe that, when they make a fool of someone by ridiculing their appearance, they make a hero of themselves. However, what they fail to observe is that onlookers of their bullying (other than ourselves) see that their victims are usually those who far outshine them. Furthermore, it does not go unnoticed that the aggressors are only able to continue to practice their tauntings because their victims are either too timid, or nice, to protest with retaliation. Hopefully, we will conclude from this that we must have had a lot going for us even in childhood days, otherwise we would not have warranted the mindless abuse from the idiots who didn't. Then we should wonder if – because bullying of this kind continues throughout life – we should learn to disregard belittling comments as the folly of those who deliver them. After this, all that is left is to accept the physiology that nature endowed us; be grateful for our health and, learn to believe that it is the person inside the body who can gain love and respect, not the body itself. To remember also that the body is the temple of the spirit.

Time to remind ourselves that we are souls on a mission, who have arranged tests to be battled and conquered. There is a subconscious exercise we can perform that can help dispel the negative and destructive influences that other people have over us, for these are harmful and, apart from creating our hang-ups, can cause us to develop illnesses. So, although the exercise might sound pagan and bizarre it is recommended that it is tried. What we must do is to picture 'our problem' person in our mind's eye and witness them being consumed by flames. No – the exercise is not undertaken to transmit malicious thoughts towards others. Its contrary purpose is to remove these from our own minds so that we are free to move on in peace.

As we courageously battle to kill off our 'dragons', so that we can become worthy of ourselves, and not afraid of ourselves, we have much to do. Firstly we must remember that most of the time we inflict our own misery, so only we can curtail it. Here again we need to apply logic to our thoughts and take note of what causes us pain, and to be mindful of the things that bring us happiness. Imperative too is the need for us to establish our aims so that we can fulfil our right to discover who we truly are and, where we want to be going. However, maintaining these aims will take great courage, for, throughout our lifetime, pressured endeavour will arise to render us on a par with the socially acceptable conditions which prevail because of political manipulation and control of society. Nevertheless, the fight to retain our bearings will be worthwhile if, at the end of it, we find ourselves where we wanted to be.

Usually, if hang-ups plague us we will be submerged in 'the self', whereby we crave attention and sympathy as our attendants. Unfortunately, however, when we are caught in this trap these are the last things that people will be prepared to offer. Instead they will tend to regard us as selfishly demanding folk intent on lumbering them with permanent troubles and woes. Hence they will try to avoid us whenever possible. Because this is not conducive to happiness, perhaps what we should do, to get a little attention, is to step outside ourselves to look in. If we did this we would focus on the well-being of others and forget about ourselves for a while. From this would come a display of pleasure toward us in response to the care we had shown. On top of this a two-way conversation might reveal that other people's worries were on a par with our own, or alternatively they were worse. Should the latter be the truth, then no doubt our own concerns would minimise and our well-being increase.

In partnership or marriage the 'unlovable' aspect of hang-ups will present in the form of jealousy. Here couples will become suspicious if mention is made of connections with any person other than themselves. This will cause arguments to soar from the flames of temper that come from words fuelled with outrageous thoughts of infidelity. This pastime is indeed futile for it achieves only unhappiness and stalemate. There is nothing that can be heard, let alone solved, from argument so we should learn this quickly. In its place we need to try to see that our jealousy is produced from a lack of esteem which makes us unsure of ourselves. To correct this we should aim to discover what our qualities are so that we can find our way to the greatest love. The sooner we arrive there the better, for jealousy is another destructive emotion that can bring us illness and unhappiness.

If we want to build our self-worth then, on top of being logical, we should be open-minded, for as the saying goes – the mind is like a parachute – it does not work until it is opened. By committing to this we will become aware that there is much to be learned from listening and observing well. As we develop this skill, not only will we gain the ability to measure the consequences of our own actions automatically, but we will also apply this to others. By means of this exercise we may consciously decide that the only routes we want to tread are those which lead to the 'feel good' areas. Open-mindedness can also alert us to the fact that however educated we believe ourselves to be, those regarded as uneducated can teach us a thing or two if we listen carefully. Importantly too, by observing cultures that differ from our own, we might learn of philosophies that could be incorporated into our own to aid our worthiness.

With visions of this in sight, now will be the time to try to discover our hidden qualities. However, we need to appreciate that because it was us who buried these, because we feared their release, this fear must now be annihilated. To help in our quest to find what we're made of we must tell ourselves repeatedly, we'll never know if we never try. After this, any notions of possible failures must be hurled out of our minds. When this is done they will be free to accept only thoughts of success. Very often though we avoid attempting tasks which are alien to us as we dread that our inexperience will portray us as fools. This state is born from the egotism we have that says we must be seen only as perfect at all times. If we retain this idea we will never move on because the fact is that perfected humans are extinct. So, let's have the courage to be ourselves and give the efforts which are humanly possible – our imperfect best. Remember that self-worth is derived from our own achievements. No matter how humble our ventures may seem in comparison to others, it is us who have undertaken them and of this we must be proud.

We are entitled to give ourselves a pat on the back also when we try our best to be kind and considerate; truthful and honest; sincere and helpful as we go about our business. We may become a little peeved if others around us do not conform to this pattern but this should not matter, for at the end of each day it is us who have to live with ourselves. If what we do creates a good feeling inside us then we're going to live with a smile in our hearts. However, if we live to think of ourselves first at all times without regard to others, this feeling will escape us. Then if our selfish actions have caused fellow beings annoyance or anger; inconvenience or hurt; rejection or even pain or death, we will find ourselves inside a vacuum of unhappiness. Escape from this will be hard for there will be no ladders made of smiles to help us climb the slippery slope. We need to remember too that all we give is returned; if not in this lifetime then in a future one.

The greatest self-worth we can earn does not develop from telling someone we love them but, by proving it. The only way we can do this is by offering others the most precious asset we possess – ourselves. However, if we donate our valuable time to those who need it to gain their respect, praise or a mention in their will, and do this grudgingly, worthiness will escape us. But if we put another person's needs above our own and offer our time gladly, because we love them unconditionally, then we're going to feel happy inside. If we commit to helping others in order to broadcast our actions, then what we seek is admiration of all. However, if we perform good deeds silently but happily, then what we shall have is the admiration of ourselves.

There will come many times when thinking of others before ourselves will not come easily, especially in cases of illness where our patient's condition may render them incapable of showing anything other than their pain. Here we will feel angry that they are suffering; frustrated that we cannot take their pain away; physically exhausted through our efforts to bring them care and comfort. Some patients may also react aggressively to their illnesses and display nothing but ungratefulness to us. They might also speak words intended to undermine our character and worth. This will upset us so much that we will feel like 'throwing in the towel,' but we won't. Instead we'll have a good cry then come to terms with the fact that our patients are people who are frightened by their own suffering. Some who witness our situation may suggest that we donate our time and energy to our own lives instead of wasting it this way. However, how could they see how little is wasted by caring for the sick and how much is gained by the carers, for only they will see self-worth oozing from their eyes as they gaze into a mirror. Self-worth which is theirs to keep forever.

Throughout our lives there will come times when we will feel we can't cope with the traumas that present to us. During these times we will feel ill with despair and might rush to acquire medical attention. However, whilst drugs are available that can help mask the deep emotions that can cause body malfunction, depression or temporary mental breakdown to occur, it cannot be said that these are the answer to ongoing problems of this kind. On the contrary, for if we develop a long-standing dependency on a cocktail of drugs to mask our natural emotions, so that we can get through our days, then we will never learn who we are or what we could achieve. It is only by letting our emotions free to be examined, and then learning to come to terms with them, that we will bravely begin to cope with them, and life itself, to restore our good health. The fact is that drugs cannot cure mental breakdown or depression, because these conditions are not a disease. What they represent are the emotions that normal human beings experience when they are unable to deal with some of the downsides of life. They are, therefore, as natural as the emotions that promote laughter and happiness in us when everything is tickety-boo in our lives. So we need to learn that the human body is equipped with its own natural tranquilising system that will spring into action to help us whilst we struggle with life. But this, like drugs, is not able to eliminate the emotions that accompany all aspects of living. If we recall, these are integral to our very being and are the source of our learning. Therefore if they are numbed unnaturally what happens is that a void appears in our lives, for without the natural release of both laughter and tears we become entombed within vessels of nothingness. So we must allow our tranquilising systems to work to capacity by laughing as much as we can; crying as we need to and pursuing those things in life that may bring us peace of mind.

Whilst the intangible is of unprovable measure it would appear that there is one exception to the rule, for people throughout the ages have portrayed that the human spirit can be proven without any shadow of doubt. These are the millions of people worldwide who have conquered the dire circumstances, and dramatic happenings that have daunted their lives; then, have gone on to recognise inner happiness. With always a positive aim in sight, they undertook to continue their journey irrespective of overwhelming pain or anguish, and to walk every avenue determined to acquire the self-worth that would result from their efforts. Irrespective of the doubts that sometimes appeared, they did not give up, instead they stumbled forward and eventually came up smiling with pride in their achievements. What they had won was the element no one could ever take away from them – the inner happiness that would carry through with them into eternity.

Some, by virtue of their contentment with 'their lot', and the reflection of the outcome of their lives, have come to a conclusion. This is that human beings are souls first, and people second. Souls who are at peace after having completed the tests set by themselves. Others cannot justify the reason for their current contentment other than to humbly state, they have always 'just got on with it' and 'done their best'.

Whilst some happy people may know why they are happy, and others may not, none need to contemplate when it comes to expressing the feelings their happiness has produced.

It has been said by many that their belief in themselves is all they could want from their living, and they fear nothing the future could bring.

It has been said by some that they have always left room in their lives for the true riches of life, and have left the past where it belongs – behind them.

It has been said by others that they regard themselves the sum total of their living experiences and are free of regrets, remorse, self-pity and bitterness, but full of self-belief and life acceptancy.

It has been said by all that when inner happiness develops through self-worth everything else just follows. (Might it be that we would have a sorry situation if people like this were not around, for those who are unable to love themselves are also unable to love others?)

Although our world is an imperfect place where inner happiness ducks and dives to try to avoid our powers to spot it, the testimonies given prove that it can be harnessed. Therefore, is there any reason why any one of us, the children of the future, should be without hope of capturing this precious asset?

The twentieth century and then what? Life will continue as it always has – as we humans make it.